WILLIAM HARVEY

HIS LIFE AND TIMES:
HIS DISCOVERIES: HIS METHODS

PLATE I. William Harvey aged about 72, from a contemporary portrait now in the library of the Royal College of Physicians

WILLIAM HARVEY

HIS LIFE AND TIMES:
HIS DISCOVERIES: HIS METHODS

LOUIS CHAUVOIS

Foreword by
SIR ZACHARY COPE

THE SCIENTIFIC BOOK GUILD
Beaverbrook Newspapers Limited
LONDON

THE SCIENTIFIC BOOK GUILD
Beaverbrook Newspapers Ltd, 1961

First published in Great Britain by
Hutchinson & Co. (Publishers) Ltd

Reprinted by lithography in Great Britain
by Jarrold & Sons Ltd, Norwich

CONTENTS

LIST OF PLATES

LINE ILLUSTRATIONS

FOREWORD

The fame of William Harvey increases with the years. Three centuries have passed since he died, yet the importance of his work has not diminished. He inaugurated a new era and laid the foundation of the present imposing edifice of modern scientific medicine.

The magnitude of the revolution in medical thought brought about by Harvey's discovery is not even now sufficiently realized. For fourteen hundred years the teaching of Galen had been regarded as infallible and to depart from it was dangerous to reputation and sometimes even to life. Harvey, after he had convinced himself of the truth of his discovery, waited several years before he published it in print, and it took many years before his clear demonstrations carried conviction to his contemporaries.

The work Harvey did in proving the circulation of the blood was of greater significance than serving as the foundation of physiology; it showed how research should be conducted. Bacon had laid down rules for the collection of facts and for inductive methods of thought, but he did not sufficiently realize the value of experiment. Harvey used and by his example taught the correct place of experiment. The sequence was careful observation, thoughtful deliberation, the appropriate experiment, and further consideration upon its results. This has ever since been the model for research students.

It should therefore be incumbent on all medical students and practitioners to know as much as can be known of the life and times, the discoveries and the methods of William Harvey, and in this book Dr. Chauvois, a distinguished French physician and medical historian, has provided exactly what is required. To Harvey's countrymen it should be regarded as a sincere and great compliment that such an enthusiastic biography should now be forthcoming from France, a country in which (as the author points out) it was due rather to lay than to medical opinion that the new views were accepted.

Dr. Chauvois has carefully read, studied and sifted all available information about Harvey, and has inspected all the memorials of that great man. In addition, as an accomplished scholar, he has very closely studied the Latin texts of Harvey's published writings.

Using all these materials with balanced judgement he has produced a lifelike portrait of Harvey the man and Harvey the scientist. He writes with wit and charm, and with an imagination which adds piquancy to the narrative while not going beyond the probabilities of the case. His evaluation of the preliminary forecasting of the circulation of the blood by Servetus, Colombo and Caesalpinus is remarkably clear and just; he gives them all due credit but shows that their work in no way detracts from the major glory which belongs to Harvey.

This very readable book with its up-to-date information and review of Harvey's life and work comes at an opportune moment when all the world is about to celebrate the tercentenary of his death; it deserves and should obtain wide recognition and appreciation.

ZACHARY COPE.

Preface

I have striven to make my account of Harvey's life worthy of its extraordinary character. I have endeavoured to portray it as it was, tense and active, as I have felt it to be during my repeated readings of Harvey's works in his original Latin text. And since I desire to communicate to others something of the force and the excitement that emanate from the great physician's writings, I have dealt with my subject in a way different from that of conventional biographies.

Instead of beginning with his date and place of birth, and his early upbringing, I have first depicted Harvey as he was at the height of his powers, in full maturity, in action, with the hope that the memory of the man will remain vividly in the reader's mind. Thus the first chapter of this book is entitled 'A Day with William Harvey, London, 1627', for he was then aged forty-nine and was about to publish his immortal discovery. Perhaps in this way readers may have their appetites whetted for further information about all that concerns so eminent a man, the different stages and phases of whose long career I deal with later in this book.[1]

As we examine the life and work of this great Englishman we shall see that he appears before us intensely human, a man serene in his science, so honest and upright, so enthusiastic for truth, so incomparably sure in judgement and in scientific method, that no finer model can be offered to those who would go forward with unfaltering steps in the pursuit of scientific knowledge or in the achievement of discovery.

Such a story as is told in this book must also inspire, guide and sustain those who would taste the intense satisfaction of a life inspired by a dream and informed with great accomplishment. Harvey's destiny was, indeed, though in another domain, not unlike that of Christopher Columbus. The two men were both realists and idealists, men who knew how to combine with a love of what was true and beautiful and of good repute a practical sense of a definite aim, doggedly pursued. It is for this reason that I have said, and

[1] This was the method I adopted from 1933 to 1937, when I was writing the life and the discoveries of my friend and master, 'D'Arsonval, Soixante-cinq ans à travers la science'.

13

repeat, that it would be legitimate to call Harvey 'the Christopher Columbus of the Circulation of the Blood'. No doubt, some will say that I exaggerate, that my language is too extravagant, too poetical, but my mind and imagination have been so conquered and subjected by my hero that I would almost deify him.

Those who would reproach me with too much enthusiasm for my subject can hardly know it well, cannot have practised the art and science that owes all to Harvey. They cannot, therefore, perceive the 'treasure of incredible genius', as Bossuet wrote of Cromwell, that was hidden in this little man—the genius which animated him from the beginning to the end of his career, and drove him to explore so pertinaciously the path he was the first to have glimpsed, and upon which he was finally to walk with such assurance and self-confidence. Indeed, this track of the circulation of the blood was much more difficult to follow than the way to the New World.

Let us reflect a moment. In recent years we have been able to date the earliest traces of the human race, and find that *Homo sapiens* is many tens of thousands of years old. From the first, Man must have asked himself what was blood. The problem of blood must have been one of the most insistent and important of all those presenting themselves to Man's natural curiosity. He saw it flow from wounds given and received, he saw blood gush forth from the animals he killed, he saw it trickle from the beasts he sacrificed in holy rites. Later on, augurers disembowelled animals to read in their entrails the intentions of Fate. Men would hold in their hands the palpitating hearts of victims whose life ebbed away as blood spurted from the open vessels.

Still, during all these many millenia, no one was able to explain and to bring into proper relation the facts that were observed every day. Here and there, indeed, a few feeble attempts at explanation were attempted—efforts that seem to us today not only absurd but almost inconceivable. Humankind had to wait until less than four centuries ago, when the genius of one man cut through the immense accumulation of ignorance and incomprehension and brought the truth into the light of day.

Harvey, again, did not devote to his task a few months or even a few years. It was decades before he dared to publish the results of his investigations—so great, we may well imagine, was his own amazement at what he had found. There were so many legends to be swept away, so many false bypaths to be avoided, so many obstacles and ancient errors—held as sacred as the words of Holy Writ—to be overcome, so many mists to be dissipated. And what was even worse, there were so many mirages to be shunned hovering over the landscape into which he had strayed that he must have possessed a gift of method and a mastery of 'navigation' that are almost without parallel in the history of science.

We can certainly propose nothing better for those who would tackle any scientific problem than a study of how Harvey manœuvred in this matter of the movement of the heart and blood in animals. In this connection the author of this book will also, taking as his starting-point the original Latin text of Harvey's works, attempt to correct some of those pieces of gossip piously transmitted from copyist to copyist. He ventures to hope that these corrections will re-establish in its integrity the thought of the great discoverer and free it from a number of absurd but often repeated statements which cannot justly be attributed to Harvey himself.

Again, in order to judge of the quality of Harvey's method of observation, we may remember that at about the same time another man, René Descartes, had his method, too—a method based upon ratiocination; it was a method which, as far as the nature and movement of the heart were concerned, led its author into lamentable errors. Harvey refused to accept as evidence any such axiom as that from which Descartes, by impeccable reasoning, deduced all his theories. Harvey's method was based upon experiment only, experiment a thousand times repeated, experiment with no *a priori* postulate accepted as certain or even probable. The truth, he would often say, can emerge only from the multiple confirmations or contradictions of experiment. Compared with experiment, all the rest is metaphysics and dialectic—smoke and inanity.

I did not myself begin my study of Harvey with any preconceived notions. I set myself to examine the works of Harvey quite dispassionately. I set out, first of all, to read in the Latin texts themselves what the English physician actually did write, not just what he is reported to have written. In fact, I was at first rather suspicious about Harvey's work. Too many fulsome apologies from too many more or less well-inspired commentators had made me wary, so that from the first I strove to free myself from all preconceived notions. I now confess that after years of study devoted to Harvey's works, I feel inclined to go farther than most of the apologists and to declare, with the text of Harvey before my eyes, that he was really a much greater man than any of them has imagined.

It is true that for the chronological part of my documentation I have had to borrow from a number of earlier historians of Harvey, but, as will be seen in my text, I have been careful to acknowledge my indebtedness. Indeed, these historians themselves got their information from other authors who wrote earlier, and who in their turn link up by a chain of chroniclers to the most copious source of our information about the man Harvey—that contained in the writings of his contemporary and friend, Aubrey. We cannot invent the facts nor the dates of a life. We must, in this case as in others, rely upon the documents left to us by those who had known the man as he lived and who described him for us. But once we have assembled the necessary chronological material, we shall find that on reading and re-reading the original texts, even if they are in Latin, we shall in some measure penetrate into the author's mind and thus obtain information most certainly more valid and valuable for an understanding of the man than any anecdotes or legends about him. By comparing this information with contemporary stories about him we may be able to make the man live again and need no longer regard him as a lay-figure, lifeless and inert, a mere name in history.

If I have been able to bring forward some documents and personal judgements that throw a new light upon certain problems of Harvey's life and work, I should like nevertheless to acknowledge here my very real debt to those judicious and acute writers who, long before me, examined Harvey's works and achievements. Among these I must mention Sir D'Arcy Power, Dr. Bayon and Mr. Wilmot Herringham, none of whom is now living. I am much indebted also to many still with us, such as Lady Moran, Sir Geoffrey Keynes, Sir Harold Boldero, Sir Zachary Cope and Mr. Payne, whose names often occur in these pages. The Registrars and Fellows of the Royal College of Physicians and other famous medical bodies in Great Britain, as well as the librarian and the archivist of St. Bartholomew's Hospital, have been most generous in placing at my disposal a wealth of facts and documents. I must also express my gratitude to the Rev. J. V. Hooper, Vicar of Hempstead, in whose small village church the body of the great discoverer reposes among the graves of his family, and to my friend Mr. D. N. Chester, the Warden of Nuffield College, Oxford, who, with his wife, have been my valued advisers on translations from several English texts. I am, indeed, profoundly grateful for the kindness I received from many other distinguished members of the Universities of Oxford and Cambridge, especially Sir James Chadwick, Mr. E. K. Bennett, Colonel Stratton, Dr. Needham, the late Professor Whitby and Professors Gardner and Trueta and Mr. M. Thomas. And I should like to express my most grateful thanks to my Brazilian friend and colleague in the Scientific Society of São Paulo, G. F. de Almeida, whose great erudition and lively curiosity have been so valuable. (I am proud to belong to those two great institutions of Portuguese language and culture, the Scientific Society of São Paulo and the ancient and illustrious Academy of Science and Letters of Coimbra, the most ancient in Europe.)

I am indebted to my old friend and colleague, Dr. Pierret, physician at La Bourboule, for putting at my disposal his invaluable aid in facilitating my contacts with the leading figures of the Royal College of Physicians in London (of which he is an honorary fellow) as well as with others of his British friends.

I should also like to mention the help I have received from Lord Harvey of Tasburgh, formerly His Britannic Majesty's Ambassador at Paris. His name and fame seemed to link him so clearly with my subject that I did not hesitate to address some enquiries to him. I shall not readily forget his cordial response to my queries. If, after research, no connection could be traced between his family and that of William Harvey, my enquiries did lead to some interesting considerations on the coats-of-arms of the two families. I must also express my thanks to another 'Harveian' name, that of Mr. Harvey Wood, formerly Representative of the British Council in Paris, as well as to his successor, Miss MacLeod, Mr. Hawkins, Assistant Representative, and Mr. Milner, the Librarian. They were good enough to read through the French MS. of this book and to make a number of comments and annotations which have been of great value.

I cannot pass in silence over the valuable help given by the English translator and editor of my work. I should like to put on record my gratitude for their unlimited patience and understanding.

I hope all my other British friends who have aided me in any way will accept here a general expression of my grateful thanks. The affection that I feel for the person of their illustrious fellow-countryman has extended to his whole land (to which I was already attached by my ancient Norman origins). I may say that it was while studying the works of Harvey, and as a result of my visits to England, that this feeling grew, little by little, until—at the end of a long acquaintance—it is my pleasure to record that I have been wholly captivated.

And now, if in view of the living personality I have sought to present, there should be some who still feel that the biographer should be nothing more than a simple enumerator of facts and dates—the teller of a sort of necrology of a life and an epoch—or any who complain that, here and there in this book, I have introduced scenes of my own imagining, I would put this general question: is not the true biographer the man who, by force of observation and frequentation, has been able to penetrate into the heart of his hero, and who, therefore, feels compelled to bring him to life again and cannot be content to be a mere enumerator of dead bones? So, it seems to me, a biographer should proceed, always provided that he is able, by the co-ordination of facts and documents, to justify the character he has evoked. I hope that, having read this book, the reader will feel that I have accomplished, at least in some measure, what I have set myself to do.

Paris, 1956   L. Chauvois

Il y a des hommes qu'il n'est
pas permis d'ignorer.

Chapter I

A Day with William Harvey, London, 1627

A morning visit to St. Bartholomew's Hospital—A Royal Command to appear at the Palace of St. James—A quarrel among the Royal Physicians—Dr. and Mrs. Harvey at dinner—A newcomer to London: 'Monsieur Coffee'—The consulting-room, laboratories and museum—The afternoon visits to patients—A mysterious outing after supper—Midnight work—The last touches put to the book which was to astonish the world

BEFORE we come to deal with the incidents and details of a life which, though devoid of most of the clamours and clangours that rise about the favourites of the crowd, proved in its social and human significance to be of such transcendent importance, perhaps we may be permitted to draw a picture of our hero as he appeared in his prime—as he lived and thought and acted at the time when he was in full possession of his powers, and when he was on the point of revealing himself to the world as the greatest and most daring of scientific innovators. Once we have viewed the man in full activity, we shall, so it seems to me, be able to follow with greater interest the successive phases of his amazing career.

Let us, then, view him when he was between forty and fifty years of age, say at the end of the year 1627 when he was indeed just forty-nine years old. This was a very short time before the publication of the immortal Treatise which was, in the short space of seventy-two pages, to overthrow doctrines that had held the field for millenia, and to present for the first time in human history an exact and an illuminating description of the actual circulation of the blood through the body. Although at the age of forty-nine he had as yet—deliberately—published nothing concerning his investigations, his conclusions were well known to his medical colleagues in London. For ten years and more he had publicly proclaimed his teaching both at his hospital and at the College of Physicians (now the Royal College of Physicians). Indeed, although his novel theories were questioned by many of his brother physicians, Harvey was already recognized as one of the leading medical practitioners in the realm. He was admitted by all to be a remarkable anatomist of unequalled manual dexterity, a man of wide general culture and one tireless in his investigations as well as 'curious of the sciences'.

In this year of 1627, he occupied at the College of Physicians (of which he had been a Fellow since 1604), for the eleventh season in succession, the important and envied post of Professor of Anatomy. Three times a week he delivered the Lumleian Lecture. Since 1607 he had been principal physician at the celebrated St. Bartholomew's Hospital. Although he did not, until 1631, receive the title of Physician in Ordinary to the King, he was often consulted by Charles I.

Harvey was also consultant physician to many great lords and other highly placed personages. For example, in the preceding year, that is to say in 1626, he had been called in by the former Lord Chancellor, Francis Bacon, whose health was rapidly declining. His remarkable success in his profession does not, however, appear to have rendered Harvey at all arrogant or haughty, nor caused him to lose in any degree his extreme simplicity of manner and of manners.

Let us glance at him on this December morning of 1627 as he leaves his house—a man pensive and hurried, wholly absorbed in taking up the thread of the previous day's work, for his growing creation was never out of his thoughts.

Here he is on the threshold of his house, his head uncovered, and dangling from his right hand is a large broad-brimmed felt hat. A cape is draped over his left arm. He is a small man. In fact, he was usually called—by some respectfully and by others a trifle ironically —'Little Dr. Harvey'. But he is quite sturdily built, his shoulders square. He has no bulging belly. There is no surplus fat upon his bones.[1] His face is spare and high in colour, though his skin is so dark as to be almost olive.

He is neatly dressed in a fustian doublet, puce-coloured, with breeches of the same hue. His appearance would be sombre were it not for the large, turned-down white collar that strikes a lighter note in his severe and plain costume.[1] Such collars had, some years

[1] See the series of Harvey's portraits in Sir G. Keynes's *The Portraiture of Harvey*.

before, taken the place of the old-fashioned starched and goffered ruffs. The little man had obviously a head of the 'cerebral' type, as we might say nowadays—that is, the head, broad and massive above, narrowed to a point at the chin, which bore a small tuft of beard under a thick moustache. The thick black hair of his head receded from a lofty and broad forehead beneath which were two dark eyes, singularly lively and penetrating. Some habit, it may be of spiritual tension, raised the left eyebrow above the right, a feature that his portraitists show to have become more marked with age.[1]

Stopping for a moment on his doorstep, the little man glances to the right and to the left as though surprised at not seeing his hack and groom, which were usually waiting for him every morning. (It was, indeed, the custom of the time for physicians—at least, those of a certain importance and celebrity—to pay their visits on horseback, the horses being attired in a long draped housing reaching nearly to the ground and known as a 'foot cloth'.) After a few minutes' wait the little man, obviously impatient, puts on his broad-brimmed hat and flings his cape over his shoulders, for the December air is damp and chilly. He walks down the roadway and takes the path—so often trodden—that leads him to his daily goal, St. Bartholomew's Hospital. The streets of London before the Great Fire were narrow and winding. They twisted and twined between tall gables, and as

[1] The text of this book was already being translated when I happened to light upon an interesting work published in 1879 by Benjamin Ward Richardson, F.R.S., M.D., entitled *A Ministry of Health*. Chapter II of this book is devoted to a day in the life of Harvey. The date chosen by Richardson was 1st April, 1629, his birthday, and also a year after the publication of the *Exercitatio*. I read Richardson's text with much interest and was happy to think that I had not known it before writing my own 'day in Harvey's life'. Richardson's picture is a fascinating one and I might, perhaps, have been prevented from writing what might be thought to be an imitation. But after reading Richardson (whose account encouraged me by a coincidence of ideas and sentiments which was quite accidental) I decided not to change one word of my own text. The independence of my picture is obvious especially in the choice of scenes. Mine are purposely set in the year preceding the publication of the *Exercitatio*. Then, peculiar to my account are the conversation between Harvey and his students at the hospital in the morning, the messenger sent in vain to seek the physician (then only Physician Extraordinary) at the King's command; the encounter with the two Physicians in Ordinary and with Queen Henrietta Maria; the scene of the dinner with Mrs. Harvey and the parrot; the incident of the nocturnal outing for clandestine dissection at St. Bartholomew's and finally the finishing touches put at dawn to the MS. impatiently awaited by the Frankfurt publisher. But certainly there is a point in common between my account and that of Richardson—a common admiration for Harvey.

Harvey threads his way through the maze the shops are just opening their cramped stalls.

From Harvey's house to the hospital is no great distance, even if we suppose that he had not, by 1627, left his first residence in the parish of St. Martin-extra-Ludgate where, as we shall see, D'Arcy Power thinks that he took up his quarters when he first settled in London in 1604. The house was near the Ludgate and close to a little church that was destroyed in the Great Fire of 1666, but which was rebuilt and today raises its small, graceful nave and tall-pointed steeple against the background of Wren's imposing cathedral.

Some think that before 1627 Harvey had come to dwell much nearer to the hospital, which lay on the west side of the great open space known as Smithfield. Smithfield on certain days served as a fair-ground, after having been the theatre of the burning of many martyrs at the stake during the reign of Bloody Mary.[1] Since, however, we are not quite sure where Harvey lived in 1627, and as, moreover, the matter is not one of any great importance, we shall, in our imaginative reconstruction of Harvey's day, keep to the house D'Arcy Power refers to. Therefore we must think of Harvey as making his way from Ludgate through narrow ways and alleys to St. Bartholomew's. The pictorial map shown in Plate II, though made a little earlier, gives a very fair idea of the London of that period.

In Harvey's time, St. Bartholomew's Hospital was situated to the north of, and outside, another of the City gates. It was built upon a triangular site whose southern base touched the Roman Wall and whose northern point projected into the huge waste ground of Smithfield which, in its central part, has remained unbuilt over to this day (see Plate III). The buildings, chapel, gardens, courtyard and burial-yard of the hospital occupied an even greater area than that shown in the map of modern London (see Plate IV). We can see the site occupying a triangle with the northern point quite near the church of St. Bartholomew the Great (a church and a parish independent of the hospital) and with the sides formed by Giltspur Street on the west and by Little Britain on the east.[2] We may say,

---

[1] The allusion is to the stakes set up here on not a few occasions during the reign of Mary Tudor and during the violent Catholic reaction of her time. Some forty Protestants were burned at Smithfield. On the walls of St. Bartholomew's Hospital is a commemorative inscription recalling these tragic happenings.

[2] St. Bartholomew's Hospital was founded by a certain Rahere in the reign of Henry I (1123) and is therefore one of the most ancient of all the western European hospitals. Rahere having fallen sick while on pilgrimage in the Holy Land made a vow that if he recovered he would, upon his return to England, establish some

here, that the ancient church of St. Bartholomew the Great, a magnificent specimen of 12th-century Romanesque architecture, never formed part of the hospital and belonged to a parish beyond Little Britain. In the 17th century the hospital, however, spread its outbuildings over Little Britain towards the east and, in fact, reached almost to Aldersgate Street. The base of the hospital's triangle (which is now occupied by the General Post Office) extended to Newgate Street—that is to say, as far as the fortified City Wall.

The *intra-muros* area on the other side of the Wall—and between it and old St. Paul's—was occupied by the pious and charitable foundations of Christ Church and Christ's Hospital. These were thus separated from St. Bartholomew's by the City Wall (clearly marked on our plan) and for this reason the two *intra-muros* foundations were completely destroyed by the Great Fire of 1666 while St. Bartholomew's Hospital, being without the walls, was happily spared, as was also the church of St. Bartholomew the Great.

But we must return to Dr. Harvey walking in the early December morning to his hospital. He moves rapidly, carried along by supple and muscular legs that never seem to tire. His leather, silver-buckled shoes appear to skip along over the puddles and gutters and through the mud that the damp and lack of sunlight conspire to maintain in the narrow streets. He proceeds without conscious difficulty, but if, on some other occasion, we had met him and chanced to get in his way, we should have seen him raise his head and dart a singularly sharp and penetrating glance in our direction—a glance that betrayed his annoyance and impatience at being disturbed in his cogitations. But should he meet one of the few friends who are devoted to him, and who understand something of what is going on in his busy mind, then an affable and almost grateful smile would welcome the encounter. A conversation would be engaged, lively, urgent, convincing; a conversation about the work in hand, expressing a conviction ever more explicit that the truth had not only been discovered but had been proved. The man who but a few moments before had been so silent, so meditative,

---

pious foundation. It is said that in a dream he beheld the Apostle St. Bartholomew pointing out to him the site of Smithfield where he should found both a hospital and a church. The church of St. Bartholomew the Great dates, indeed, from the 12th century. The Augustinian Canons (to whose Order Rahere belonged and whose prior he later became) received from Henry I the permission they begged for and work on the foundation began in 1123. Rahere died in 1144 and his tomb still exists in the church he built. In Harvey's time the hospital was staffed by laymen, all the religious Orders having, of course, been suppressed by Henry VIII.

would become eloquent in his desire to instil into the spirit of his friend the conviction and the certitude that he himself felt.

The physician, if need be, would pause from time to time and finger the little dagger that since his Padua days he always wore at his left side. He would unsheath it and then, with of course no hostile intention, would place the point or the flat side in the palm or on the back of his hand, as though the better to support his arguments for the principle of the circulation of the blood which the ignorant and the wilfully obstinate would still not accept. If he raised his dirk to the heavens there was no need to be afraid. The gesture was not that of an Italian bravo; the movement was just that of a man exasperated by the obstinacy of fools.

But on this day Harvey makes no encounter, opportune or inopportune, before he gets to the hospital, which he enters by the great north-west gate. He passes near the chapel (known today, as it was in Harvey's time, as St. Bartholomew the Less) and walks quickly to his own department. At the door he is awaited by all his assistants as well as by a number of visitors. The students are at work in the wards. Everyone knows the regularity and punctuality which the great man invariably observes. The assistants have to be always ready to answer the stream of questions that he addresses to them— on the state of serious cases that are giving him anxiety—the new patients—all sorts of incidents and happenings. His questions and comments are concise, and he likes answers succinct and to the point, for he hates all verbiage not related to fact. This done, he now turns his whole attention to his patients.

He enters a ward, stops at each bed and begins by scrutinizing the patient closely, examining him, looking through him as it were, and neither questioning him nor making any remarks until he has finished a close inspection that is often followed by silent meditation.

The fact is that in acting thus Harvey is not only thinking about his patient's case. He is also gathering up for himself a provision of observations and information. He is always concerned to understand, to learn, to link up what he sees with what he has seen before, to add to what he already knows, or to correct his earlier impressions, for he is the personification of scrupulous honesty and a very slave of truth and duty. And, as he is essentially a kind man, he never leaves a patient's side without a few words of friendly encouragement and comfort which contrast markedly with the silent severity of his first manner.

He has not only to deal with the medical cases but with the surgical ones also, of which the neighbouring wards are always full.

Harvey is the chief in the house, the principal doctor responsible both for medicine and surgery for (in his day) the master-surgeons could act only under the orders and surveillance of the physicians. One of the surgeons who enjoy the highest reputation is Master John Woodall,[1] who was received a Master at the age of twenty-two and is now both the subordinate and the friend of Harvey and accompanies him each day on his round of the wards of the great hospital. Together they discuss the surgical cases. Finally, Dr. Harvey gives his instructions and his authorization to proceed with such and such an operation, or to apply such and such a treatment. Such is his lively temperament and his intimate knowledge of anatomy, that he will not hesitate, on occasion, to perform operations with Master Woodall, without considering (like so many other physicians) that 'manual work' means loss of dignity and caste.

After his visit to the wards Dr. Harvey is in the habit of gathering together in his private office all the assistants and students who have accompanied him. Here, he recalls the cases that he has especially studied during the morning. He points out that if he has ordered a blood-letting to be practised on two pneumonia patients, whose eyes are glassy with fever, whose faces are congested and whose respiration is painful, it is because he knows that the treatment is entirely justified by the fact of the circulation of the blood, the main object of all his thoughts for the past thirty years.

Now we find him referring to the death, the night before, of a poor young man, an orphan. He died, so it is thought, of a 'serous apoplexy' of the brain. Harvey does not hide his disappointment that the rigid rules of the day forbid a physician to open a body in order to search for lesions and perhaps to discover the explanation of the symptoms that had been observed. What a blessing it would be for patients with similar symptoms if one could verify, confirm or invalidate the diagnosis of this disease, find the cause of death and compare the states of all the organs. But, alas! vain obstacles had been placed in the way of necessary knowledge—of indispensable knowledge. It was not possible to study the lesions in the dead in order better to protect the living. This prohibition against seeking instruction and enlightenment directly from nature was, as Harvey feels, an antiquated superstition, belonging to an outmoded way of thought shot through with chimerical fears.

[1] 'Master in Chyrurgerie' is the title that follows Woodall's name at the foot of the title-page of his work, *The Surgeon's Mate or Military and Domestique Surgery*, published in the same year as Harvey's, *Exercitatio* and, like that work he dedicated to 'The King's Most Excellent Majestie CHARLES . . .'.

Of course, Harvey would say, such explorations must be hedged round with all the respect and the circumspection possible; such experiments must not be left to the caprice of the first comer. But once these precautions were generally adopted, would not every intelligent man give permission to the physicians to examine his body after death, in order that the course of his disease could be ascertained and valuable lessons learnt?[1]

'We have not,' declares Harvey to the assembled company, 'more than three or four days each year, generally in the months of March and April, when we are authorized to dissect publicly the corpses of a few criminals executed for felony. Thus it is only at the end of the winter, during my Lumleian Lectures, that I shall be able to show you *de visu* some of the rudiments of normal human anatomy. I shall be able to show you nothing at all of the long-standing maladies which slowly kill patients by progressively deteriorating their organs, nor shall I be able to demonstrate anything concerning the maladies called "acute"—though these, too, take several days to accomplish their deadly work. Moreover, the corpses of hanged men are most often those of robust and healthy fellows, and are of little use for the study of pathological anatomy. Yet we must learn all we can about pathological anatomy so as to be able to compare it with normal anatomy. While we are awaiting these all too brief and incomplete sessions of our annual dissections, I give you as my Lumleian Lectures—that is, on Tuesdays, Wednesdays and Thursdays—theoretical lessons on diverse subjects relating to our profession, but I cannot conceal from you that I regret bitterly, each day, the lost opportunities of learning from the bodies of those who die in our hospitals lessons that are absolutely necessary in view of our great ignorance of so many important things.'

Dr. Harvey is still voicing his complaints when he is handed a letter. The messenger is waiting outside for an immediate answer. The missive is sealed with a large, thick impression of red wax on

---

[1] I should like to recall here a moving scene that I witnessed about fifty years ago in the old Beaujon Hospital in Paris. This anecdote will show what respect and dignity prevailed at autopsies in my time as a student. The scene was also cited recently (15th June, 1953) by my friend Dr. Crinon, recently deceased, in the medical review *Pallas*, of which he was the editor. Before the body of a very beautiful young woman who had succumbed to an embolism due to endocarditis, Professor Debove, who had come into the amphitheatre to practise the autopsy accompanied by his students, took off his hat and retired, saying: 'Gentlemen, this autopsy would not tell us anything that we do not know already. Let us leave this poor dead girl unscathed in her beauty.' Doctors are often more sensitive than their detractors would have us believe.

which the physician at once recognizes the Royal Arms. He reads rapidly through the communication and orders the messenger to be admitted. The man is wearing the King's livery, and Harvey says to him simply, 'I am ready.' They walk together down to a coach whose horses are champing before the entrance of the hospital.

Dr. Harvey has been commanded to the Palace. The King is ill. Harvey is, as we have said, Physician Extraordinary, which is to say that he is consulted upon occasion. (It was not until four years later, in 1631, that he became Physician in Ordinary to the King.)

On leaving the hospital, the coach takes the direction of St. James's Palace and skirts first of all the outer side of the City Wall. Then it drives west across the more or less deserted open fields of a suburb that is just beginning to encroach on the countryside. After approximately one mile the Palace in its gardens is reached.

King Charles I is, at this time, but twenty-seven years of age and has reigned but two years since the death of his father, James I, the son of Mary Queen of Scots. Charles is rather a small man but so slender that he appears somewhat taller than he really is. He is fond of sports and is an enthusiastic huntsman. He is, moreover. intelligent (as even Cromwell later admitted, though the Protector was to add that the King was also an inveterate liar). His general appearance is well portrayed in Plate V, though the scene there illustrated took place some years later.

When he was a young man, Charles had not often had to worry much about his health. However, on this day, as little Dr. Harvey enters the royal bed-chamber, he perceives in the half-light of a four-poster bed the monarch, half-sitting, his red, puffy face bathed in sweat, his breathing obviously painful and his frame shaken frequently by distressing bouts of coughing. In one corner of the apartment, and withdrawn from the bed, are standing the two Physicians in Ordinary who, to judge from their low whispers and lively mimicry, are discussing some subject on which the teachings of Hippocrates and Galen were opposed both from the point of view of diagnosis and of therapeutics.

Harvey, without appearing to notice the two masters of the healing art, silently draws near to the royal couch, and after a deep bow takes the sovereign's hand, carefully feels the pulse and checks it with the panting, rapid and jerky breathing. He then uncovers the King's chest and back, places his hands upon them and seems to listen to the sounds that emerge from the thorax. He palpates the abdomen, examines the legs and asks to be shown a specimen of the urine. At the end of a long examination, Harvey declares that there should be no delay in applying several leeches to the patient's right side. The King must then drink plenty of warm and expectorant potions and swallow an opiate preparation which Harvey prescribes. The King must be allowed to repose in complete quiet until the evening, when the physician will return.

The two medical colleagues have, during the whole of the examination, remained silent some paces away from the bed. Harvey soon reconciles their variant opinions by declaring without hesitation: 'This is without any shadow of doubt—is it not, gentlemen?—a slight attack of pneumonia with peripneumonia, and in the circumstances the best thing to do is to aid nature in her efforts and allow her to liberate the stagnant blood which has begun its defence against the malady, and to replace it with new blood. Thus, by the application of leeches, we may remove the blood that is immobilized and allow new blood to take its place, thanks to the marvellous stream of circulation that nature has established in the human body for its nourishment and for its purification. To achieve this end, gentlemen, I will send here my apothecary from the hospital, who will have received from me all the instructions which we have just decided together.'

Both the two physicians nod in approval and seem in entire accord with their colleague's declaration as they accompany him to the antechamber. As soon as Harvey's back is turned the two Physicians in Ordinary, who seem to have forgotten their differences, indulge in little friendly taps and subdued laughter, for they are at least agreed on the subject of Harvey's manias and his obsession by the supposed circulation of the blood through the body. As though he thought that he knew better than Hippocrates, Aristotle or Galen! It was, however, just because Harvey knew quite well what would happen once he had withdrawn that he had insisted that his own apothecary should carry out the prescribed treatment.

As he walks through the great saloon on the other side of the royal antechamber, Dr. Harvey perceives in the half-light a very young woman seated in one of the tall armchairs then fashionable, plunged in meditation. Not far from her, and in the embrasure of a multicoloured glass window, several silent gentlemen are standing close together. As Harvey enters, the young woman rises impatiently and the physician finds himself in the presence of Henrietta Maria of France, the youngest sister of Louis XIII. She has been married to Charles for about a year. To the Queen's anxious questioning Harvey replies with reassuring words, though he insists that the King must be kept absolutely quiet, that he must not be bothered with any State business and that no member of the Court be allowed to approach him. Then, repeating his promise to return the same evening, Harvey bows deeply and takes his leave.

The King has ordered, as a mark of his high esteem, that Harvey shall be driven home in a royal coach. The appearance of the sovereign's equipage causes no small sensation in the commercial district of Ludgate, where among the chaffering tradesmen tongues are sharp and curious eyes are ever peeping and peering out of doorways or from behind the stalls.

As soon as he is back in his study, Harvey punctiliously notes in his diary the observations he has made on his royal patient and the treatment he has ordered. Then his wife calls him to dinner. He sits down, facing her, in a dining-room that is lit by a spacious bay-window—a leaded light of variegated coloured glass that harmonizes well enough with the plumage of a large parrot on a high perch near one end of the table. The creature's antics and chatter amuse the two diners whose meal might otherwise be rather dull. For twenty-two years now the childless couple have daily watched the time slip by in a rhythm as regular as that of the clock facing the window, their conversation punctuated by the monotonous tick-tock coming from its tall varnished case.[1]

In this year of 1627 it is the fashion to clothe clocks in a long monkish robe, modestly closed from top to bottom. From the cowled head only is emitted, grave and sonorous, the Voice of Eternity, while a single hand marks the March of Time on a circular pathway representing the twelve hours. Later on in this book we shall have occasion to speak of the 'watches' of Harvey's day—for Harvey possessed a watch, a precious instrument which is described by D'Arcy Power as 'the minute-watch he used in all his experiments', and which upon his death-bed he gave to one of his nephews. But we must return to the Harveys' dinner-table.

The parrot adds to this rhythmically punctuated monotony a welcome note of fantasy that takes the physician out of the travail of his thoughts, and he smiles at the mingling of his wife's chatter with that of the parrot. It is during such moments of relaxation that Harvey's observant and meditative mind has suspected some connection between the vocal, and apparently mental, processes of this

[1] Harvey's clock would have been driven by a weight, but its primitive mechanism could not have kept very good time in the absence of a pendulum. Pendulums were first applied to clocks by Huygens in 1657, the year of Harvey's death.

singular bird with those of singing birds to which he has so often harkened. So it is that the acts and the attitudes of his parrot have induced Harvey to feel certain that it is a male. Indeed, the avian behaviour in which he thinks he can discern an obscure expression of the male sexual instinct has been described by Harvey in a pleasing and curious passage in his *De Generatione Animalium*, which may come in appropriately here while we are waiting for the two diners to finish their meal.[1]

'A parrot,' he wrote, 'a fine bird and a splendid talker, had, for a long time, been a favourite of my wife's. It was so tame that it wandered about freely all over the house, would call out to its mistress when she was away from it and would cover her with caresses when she came back to it. It would make signs of recognition with beak and claws, clamber up her dress on to her shoulder and then walk down her arm and often came to rest on her hand. If it was bidden to sing or talk it would do so even at night or in the dark. Impudent and sensual, it would often nestle down in my wife's bosom while, by a slight movement of the wings and a sweet, soft murmur it would mark its pleasure. I used to think that all this was but due to habit and a need the creature felt to have notice taken of it. Moreover I had always thought the bird to be a male because of its aptitude for talking and singing. For, among birds, it is rare for the females to sing and to compete in sweet music with the males, these latter alone tame and captivate their mates by harmonious warbling. . . .' (Here there is a reference to texts of Aristotle and Virgil.) . . . 'But one day not long after the demonstrations I have described above, the parrot, until then in perfect health, fell ill and after a series of convulsions, to our great sorrow died in the breast of its mistress where it had so often liked to nestle. When I made a post-mortem in order to discover the cause of death I found in the oviduct an almost completely formed egg which had there rotted away!'

A strange happening indeed, and certainly a cruel disappointment for a naturalist who was usually so accurate and competent an observer, but still an occurrence which must have caused some pleasure to a man who was such a fervent follower of the path of accuracy and verity, and a further confirmation of Harvey's conviction that true science demands always and at all times that one should be prudently distrustful of one's own opinions. However, on

---

[1] The passage is to be found in *Exercitatio V* of *De Generatione Animalium*. It begins thus: *Psittacum nempe insignem, docteque garrulum, uxor mea diu in delitiis habuit. . . .*

this December day, the parrot is still in excellent health and chatters away to Mrs. Harvey for all it is worth.

The meal is nearly at an end when there enters a sort of little wheeled armchair pushed along by a venerable maid-servant, a personage of high and ancient lineage, an exclusive visitor known to few houses in London. In the Harvey household he appears regularly at midday and in the evening—he is Milord *Coffee*. All the members of the Harvey family appear to have drunk considerable quantities of this novel beverage, which they procure at first hand from Harvey's brothers, the Turkey merchants.[1]

When, with undisguised satisfaction, the doctor has enjoyed the aroma and the taste of two cups, he withdraws into his study, which is also well-lighted by a multicoloured glass window. He is ready to begin his private consultations, but before he receives the numerous patients attracted by his ever-growing reputation, he opens a door hidden behind a thick velvet curtain and enters a very large room which he calls his 'museum'—into which the light of day streams through a plain-glass window. Against the walls are shelves with many bottles, jars and small buckets. Everywhere are living and moving things—little fish, crustaceans, eels, frogs, newts, reptiles, and others. Some birds are hung in cages from the ceiling, while before the broad window is a table covered with a thick layer of felt upon which a dissected frog has been pinned. Near the frog are some small instruments, many of them invented by Harvey himself for his experiments and among them a large magnifying-glass holding down some sheets of parchment covered with notes and sketches.

The doctor proceeds to give each creature the food appropriate to it. Then, pushing open still another door, also covered with a thick curtain, Harvey leaves his 'museum' and enters an annex to which there is no other exit. This room is a rather mysterious if spacious place, well-lighted by a window set with panes of parchment. It is a retreat fitted with rabbit-hutches and a small kennel—empty at this time—and serves the master for his more important researches and experiments in animal physiology. The use to which the room is put is indicated by various pieces of apparatus on a table near the window. There are a muzzle, some leather armlets, graduated receptacles for receiving blood or for liquids used for injections, various very primitive syringes made of pigs' bladders

---

[1] In Nos. 1–6 (1955) of the little French review *Grandgousier* are some interesting articles on the early days of coffee-drinking in Europe. We shall return to this subject when we come to deal with Harvey's will.

fixed to wooden or metal nozzles, strands of flax for ligatures and, finally, a leather case containing silver trocars, sounds and probes as well as several scalpels.[1]

It is clear from these objects, which all seem ready for use, that the table is soon to be used for an experiment on an animal, though Harvey seems to have been sparing in conducting the painful but necessary investigations which alone may yield the secrets of life and thus furnish arms for the struggle against disease and death. Harvey, was, indeed, always disinclined to cause suffering in the higher animals, whose pain and fright would be expressed in violent reflexes and in piteous cries. Whenever it was possible he used a creature of one of the lower orders since they seemed to feel pain less acutely.

On this occasion, Harvey, after a glance at his rabbits, withdraws, carefully shuts the two laboratory doors and regains his study, into which he at once calls the first of the patients who has been waiting in his ante-room. After his consultations, which are numerous and occupy a great deal of time, he takes yet another look at his animals and hurries out for his evening visits abroad. The first of these is, of course, the visit to the King.

This time the hack with the footcloth is awaiting him at the entrance to the house. He springs lightly into the saddle and, followed by a running footman trained to keep pace with him, he sets off at a trot, though from time to time he breaks into a walking pace. Thus, for the second time that day, he reaches St. James's Palace. He finds the King still flushed, feverish and breathing heavily, and still racked with painful coughing. So, without waiting for the services of the barber-surgeons, Harvey at once practices an abundant blood-letting which is followed by great relief for the patient.

Feeling much easier in his mind, Harvey now returns to his hack and running footman, and the three head back towards the City at the same brisk pace at which they had come. It is almost night when Harvey gets home. He has had time to make only two or three visits and has not been able, as was his wont, to stop and chat

---

[1] The silent film made in 1928 at the instance of the Royal College of Physicians, on the occasion of the tercentenary of the publication of the *Exercitatio* (1628), showed specimens of the instruments actually used by Harvey in his physiological experiments. These objects were either those which still survive or they were reproduced from drawings and explanations contained either in the first edition of, or in the MS. notes for, Harvey's Lumleian Lectures. In this documentary part the film is more praiseworthy than in its general conception and construction, concerning which I shall have some criticism to make further on in this book.

a few minutes with one or other of his brothers. In this year of grace, 1627, he still has five brothers living, all merchants and tradesmen prospering in the City of London. However, night has fallen and he makes haste to sit down to supper with his wife. The same ritual is observed as at dinner. The parrot makes itself even more conspicuous by its incessant chatter, and Milord Coffee makes his customary appearance.

Soon supper is over, but the little doctor, instead of going according to his custom to his study for work and meditation, takes up his hat, cape and walking-stick and runs smartly down the stairs. At the front door he glances up and down the street as though expecting someone, and in a moment he is joined by a man of rather tall stature, carrying a lantern and swathed in a long mantle. They set off together in the dark along the path we followed in the morning to St. Bartholomew's Hospital. This time, however, Harvey and his companion approach the hospital by a narrow side-street or alley, quite deserted at this time of night and with houses on one side only. By the lantern's light they find a low door in the great wall that bounds the hospital buildings. The heavy postern is covered with iron-work and studded with great round-headed nails. They give three sharp knocks and the door is opened at once. The two men slip in while the massive wooden barrier is swung back into place. The man who has admitted them says nothing but leads them across a yard to a small building, into which the three step, closing the door carefully after them.

Were we able to accompany the three men we should find ourselves in a large vaulted room, bare and cold, with extremely thick walls and but feebly lighted by smoky torches. In the centre of the apartment is a block of masonry in the form of a table. On this lies a long bundle wrapped in cloth. When this has been stripped off there lies disclosed the body of the tall young man who had died the night before. Then the smallest of the three men gets to work. It was he who, that morning, had voiced his grievances to his assistants and students. That night he secretly performs the task that he considered necessary on the grounds that it is the duty of a man of science to probe into the mysteries of disease.

After making a circular incision around the skin of the head, an incision so fine and regularly cut that when resewn it will be invisible under the long thick hair of the head, Harvey delicately scalps the corpse, and then rapidly breaks open the cranium by means of a few hammer strokes delivered on to a metal punch. The strokes awake strange echoes in the great nocturnal silence of the room, into which no sound filters from without. Harvey then makes an incision in the brain and its membranes, and an abundant flow of serous matter gushes forth. This is much greater than is considered normal, and it is apparently under great pressure. He next enlarges his incision so as to be able to observe the complex convolutions of the brain. They are of a rosy pink colour, except in one area where the membranes are, so to speak, drawn unnaturally together in the form of a spider's web. 'Here,' mutters Harvey, 'must be the original centre of the irritation that provoked this abundant exudation.' To his acute and generalizing habit of mind the idea at once occurs that a superabundance of serous fluid, whether it is found in the meninges, the pleuras, the peritoneum, the pericardium, or elsewhere, may be a sign of irritation, of lesions localized somewhere in those membranes. He makes up his mind to use every opportunity to test his theory, and if possible to trace the cause of such irritation.[1]

He decides at once to find out whether the viscera of the abdomen and the thorax are normal in the poor lad's body, so he opens up these cavities with a skill and rapidity that are characteristic of all that he does. He is struck to discover in one of the pleura a considerable amount of liquid much like that which had welled forth when the meninges were incised. He notices, too, that the pericardium, around the heart, also contains some similar liquid. He notes how the heart itself appears to be large and over-developed for the slender frame of the young man—it is as though the cardiac muscle has had extra work to do. Last of all, he sees in the lungs nodules or hard knots. These cause him to ask if there may not be some connection between them and the inflammation he has already noted in the pleura, the pericardium and the brain. Once more, he makes a note to 'verify when a similar case should occur, if there

---

[1] If any should express doubts about this clandestine autopsy undertaken by Harvey and should cite the then existing regulations and the legislation then in force, and thus charge me with a too highly coloured imagination, I would reply by quoting this passage from a letter dated 4th March, 1953, and written by one of the most eminent authorities on British medical history: 'I doubt if anything would have prevented Harvey from opening an interesting case, but I very much doubt whether he would have risked asking permission.' Moreover, it is interesting to hear from Harvey's own mouth the admission that he did, in certain cases, practise dissections. There is a passage in his first Letter to Riolan (1649) in which he mentions his numerous autopsies performed on the bodies of those who had died of disease. I gave a translation of this passage in my *'Nouvelle traduction française des deux lettres de William Harvey à Jean Riolan sur la circulation du sang'*, in *Biologie Medicale*, April, 1953.

should be found in the brain and the lungs, conditions similar to those found today'.

It is always in this methodical manner that Harvey advances along the road of objective observation, constantly comparing conditions previously noted so as to discover if, in cases apparently identical, the same sorts of lesions are always present. This is the method he has employed in building up, step by step, and by long and laborious work, his conviction (now a certainty) that the blood circulates continuously without any interruption throughout the body. Comparative anatomy, as he has observed it in animals during his varied and numerous experiments and vivisections, have forced him, little by little, to see clearly into a jumble which at first appeared absolutely incomprehensible.

This night, Harvey, tenacious and energetic as ever, after having carefully sewn up the abdomen and the thorax, as he has already replaced the scalp, retires from the mortuary with his assistant as quietly and as mysteriously as they came. The heavy postern closes behind them as by magic, and the mortuary is once more engulfed in the silence of the night.

Directly he gets home Dr. Harvey sits down at his table and scribbles some notes, which he slips into a folder. He then retires to snatch some hours of well-earned rest, for at the first hours of morning light he will, as usual, be at his work-desk, where he is putting the finishing touches to the manuscript of his *Exercitatio Anatomica de Motu Cordis et Sanguinis in Animalibus*, the fruit of no less than twenty years of observation and reflection.

So ends our day in the life of Harvey, in the year 1627. He was at this time at the height of his powers, and for some time past Wilhelm Fitzer, the Frankfurt publisher, had been impatiently demanding that Harvey should send in his manuscript, for at the beginning of the New Year, 1628, the great Book Fair would make a great stir in both Frankfurt itself and in all the surrounding country. 'We must not,' wrote Fitzer to Harvey, 'let slip this opportunity of getting your book known throughout all Europe.'

Only the Preamble remained to be finished, for the whole body of the work was ready for the printer. Harvey now felt more ready than ever before to declare why he had undertaken to write his book and to point out boldly all the contradictions, the impossibilities and incoherencies in the traditions and teaching of the Ancients.

Harvey's Preamble, or *Proemium*, had indeed been already enriched by the following passage of judicious criticism directed against ancient assertions still generally accepted and taught, such as that of a supposed transmission of venous blood from the right to the left ventricle of the heart, through the septum or muscular wall which was held to be perforated. I have translated Harvey's Latin text:

'The substance of this septum is harder and more compact than that of any other part of the body, after the bones and tendons. If there were any orifice, how—when both the ventricles are dilated—would it be possible that one should draw off anything from the other, as it is held that the left ventricle does from the right? And why should I not be quite as justified in thinking that it is the right ventricle which attracts, through these same orifices, the blood from the left ventricle? On the other hand, it would be astonishing indeed, in fact it would be absurd, to maintain that the simple passage of the blood should take place by such obscure and blind channels when, at the same time, air demands so much larger a passage?[1] Yes, I ask why must there be postulated the existence of mysterious and uncertain pores for the passage of the blood from the left ventricle, when by the venous artery there is a way that is wide open? For myself, indeed, it is discouraging to reflect that men have preferred to seek or to imagine a passage through the septum of the heart, a wall that is thick, resistant, dense and very compact, rather than through a venous vessel that is capacious, or through the substance of the lungs that is not compact, that is slack, soft and spongy. Furthermore, if the blood could thus pass through the substance of the septum or be extracted by it from the ventricular cavities, what need would there be for this septum, in order to nourish itself, to have recourse to the ramifications of a vein and to a coronary artery? And here is, again, something well worthy of note: if, in the foetus (when all the substance of the body is less dense and thus more easily permeable than in later life), nature is forced to transmit, by means of the oval orifice, blood from the *vena cava* into the left ventricle by means of the venous artery, how can it be thought probable that in the adult blood passes with such ease and freedom through the very septum of the heart that is by age made so much more thick and resistant than in the foetus?'

Harvey continues:

'Andreas Laurentius (Book 5, Chap. III, Question 12), following Galen (*De Loc. affect. Lib. VI, Cap. vii*) and relying upon Holler's experiments, states and proves that the serous matter and the pus of empyema can pass into the venous artery and then through the left

[1] The passage, said the disciples of Galen, of the venous artery, which they maintained brought air from the lungs into the left ventricle.

ventricle of the heart into the arteries until evacuated by the urine and the faeces. He advances in confirmation of this the case of an individual afflicted with melancholy and frequently stricken with mental disorders, who was relieved on the occurence of each paroxysm by an excretion of turbid, foetid and acrid urine. When, finally, this patient succumbed to his malady and his body was opened, no matter similar to that excreted was discovered in the bladder or kidneys, but there was a quantity of this liquid in the left ventricle of the heart and great quantities in the thoracic cavity. And Laurentius boasts that he discovered the exact cause of the sickness. For my part, I can but say this: while Laurentius guessed and foretold that undesirable matter may be evacuated by this channel, he did not notice that by the same channel the blood might be quite naturally brought from the lungs into the left ventricle, or, in any case, he could not, or would not, state this fact.

'From this, and from many other things of like nature, it is clear that many of the ideas handed down by our forefathers concerning the movements and functions of the heart and of the arteries, appear to those who will give these things fresh consideration to be full of contradictions, obscurities, or impossibilities, and that, as a consequence, it would be most useful to examine the whole question more profoundly and to observe carefully the movement of the heart not only in Man but also in all other animals. But, in order thus to pursue and to overtake the truth, we must conduct many vivisections and dissections.'

With that, Harvey laid down his pen. He had finished his *Proemium* as he had willed it. He had already written his dedication to King Charles, and that to his colleagues of the College of Physicians and its President, his great personal friend, Dr. Argent. He had, therefore, now completed his manuscript and on the morrow the courier leaving for the Continent could take the document to the impatient publisher at Frankfurt. For Fitzer, either divining the great value of the work, or having received good advice, was most anxious to publish the *Exercitatio* in time for the great International Fair, and that he did not hesitate to assume all the expense in connection with the book may be seen from the title-page, at the foot of which we may read:

Sumptibus Guilielmi Fitzeri

That is to say, 'At the expense of Wilhelm Fitzer.'

We need not enquire whether there are today many publishers

who would, on mere hearsay as to the merits of a book, offer not only to publish it but also to take the risk of all the expenses connected with the printing, but we must pay homage as we pass on to the learned and erudite Fitzer, whose greatest reward was that his name should be for ever associated with that of the great William Harvey.

Chapter II

Childhood at Folkestone and Canterbury
(1578–1593)

Birth at Folkestone, 1st April, 1578—Origins of the Harvey family—The
'Pepperer', head of the Guild of Grocers—Coats-of-arms of the various Harvey
families—The tardy knighthood in the Harvey family after William's death—
Harvey's relations and their careers—His own early awakening to curiosity and
the desire to know and understand—Entrance as a boarder at Canterbury Grammar
School—The Spanish Armada

It was in the little town of Folkestone on the coast of Kent that
in the reign of Elizabeth I there was born on 1st April, 1578, the
eldest son of a family of seven sons and two daughters. He received
the Christian name of William and was destined to make the name
of Harvey immortal.

We need not discuss whether the actual date of his birth was the
1st or the 2nd of the month since, as Robert Willis pointed out,
those who prefer the 2nd April can invoke no other reason than the
inappropriateness of All Fools' Day as the birthday of so eminent a
man as Harvey.[1] Obviously it would become rather difficult to
write history if we have to take into account such sentiments!

The name of Harvey is one of the variant spellings of a family-
name derived from the old Breton baptismal name, generally spelt
in French *Hervé*. There are, however, many other forms in France
—Hervey, Hervy, Harvey, Hervier, and so forth. Possibly some of
the English Harveys are derived from some far-off Breton ancestor
who emigrated to the lands north of the Channel. It is pleasing to a

[1] Robert Willis, *The Works of William Harvey*, published by the Sydenham
Society, London, 1847.

Frenchman to think that such a remote Breton origin may be indicated in what we can see of Harvey's skull in the portrait now in the possession of Glasgow University and which, in agreement with Sir Geoffrey Keynes,[1] we hold to be the best extant. This form of skull, common in Brittany, accords well with the tenacity of purpose evident in nearly all the members of Harvey's family.

In connection with Harvey's ancestry we may perhaps quote the opening passages of *William Harvey* by the late Sir D'Arcy Power:[2]

'The history of the Harvey family begins with Thomas Harvey, father of William, the discoverer of the circulation of the blood. The careful search of interested and competent genealogists has ended in the barren statement that the family is apparently descended from, or is a branch of the same stock as, Sir Walter Hervey, 'pepperer' or member of the ancient guild which afterwards became the important Company of Grocers. Sir Walter was Mayor of London in the year reckoned from the death of Henry III in November, 1272. It was the noise of the citizens assembled in Westminster Hall clamouring for Hervey's election as Mayor that disturbed the King's deathbed.

'The lineage would be a noble one if it could be established, for Hervey was no undistinguished Mayor. He was the worthy pupil and successor of Thomas Fitzthomas, one of the great champions in that struggle for liberty which ended in the death of Simon de Montfort, between Evesham and Alcester, but left the kingdom without a Parliament.[3] Hervey's counsels reconstituted in London the system of civic government, and established it upon its present base; for he assumed as chief of the executive the right to grant charters of incorporation to the craftsmen of the guilds. For a time his affairs were successful, and they wrought him much harm. But his idea survived, and in due season prevailed, for the companies have entirely replaced the guilds not only in London but throughout England.

'It would be truly interesting if the first great discoverer in physiology could be shown to be a descendant of this original

[1] Geoffrey Keynes, *The Portraiture of William Harvey*: Thomas Vicary Lecture, 1948, at the Royal College of Surgeons, 52 Plates. *The Personality of William Harvey*: Linnean Lecture, 1949, at St. John's College, Cambridge, with 8 portraits. Cambridge University Press, 1949.

[2] D'Arcy Power, *William Harvey*. Fisher Unwin, 1897.

[3] This passage refers to the revolt in 1258 against Henry III (1216–72), when the barons, who had already forced his father, John, to promulgate the Magna Carta, now went much further and, led by Simon de Montfort, subjected the sovereign entirely to their will.

thinker on municipal government. The statement depends for the present upon the fact that both bore for arms "argent, two bars nebulée sable, on a chief of the last three crosses pattée fitchée; with the crest, a dexter hand appaumée proper, over it a crescent inverted argent", but arms were as often assumed in the reign of Elizabeth as they are in the Victorian era.'

Let us take a look at this coat-of-arms of 1272, as D'Arcy Power has described it (Fig. 1, left, top). He thought it formed part of Harvey's blazon, but had this been so then we should, of course, have to consider whether such a display of arms did not imply a claim to connection with the 13th-century 'pepperer'. But in his attempt to show that the arms of the 'pepperer' Mayor of London were marshalled with those of William Harvey's family, D'Arcy Power relied upon the coat-of-arms reproduced in Fig. 1, centre, which is to be seen, clear and distinct and without any sort of doubt, on the Ditchingham Hall portrait and, also, it would seem (though this time rather indistinct and confused) on the shaft of a column in the background of the portrait of Harvey at the Royal College of Physicians (Plate I). The same achievement is to be found on the marble high-relief that surrounds Harvey's bust in the chapel of Hempstead Church (Plate XII).

On examining this rather imposing-looking quartered shield we can easily recognize in the second and third quarters the arms attributed to the London Mayor of 1272. In the first and fourth quarters is another coat which, as we shall find, was the sole armorial bearings borne by his family during Harvey's lifetime (*see* Fig. 1, left, foot). These appear to have been first used (between 1616 and 1620) by Thomas Harvey the father, five of whose sons were Turkey merchants in London. The crescents may have been allusive arms relating to the Levant, but however that may be, this coat was certainly the only one borne by William Harvey's family during the illustrious physician's life. Moreover, these arms were either confirmed or granted to Daniel Harvey of Combe Neville, Surrey, about the time that he was knighted by Charles II in 1660 (three years after William Harvey's death). This Daniel, son of William Harvey's brother, bore arms: 'or on a chief indented sable, three crescents argent', and we find no attribution to this Daniel of any coat resembling that attributed to the 'pepperer'.

Thus, it is clear that until 1660, and indeed for some time after that date, the arms of the Harvey family were only those we have indicated. This is the opinion also of the critic of *The Times Literary Supplement* who in his notice (dated 11th November, 1949) on

Sir G. Keynes's Vicary Lecture states that in the quartered shield 'Harvey's own coat is, of course, in the first quarter'.

Whence, then, came the quartered coat (Fig. 1, centre)? Although it is to be seen on three likenesses of Harvey it was almost certainly an 'improvement' effected after Harvey's time. What seems most probable is that after Daniel's knighthood and his grant of arms an attempt was made to claim some connection with the 13th-century 'pepperer' by quartering his arms. Over these 'ameliorated' arms was placed a crest suggested, maybe, by the *stemma* displayed by the illustrious uncle at Padua—a flaming torch with intertwined serpents. We shall come across this *stemma* again when we come to deal with Harvey's student days at the Italian university town (*see* Fig. 3, page 64).

Sir G. Keynes is inclined to think that the Ditchingham portrait of Harvey was executed after his death. If this were the case, then, of course, the coat-of-arms displayed on the picture must be later than Harvey's time. With regard to the portrait in the Royal College of Physicians we may remember (as Keynes points out) that there is documentary evidence to show that this picture was restored in 1706 when some retouching was done, especially to the right hand which is poorly redrawn. There is nothing at all improbable in the quartered coat's having been added at this time. The arms on the marble frame surrounding the bust at Hempstead prove nothing, for it is as likely as not that the frame was executed after Harvey's death. These questions have been well dealt with by Keynes and we shall refer to them again in Chapter VII when we come to consider the tomb, the will, the portraits and other souvenirs.

From what has been said above it is clear that the arms attributed to the Mayor of 1275, and those borne by the Harveys at least as early as 1620, are quite unalike. But D'Arcy Power (when discussing a possible connection between William Harvey's family and that of the 13th-century 'pepperer') took, as the authentic blazon of William's family, the composite and quartered coat Daniel Harvey adopted after he had received his grant of arms. However, if we compare the coat-of-arms (Fig. 1, right) borne from the 18th century by a family of Norfolk Harveys with that which was the original blazon of the London Harveys, we shall notice that the two present undoubted resemblances though no sort of connection between the two families can be traced.

From all this we may conclude that, as I mentioned at the beginning of this discussion, families of the same name often assume more or less similar or even identical arms, without such an assumption

FIG. 1. *Left (top):* Blazon of Sir Walter Hervey, the 'Pepperer', elected Mayor of London in 1272. *Left (foot):* Blazon of William Harvey's family confirmed or granted to Sir Daniel Harvey by Charles II. *Centre:* Blazon affixed to Harvey's portraits after his death and probably an attempt to claim some connection with the 13th-century 'Pepperer'. *Right:* Blazon and crest of Lord Harvey of Tasburgh, Norfolk, whose family have borne these arms with slight changes since the 18th century. Although it recalls the blazon of William Harvey in certain details, the families are not known to be related.

proving (though it may be intended to suggest) any connection or relationship between the stocks.

But I have, perhaps, spent too much time over this heraldic problem, suggested by D'Arcy Power, interesting and puzzling though it may be. To return now to the history of the man Harvey, all that can really be proved about his ancestry is that his father was a certain Thomas Harvey, born in 1549, who had two brothers and three sisters, who all married and left issue.

Thomas Harvey married his first wife Juliana, the daughter of a William Jenkin, about 1575. She died in childbirth in 1576, leaving a daughter. A year or two later Thomas Harvey married again, this time a girl named Joan Halke or Hawke. She was apparently some relation of the first wife and she bore Harvey seven sons—a 'week of sons', as Fuller says—and two daughters. All the children seem to have been born at Folkestone, where Thomas Harvey was engaged in the trade of Levant merchant. William was the eldest child of the second marriage.

Thomas Harvey served as jurat or alderman of Folkestone and in 1600 was mayor of the town. He was reputed to be a man of considerable intelligence and a skilful manager both of his own fortune and of that of the town. His sons always professed great respect for him. They confided in him and sought his advice in all things, so that Fuller says he was able to watch their rise to situations superior to his own.

D'Arcy Power considered it not improbable that this prominent citizen was, as alderman of Folkestone, a member of the special commissions created during 1588 and the succeeding years in the Cinque Ports. The object of these boards was to prepare the defence of the realm against the aggression of the King of Spain. We shall have occasion to refer to this again later on.

In 1605, on the death of his second wife, Thomas Harvey left Folkestone and settled in London. He lived for a time at Hackney, where he died in 1623 surrounded by all his children except his third son Thomas, who had predeceased him in 1622. The elder Harvey was buried in Hackney Church.

Of Thomas Harvey's wife, Joan Halke, we know little beyond what may be learned from the inscription to her memory on a brass tablet which still exists in the parish church at Folkestone. The inscription may have been composed by her son William. When she died he was twenty-seven years of age and was already practising as a physician in London. The inscription reads:

A.D. 1605 Nov. 8th died in the 50th yeare of her age
Joan Wife of Tho. Harvey. Mother of 7 sones & 2 Daughters.
A Godly harmles Woman: A chaste loveinge Wife:
A Charitable qviet Neighbour: a cofortable frendly Matron:
A provident diligent Hvswyfe: A carefvll teder-harted Mother.
Deere to her Hvsband: Reverensed of her Children:
Beloved of her Neighbovrs: Elected of God.
Whose Soule rest in Heaven, her body in this Grave:
To her a Happy Advantage: to Hers an Unhappy Loss.

Harvey had the good fortune to be nurtured in a healthy home, surrounded by an affectionate and contented family, and we can trace all through his ardent and courageous life the deep and precious influence of his upbringing.

It is also worthy of remark (as Fuller long ago pointed out) how, under wise parental guidance, the seven Harvey sons all made their way with unfaltering steps to positions of importance. They were certainly robust and healthy, of good sound country stock, and

they were naturally of a diligent and enterprising turn, but from
their earliest years they received from their parents a sound training
in method, aim and continuity of effort—qualities which, in our
day, are too often replaced by incoherence, instability and lack of
foresight. It was, then, under the able direction of their parents, and
indeed inspired by their parents' example, that the Harvey boys and
girls lived through their early childhood and acquired the first
rudiments of education—no doubt in reading, writing and arith-
metic, and general instructive observation of the things and people
around them.

William, the eldest, was no doubt distinguished by his lively
curiosity and by his ardent desire to learn, and it was certainly
because of these qualities that his parents sent him at the age of ten
to King's School, Canterbury, so that he might have full scope to
develop his aptitudes and tastes. John, the second son, became (jointly
with his brother Daniel) King's Receiver for Lincolnshire and sat
in Parliament as member for Hythe. Then followed Thomas,
Daniel, Eliab, Michael and Matthew (the two latter twins), all of
whom became prominent merchants in London trading with the
Levant, and all acquired comfortable fortunes. The brothers
remained closely united and were on intimate terms with their
eldest brother, whose material interests were the especial care of
Eliab Harvey while the great scientist was absorbed in his researches
and with his professional duties. It was at their houses in the country,
visited in turn, that William Harvey spent most of his declining
years. He was then a childless widower, and had been through the
horrors of the Civil War, though his mind, despite his years, never
lost its power of interest in research or study. Of Harvey's two
sisters, Sarah died young and nothing is known of Anne.

The seven brothers died at the following dates:

> Thomas in 1622, aged 38.
> Matthew in 1642, aged 48.
> Michael in 1643, aged 49.
> John in 1645, aged 63.
> Daniel in 1649, aged 62.
> William in 1657, aged 79.
> Eliab in 1661, aged 72.

When, then, William Harvey died in 1657, only one of the brothers
remained alive—Eliab.

There is a precious copy of *De Generatione Animalium* (First

Edition, London, 1651), bearing MS. notes in Harvey's hand and containing the following *ex-libris* dated in the handwriting of the owner:

> *Eliab Harvey*
> *His Book*
> *Anno Dom.*
> 1674.

Obviously this *ex-libris* was not designed by Eliab, the brother of William Harvey, since he died in 1661. The Eliab Harvey of 1674 was the youngest of the elder Eliab's children—the one who was knighted at the Restoration.

There is an account concerning the last male representative of the Harvey family (which became extinct in 1830 on the death of still another Eliab, a descendant of William's brother) in a letter from Horace Walpole[1] to Mann, dated 6th February, 1780:

'Feb. 6, 1780. Within this week there has been cast at hazard at the Cocoa Tree, the difference of which amounted to one hundred and fourscore thousand pounds. Mr. O'Birne, an Irish gamester, had won £100,000 of a young Mr. Harvey of Chigwell, just started for a midshipman into an estate by his elder brother's death. O'Birne said, "You can never pay me." "I can," said the youth, "my estate will sell for the debt." "No," said O'B. "I will win ten thousand—you shall throw for the odd ninety." They did and Harvey won.'

This midshipman became, later on, Sir Eliab Harvey, G.C.B., who commanded the *Téméraire* at the Battle of Trafalgar and was Admiral of the Blue. He sat in the House of Commons from 1780 to 1784 for the town of Maldon, and for the county of Essex from 1802 until his death in 1830. He was, as we have said, the last male descendant of William Harvey's family.

The estate of Chigwell, then some ten miles to the north-east of London (but now almost in the suburbs), was bought by Eliab, William Harvey's brother, and the portraits of the elder Thomas Harvey and his seven sons could be seen on the dining-room walls there until a few years ago. These pictures are now at the Royal College of Physicians, and a fuller account of them will be found in Chapter VII.

[1] Horace Walpole (1717–97), fourth son of Sir Robert Walpole (1676–1745), during his first tour on the Continent with the poet Gray made the acquaintance at Florence of Mann, the British envoy to the Tuscan Court, and thereafter exchanged with him a correspondence that lasted for forty-five years and was first published in Walpole's *Letters* (1837–39).

Now that we have some idea of the Harvey family's fortunes, let us return to Folkestone and to William Harvey's childhood days. William's first ten years were spent with his brothers and sisters in this small Channel port. After receiving at home the first rudiments of education William (whose lively mind and curiosity did not seem to mark him out as fit for trade) was sent to King's Grammar School at Canterbury.

No doubt the grammar schools did not make any very great demands upon the intellect of their pupils, and nothing like the demands that so soon were to be made on boys in the French 'colleges' that Villon, Clement Marot and Montaigne had attacked so vigorously. In England, the schoolmasters' own habits were influenced by the practice of physical exercises and by sports, so that these things came to be thought of as integral parts of the scholastic curriculum, necessary for the formation of the ideal 'complete man' and a gentleman. Nothing of this sort existed in the French provincial 'colleges' or at the Sorbonne. At the English grammar schools and universities all manner of sports were practised, for the English have never lost sight of the legitimate demands of the body. (Maybe the body demands more sport and exercise in the English climate.[1])

At Canterbury, young Harvey must have tempered and made supple the fine steel of his body and acquired that physical vigour which, later on, was to allow him to meet without flagging the insistent demands of his scientific and professional pursuits. To his vigorous outdoor life, both at school and during his holidays among his friends at Folkestone, we may also attribute not a little of his keen observation, his unerring rapidity of glance, his decision of manner, and that precision in execution that he was, throughout his life, to display in so eminent a degree.

We have no documents or souvenirs relating to Harvey's schooldays at Canterbury, but we may, however, note two facts of some interest. The year of his admission to the King's School was 1588. All England was then in a great state of excitement before the menace of Spain. It was common knowledge that Philip II was equipping a formidable Armada, which he had dubbed the 'Invincible' and which was to bring rapidly to heel the English merchants who, for years past, had challenged the Spanish mastery of the seas and

---

[1] I cannot too often recommend the excellent book published in 1888 by Pierre de Coubertin (who revived the Olympic Games), *L'Education en Angleterre*, where the author incidentally recounts the history of the more famous Public Schools.

had disputed with the Spaniards the riches of those new lands that Castile owed to Columbus's genius—and good luck. The English pirates must be stopped once and for all, and, in the view of Philip and his counsellors, the hundred and fifty large ships, armed and equipped (and fitted to take on board more troops in the Low Countries) for the express purpose of invading England, must achieve rapid and complete success. But, under the threat, the English worked at fever heat in all the southern ports; the 'Brodereild' or Confederation of the Cinque Ports was formed, Folkestone and Dover playing an important part in the plan of defence. As many vessels as possible, of all sorts and sizes, were gathered together. They were very inferior in tonnage to the ships of the Armada but they were (as in olden times were the Greek triremes at Salamis) much lighter and easier to manœuvre, and they were commanded by tried and experienced seamen.

The English surprise tactics in the Channel worried the enemy, repeated bouts of foul weather lashed the Spanish fleet and the huge, heavy convoy soon broke up. Finally the Armada had to execute a disastrous voyage around the whole of the British Isles, and the surviving vessels lumbered home and made their way crippled into the Spanish ports. It is not difficult to imagine how great was the rejoicing in England. Those were days of triumph and pride that the soil of the realm had been kept inviolate. The younger people who were the witnesses of these events might have been excused if they showed themselves a little 'chauvinistic', as we might say today. The year 1588 and those following must have been exciting ones for young William Harvey, especially when he was home for the holidays. He must have spent long hours in the port watching the embarkation of troops headed for Portugal and Spain, for the English were soon to take the offensive. So when, at the age of twenty-one, he left England for Padua, young Harvey must have had the feeling that since he was an Englishman he was someone of consequence. Indeed, as we shall see, in all the disciplines of his celebrated university Harvey impressed all-comers not only with his well-stocked brain but also with his juvenile authority.

The other incident that links us with Harvey's schooldays relates to events long after Harvey's death. On 7th July, 1764, there was a ceremony performed at the Royal College of Physicians in London. On that day the 'reverend and learned Osmond Beauvoir, Master of Arts and former Fellow of St. John's College, Cambridge, Headmaster of King's School, Canterbury, handed over the diploma (of Doctor of Medicine granted on Thursday, 25th April,

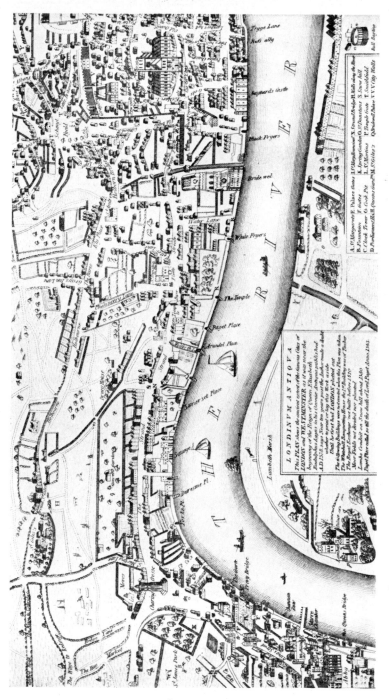

PLATE II. Part of a map of the cities of Westminster and London, c. 1560. Westminster Abbey is in the bottom left corner and old St. Paul's near the right margin. St. Bartholomew's Hospital lies between Smithfield (here Schmyt Fyeld) and the Roman wall. From 1602 Harvey lived for some years near old St. Paul's, just outside the City wall

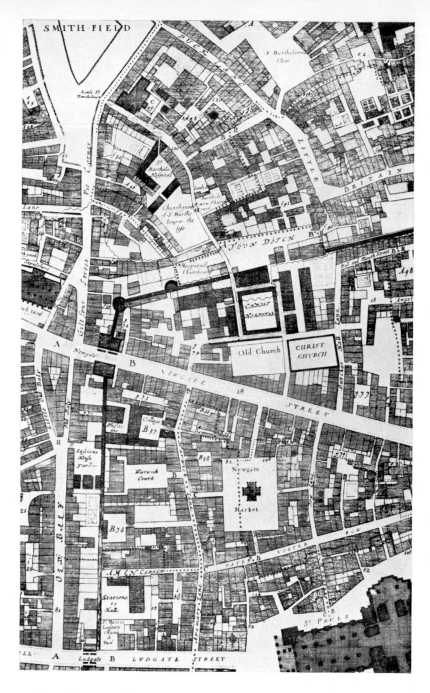

PLATE III. Part of a map of the City of London by John Ogilby, 'His Majesty's Cosmographer', 1677. Harvey's house was not far from the Ludgate. (From a copy in the Guildhall Library, London)

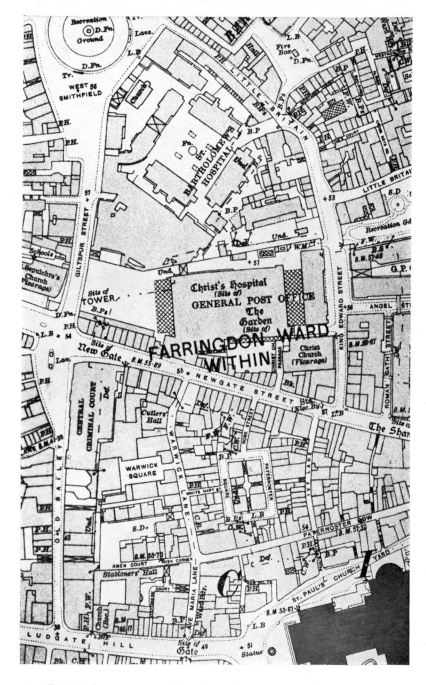

PLATE IV. The same part of the City of London as is shown opposite, but some 260 years later. Note the replacement of old St. Paul's by Wren's masterpiece, and the disappearance of the Roman wall

PLATE V. Charles I demanding the five members at the Guildhall, London, 1642. From a modern mural painted by S. J. Solomon, R.A., in the Royal Exchange

1602, by the University of Padua to William Harvey) with much liberality and kindness at the demand of Sir William Browne, Knight, Fellow of the Royal College of Physicians, London, whose veneration for the name of Harvey is almost religious, in order that this precious relic may be perpetually preserved among the most valued treasures of the College'.[1] This would indicate that for some time at least before 1764 the diploma had been preserved at Harvey's old school in Canterbury.

It was with considerable emotion that, during a Harveian pilgrimage undertaken in October, 1955, to Oxford, Hempstead, Cambridge and London, I examined this splendid document at the Royal College of Physicians. Here also may be seen other interesting, if less outstanding, souvenirs of William Harvey. We shall have occasion to refer to these things again, but our immediate task is to follow Harvey from Canterbury to his university of Cambridge.

---

[1] This is a translation of the Latin account written on the back of Harvey's diploma on the day of the ceremony. The College had just decided to issue a new edition of the Work of the 'Divine Harvey'. . . . *Dum collegium Medicinae suique honori consulens ad accuratius edendum Divini Harvei! Opera animum appulerit: Reverendus admodum doctissimusque Vir. D. OSMUNDUS BEAUVOIR . . . etc.*

Chapter III

Youthful Days at Cambridge
(1593–1600)

Harvey admitted to Gonville and Caius College—The City and environs of Cambridge—The origin and traditions of Gonville and Caius—Interest displayed there in medical studies and the link with the University of Padua

H ARVEY had been at King's School, Canterbury, from his tenth to his fifteenth year; at the beginning of his sixteenth year, 1593, he matriculated at Gonville and Caius College, Cambridge, a foundation which had been developed from old Gonville Hall, so-called from the name of its founder.[1]

Thirty-six years before Harvey went up, that is to say in 1557, Gonville Hall had been rebuilt and enlarged by one Dr. Keys, Kays or Kaye, Latinized as 'Caius'. Keys, who was born at Norwich, after having studied at Cambridge had gone to Italy in 1529, and there he had pursued his studies at the University of Padua under the famous teachers who were the glory of the ancient academy. Keys had been the pupil of Montanus, whose name is associated with that of Galen in a book Caius published at Basle in 1544 under the title of *De Medendi Methodo, Ed. Cl. Galeni Pergameni et Johannis Baptistae Montani*. In that same year, 1544, Caius also published at

---

[1] Gonville, who founded the hall at Cambridge in 1348 and endowed it with a number of scholarships for poor students (and who died in 1351) was, successively, incumbent of several parishes in Norfolk and Suffolk, where he also acted as bailiff and land-agent. In the latter professions he acquired a considerable fortune which he employed in founding his college or hall which, during the ensuing two centuries, was always protected by the prelates of the region. Gonville Hall was several times moved until finally, in 1558, it took the name it still bears today of Gonville and Caius College.

Basle his *Cl. Galeni Libri aliquot graece.* This was also the year during which, having taken his doctor's degree at Padua, he returned to England where he was soon appointed Physician in Ordinary to the young king Edward VI (son of Henry VIII) and later to his two sisters the queens Mary and Elizabeth I. Gonville Hall, enlarged at Caius' expense and endowed with twenty-five scholarships for poor students, enjoyed as 'Gonville and Caius College' a considerable renown. Dr. Caius died in 1573.[1]

So it is clear, from what we have said, why William Harvey later took the road to Padua. Meanwhile he was admitted to the College on the last day of May, 1593. The entry (translated from the Latin) reads as follows:

> William Harvey the son of Thomas Harvey, a yeoman of Kent, of the town of Folkestone, educated at the Canterbury Grammar School, aged 16 years, was admitted a lesser pensioner at the scholars' table on the last day of May, 1593.[2]

Perhaps we may, for a few minutes, take a glance at the town of Cambridge when Harvey matriculated there. The university, even in his day, was rich in academic foundations whose picturesque and splendid buildings rose like kings' palaces on each side of a central highway. One might think of this fine old medieval town as a northern Venice were it not that the north-south artery of the place is a noble street instead of a Grand Canal.

In this central thoroughfare of Cambridge (bearing successively the names of Trumpington Street, King's Parade, Trinity Street and St. George's Street), so much has been preserved from the Middle Ages and later periods that even today the visitor is apt to be overwhelmed by the succession of colleges representing eight centuries

[1] Perhaps we may note that Caius himself had been preceded in Italy by another famous physician and humanist, Thomas Linacre, who was born at Canterbury about 1460 and who, in 1485, betook himself to Italy where he studied, especially at Rome, both Greek and Medicine under the famed Barbaro of Venice and Padua. When Linacre got back he published the first books ever to appear in England in the language of Hippocrates and Galen. Linacre was appointed physician to Henry VIII, founded two chairs at Oxford and one at Cambridge, and took an important part in the founding of the College of Physicians of which he became the president in 1518. He died in 1524. It was Linacre, in effect, who taught the English to study the art of healing in the works of the ancient authors.

[2] The wording of this entry is enough to prove that Harvey's family had no right to bear arms, and indeed did not in 1593 pretend to them. Had it made any such claim Harvey's father would have been certainly described as *armiger.*— *Translator's note.*

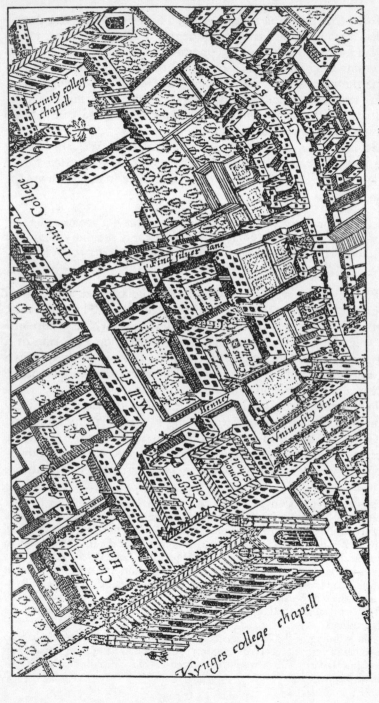

FIG. 2. Part of Hammond's map of Cambridge, 1592, showing the college buildings of Gonville and Caius.

of scholarship and erudition. The words 'Royal City' spring un-
bidden to one's lips (*see* Fig. 2).

And even if, as I have remarked, Cambridge has no central
Grand Canal it yet has its waterway, and even a modern 'Bridge
of Sighs', for the city has spread along the right bank of the
River Cam which, some distance farther north, flows into the
Great Ouse. The mingled waters, today hemmed in and embanked,
flow through a vast low-lying plain occupying the site of a huge
marsh that in former times was open to the intrusion of the sea
as well as to the waters running down from the neighbouring
hills. This area of bog and stagnant pools is now drained, though
even at the end of the 17th century Cambridge and Newmarket
(a little farther east) were quite near the waters of the Wash. It was
not until the 18th century that extensive reclamation was undertaken and the Fens pushed fifty miles farther north.

In the middle of the fens, on a slight eminence, rises the superb
Cathedral of Ely, like a lily emerging from the waters. This former
abbey-church is a constant testimony to the ardent piety of the
medieval monks and that of the strange population that once in-
habited the Fens—men seeking protection in the damp wilderness
where the snaring of sea-birds and the catching of the abundant fish
provided the only living to be got. These marshy labyrinths, indeed,
had offered asylum to fugitives for many centuries. It was into their
impenetrable lairs that the neighbouring populations fled from the
raids of Romans, and later from the Danes and the Normans. It was
in Norman times that some Saxon monks led the faithful into this
wet paradise and the abbey of Ely arose as a challenge to all who
would dispute the fenmen's way of life.

By contrast, Newmarket, on its hill to the north-east of Cambridge and also overlooking the Fens, is surrounded by downs and
dry valleys covered with short grasses and heath, became, in Stuart
times, what it has since remained—a centre of horse-breeding
and of the training of race-horses. Innumerable pictures and
drawings have perpetuated Newmarket's appearance throughout
the centuries. Many novels have been written about the place and
one such work of fiction, indeed, brings in Harvey's name in somewhat unexpected fashion. Speaking of the heather the author says
'where Harvey walking through the heather and heath discovered
his theory of the circulation of the blood'.[1]

We may well imagine that Harvey, a small, nervous man and
an excellent walker, must have walked more than once during the

[1] See Edgar Wallace's *The Green Ribbon*.

course of his long career all over the countryside around Cambridge and Winslow's Hall (near Hempstead), where he later lived. He must also have been a good rider, for otherwise he could not have so often accompanied his sovereign (who was for ever on the move) while hunting or at war. During the Civil War we must think of the King's Physician in Ordinary as more often on horseback than on foot and as undergoing, from time to time, the vicissitudes of a harsh and tragic campaign.

However, it was not, as Edgar Wallace imaginatively suggested, in crossing the Newmarket heaths that Harvey discovered his theory of the circulation of the blood. No, Harvey's imagination was fired almost certainly at Padua and was sustained in London by the success and promise of his researches. But we must return to Cambridge and to what was no doubt a significant phase in the early career of the great discoverer.

It is to the Cam's waters (often swollen by the rains) that the great university city owes its splendid lawns or 'courts', which are the Cambridge equivalents of the quadrangles at Oxford. As soon as you enter the gates of a college you are struck by the greenery of the courts, many of which lead right on to splendid gardens surrounding the collegiate buildings, and beyond them to the playing-fields. For rowing men the Cam is both a training and a racing water.

Although Gonville and Caius did not rival its brilliant neighbours King's and Trinity (which were expanded to their limits even in the late 16th century and were later on still further enlarged and freed from parasitic constructions), still, Dr. Caius's modest foundation was renowned as a hot-house, one might say, for study; both the quality of the teaching and the intellectual discipline were celebrated. If we seek out the old college, half-hidden by high modern buildings (necessitated by the University's expansion), the ancient structure cannot fail to recall the life of a departed age. The two square courts surrounded by the most ancient portions of the foundation are tirelessly attractive.

We follow the antique avenue of access, formerly narrower than now, but then, as at the present time, planted with an avenue of trees that begins at Trinity Street by the little low gateway that Caius called *Porta Humilitatis*, the Gate of Humility. This entrance has now been removed to another site, but the *Porta Virtutis* (sometimes but incorrectly called the *Porta Sapientiae*) still exists and serves as the entrance to the courts and the academic buildings. After giving them three years of study Caius's courts ushered men out into life and their future by the fine and highly decorated *Porta Honoris*, that opened into a lane called upon the old maps 'Henney', but later on made part of Senate House Passage. *Porta Honoris* was, indeed, in Dr. Caius's mind the starting point of that glorious and honoured life that he wished all his old undergraduates.

Though William Harvey could never have met Dr. Caius (who died in 1575) he certainly did find at Gonville and Caius traditions and precepts derived from the Founder himself, whose tomb on the north wall of the chapel is the predominating feature in that oratory. We shall have reason to think that Harvey, passing through the successive doors of Humility, Virtue and Honour, realized to the full the dreams and desires of Dr. Caius.

Harvey's taste for and bent towards medical and anatomical studies were encouraged and strengthened by the prevailing tendencies and traditions of the College. We may judge indeed of these traditions by the fact that Caius enjoyed what may be termed a special privilege. Each year his college received for dissection the bodies of two felons hanged at Cambridge. In fact we may ask, with Dr. Kent, whether the judges of the town could not have claimed considerable credit for having furthered the medical and anatomical vocation of William Harvey.

However, we have no document which allows us to learn how far this 'privilege' was exercised during the time Harvey was up at the University. What is most probable is that Harvey received a good general education in which Latin and Greek, with perhaps some smattering of the natural sciences (as then understood) made up the principal part of the curriculum. But such classical studies were by no means a waste of time, as we may judge by the use that Harvey later made of them. In fact, Harvey probably owed to them the fine habits of precision and the nice balance of judgement which are so evident in his scientific work, and which are so rarely attained save through the discipline of the humanities. He obtained his degree of B.A. in 1597.

We have seen that the young Harvey went to Caius College at the end of May, 1593, and stayed there—as has long been supposed on the authority of D'Arcy Power (*William Harvey*, 1897), R. B. Wyatt (*William Harvey*, 1924) and of Malloch (*William Harvey*, 1929)—until the end of 1597 or the beginning of 1598. The two first-named have him reach Padua in 1598, but Malloch gives the date as 1600 without attempting to bridge the gap between 1597 (when he graduated at Cambridge) and 1600.

Dr. Andra Bosatra makes no mention of the duration of

Harvey's stay at Padua in his article on 'British Doctors at Padua University,'[1] but L. M. Payne reopens the question[2] on the basis of the facts given in Sir Thomas Barlow's Harveian Oration, 1916.[3] Here it seems to be established from the *Exiit Book*—a record of students' absences at Caius College—that William completed the first three years of his studies (1593–96) without interruption, but that in the second period (1596–99) he was repeatedly absent for reasons of health. Indeed, according to a letter he wrote at Michaelmas, 1599, he had needed long periods of absence for convalescence. According to the *Computus Book* (account book), Harvey received a stipend for only one quarter between Michaelmas, 1599, and Lady Day, 1600, so that his scholarship lapsed at Christmas, 1599. This would put his departure for Padua at the end of 1599, in March, for example—for at that time the new year began on 25th March, Lady Day. In these circumstances Harvey would have spent a little more than two years at Padua (1600–1 and a part of 1602), not four. This would explain the absence of any record of his matriculation at Padua in 1598 or 1599.

We may now ask what were the reasons that led young Harvey to choose Padua in preference to any other of the universities then flourishing in northern Italy? First of all there was undoubtedly the consideration we have already mentioned, the tradition stemming from Dr. Caius himself. It was natural that the men of his College should turn their eyes towards Padua, in which Caius had so long sojourned. Moreover, there were doubtless old-standing friendships and perennial links between Gonville and Caius and the great Italian academy.

Then there was the renown and prestige of the University itself, made illustrious (to mention only the names in medicine) by Vesalius, Colombo and Fallopius in the recent past and by Fabricius at the time of Harvey's studies.[4]

Finally—and this is significant—for students from Protestant countries there was a sense of ease and security (not so marked in other Italian university cities) created by the atmosphere of liberal ideas that Padua enjoyed as the neighbour and dependent of the great republic of Venice, which was free of Roman ecclesiastical

[1] *Lancet*, 1955, No. 2, pp. 717–18.
[2] *Journal of the History of Medicine*, July, 1956.
[3] *Lancet*, 1916, No. 2, pp. 739–46.
[4] Among the souvenirs of Harvey that Mr. Payne, Assistant Librarian at the Royal College of Physicians, was good enough to show me was a Latin copy of Fallopius's works annotated in several places by Harvey's hand.

control and intended so to remain. Thus it came about that at Padua more than in any other Italian university there reigned a spirit of liberalism and liberty better protected against the Inquisition and less forced into a strait, narrow and crippling conformism.

Perhaps it may not be inopportune to open here a parenthesis on Harvey's attitude towards those problems which present themselves to every thinking man, problems about the Beyond and the things that lie outside our mere animal life—the things that make Man more than a simple automaton produced, directed and destroyed by the caprice of nature. In short, what was Harvey's attitude towards religion in general and religions in particular? No doubt, in common with all great liberal spirits, he was careful not to reject categorically or with a disdainful smile the comforting hopes of faith. He must have known, as a true man of science, that science itself has no power to throw any light upon these poignant mysteries.

He was convinced of—or he hoped for—the existence of a Supreme Creative intelligence, and of a future life in which there would be compensation for the trials of our earthly lot, and such a faith he affirmed, as we shall see, in the preamble to his last Will and Testament. It appears, too, that he had, early on in life, taken sides in that choice that Pascal was so soon to formulate and that Descartes himself hints at in the chapter of his Discourse relating to the moral attitude which every man would be well advised to adopt —the attitude of conformity with the usages and practices of his age. It was in accordance with this principle, and by personal inclination, that Harvey practised the Protestant religion in which he was bred (and we know only that the baptisms, marriages and burials in his family took place according to the rites of the Established Church). It appears from his life and writings that he was an enemy of all intransigeance and of all excess, and that his dearest desire was a general accord in a common mind of charity, mutual helpfulness and mutual forbearance.

Having said this much about Harvey's attitude to religious ideas, we may repeat that it was certainly the three considerations we have set forth above that led him to Padua: the prestige of the University, the example of Linacre and Caius, and the prevailing liberalism in speculation and in religious profession. And Harvey was not alone in being thus attracted to Padua. The University registers and archives of his time show plainly that there was then a large colony of British students at that University. Harvey's intellectual and moral evolution while he was in Italy is next to engage our attention.

Chapter IV

Student Life in Padua
(1600–1602)

The geographical situation of Padua—The city in 1600—Its population, activity and administration—Its universities and their organization—Harvey as a medical student at Padua—Fabricius da Aquapendente—Classical medical training—The doctrines of Servetus and Caesalpinus—Doubts of Galen's teaching expressed—Harvey is awarded his degree of Doctor—His last days at Padua

In following the young Harvey from Cambridge to Padua we are naturally first interested to know the route he followed, but of this we cannot be certain. We are not sure whether he started out from his Folkestone home or whether he began his journey at Cambridge or London. We do not know whether he took the northern route through Antwerp, Brussels, Lille, Strasbourg and Basle or whether he went through Paris, Troyes, Geneva and Milan. But what we are quite sure of is that once he had arrived at Padua his personality soon attracted the attention of both students and professors. The outstanding positions he occupied in the University afford sufficient proof of that.

But before we examine this phase of Harvey's life, when he was about to venture on to the territory of the Most Serene Republic of Venice (of which Padua was undoubtedly one of the most precious possessions), it may be as well to make a rapid sketch of the geography and the political situation of this part of Italy, as they were over three hundred and fifty years ago.

The territory of the powerful commercial and trading Republic lay at the north end of the Adriatic and beyond the mouths of the rivers Brenta, Adige and Po, whose waters with other coastal streams of lesser importance flow down from the Alps, and whose estuaries occur in the order named, reckoning from north to south. At the foot of the Alps the fan-shaped territory of the Venetian Republic spread out in plains which were stepped down to the sandy low-lands of the rivers' mouths. The State boundaries were the Austrian Alps of Carinthia and the Tyrol to the north, and a jigsaw puzzle of little countries—Milan, Parma, Modena and Ravenna—to the west and south, while towards the Adriatic the gates lay wide open. Here were the ports, here was the gateway to the Orient.

Surrounded by verdant fields and meadows, and a few leagues only away from the seashore and the City of Venice itself, Padua was a pearl set in a loop of a little stream that bears the pagan name of Bacchiglione. This river flows down from the north-western heights and, after having passed by Vicenza, strikes northward and then eastward before running south-east to mingle its waters with those of the Brenta, which empties into a lagoon to the south of Venice, not far north of the many-armed estuary of the Po.

At Padua the Bacchiglione's meanders encompass the city's walls, its right bank supporting the western, northern and eastern ramparts. In Harvey's day, moreover, the river (whose flow is very variable according to the seasons) still thrust a number of narrow arms through the city so that it was divided into three main islets—those of the west, the centre and the east (*see* Plate VI).

The western islet was the ancient heart of the city, the core around which suburbs had spread to the other islets. It was on this western islet (not much larger than the Ile St. Louis in the Seine at Paris) that the main buildings of Padua—palaces, convents, churches —were erected. The church of St. Antonio and its adjoining monastery, however, were on a neighbouring islet. In between these fine buildings were the modest dwelling-houses of the citizens. At the beginning of the 17th century all the buildings of Padua gave on to narrow, winding streets which, here and there, widened out into squares—some quite small, others of considerable dimensions. These open spaces were often bordered with the arcades that even today give a characteristic appearance to the town. Through this labyrinth of alleys, streets and lanes there pressed and jostled all day long a population that was most markedly cosmopolitan. As a matter of fact, to the permanent population of some 15,000 souls there were added no less than 3,000 students drawn from all countries.

Furthermore, within the triple girdle of walls that, little by little, had come to encircle Padua, the *Serenissima* kept a garrison under the command of a 'captain of arms'. The place ranked, indeed, as an important fortress. The civil power, however, was exercised by one of its *podestas* or mayors, assisted by a council elected by the citizens. Padua thus seemed to enjoy, under the sceptre of Venice, a considerable measure of local autonomy. But though they ruled with a velvet glove, the Venetians knew well enough how to secure the fidelity of the Paduans, for their city, by its strategical position and its garrison, was a key-point in the defence of the Republic should its interests be threatened from the landward side. The Venetians could always look after themselves on their seaward boundaries.

Life at Venice was not just made up of graceful gondolas, big business and amorous intrigue. Near the Arsenal were moored powerful galleys manned by crews often recruited by devious and, perhaps, unavowable means, crews that were subjected to a harsh training and a rigorous discipline. Moreover, the cunning and subtle Venetians knew well how to guarantee themselves on the landward side (at least to some extent) by the protection and the subventions accorded to Padua University, for, as an international centre, the famous Academy could claim a measure of protection from all the nations whose subjects resided within its walls. None of these Powers would have tolerated that Padua should fall under the exclusive influence of any one of the others, and so the Venetians could sleep soundly.[1]

On entering Padua, the young Englishman must have been greatly impressed by the milling crowds of youths from all countries come to learn at the University—Orientals, Greeks, Italians of all types, Spaniards, Germans, French, men from the Low Countries, Englishmen. All these had foregathered to enjoy what was then the

[1] The Venetian domination ended only at the beginning of the last century, after a few preliminary uprisings due to the contagion of French revolutionary ideas. It was on 28th April, 1797, that General Lahoz (preceding the main body of Bonaparte's troops) entered Padua without firing a shot and was acclaimed a liberator. For information concerning the reasons that induced the Paduans to hail with almost complete unanimity the new order of things installed by the French, we should consult two monographs by Signorina Maria Borgherini-Scarabellin; namely *La vita privata a Padova nel secolo XVII*, and *Il governo di Venezia a Padova nel'ultimo secolo della reppublica*. Extracts from these have been translated into French and were published by Luisa Acerbi under the title '*L'Université de Padoue: les academies, les étudiants, les conditions intellectuelles au XVIIe et au XVIIIe siècle*. (Published by Lidevani at Faenza, 1919.) Padua, after having formed part of the French dominions from 1797 to 1815, passed under Austrian control (always detested by the Italians) until, in the days of the *Risorgimento* of 1848, the former Cisalpine Republic was incorporated into the new Kingdom of Italy.

most advanced civilization in the western world, whether in the domain of politics, law, medicine, science, letters, arts or philosophy. In a word, Padua was a sort of new Byzantium that had arisen after the first efforts of Bologna and Ferrara at the beginning of the 13th century, and was soon to eclipse all other centres of study in Italy.

Padua was, indeed, the eldest daughter of Bologna, and like her mother was first of all a medieval *studium*. Padua appears as a place of learning as early as 1222, and did not become a university until the Renaissance.[1]

Moreover, it is interesting to recall that the foundation of the *studium* of Padua was due to the evasion, if we may so term it, of three masters from Bologna who wanted more liberty and wished to free themselves from the rigid control of thought and its expression exercised in a city belonging to the Roman ecclesiastical authorities, who watched carefully over everything that was taught in the lecture-rooms. To this day there can be seen, in the old university city of Bologna, a number of spy-holes or 'judases' hidden high up in the walls of the amphitheatre.

The masters established themselves in Padua at an old inn known by the sign of the Ox and there began their teaching. So it came about that the word *Bo* (that is, 'Ox') came to be employed in conversation as the name of the *studium*. One spoke of 'going to the *Bo*', or of 'being a member of the *Bo*'. This nickname, given by master and student to their *studium*, clung to the academy and was afterwards transferred to the famed University of Padua.

When young Harvey reached Padua, the original building of the Bo had been enlarged by the addition of numerous edifices which have been well described by the Hungarian writer, Zsolt Harsanyi, in his interesting life of Galileo, *Eppur si muove*.[2] The main University block consisted of a large yellow-coloured building two storeys high (*see* Plates VII and VIII). The entrance-gate, relatively small, was surmounted by an imposing bas-relief representing the fabulous animal of the Venetian blazon, the Winged Lion of the Apostle Mark, its head turned to the right and its paw resting upon an open Bible. This allegorical figure indicated, of course, that the

---

[1] Before the existence of the new-type Renaissance universities, which appeared only at the end of the 15th century and were in a measure inspired by the ideas of Boccaccio and Petrarch, the centres of scholastic learning were, in the Middle Ages, known as *studia*.

[2] *Vide*, Zsolt Harsanyi, *Eppur si muove* (i.e. 'Yet it does move', Galileo's famous declaration), translated by Müller-Strauss and published by Calmann-Lévy, Paris.

palace of learning depended upon the Republic of Venice, the *Serenissima*, as it was usually called.

As its buildings grew, the original *studium* evolved, little by little, into what was known as a 'Students' University', very different from the so-called 'Magistral Universities' which were then developing in other Italian towns and in different parts of Europe (e.g. at Paris, Oxford and Cambridge). In the 'Magistral University' it was the body of professors (appointed by some suzerain authority, either Church or State) that controlled the whole organization. Students must obey unquestioningly. In the other type of university it was the undergraduates themselves who both put the machine into motion, so to speak, and controlled its workings. Thus, D'Arcy Power has written:

'Hitherto Harvey had been a member of a Magistral University, now he became attached to a University of Students, for Padua was an offshoot of Bologna. Hitherto he had received a general education mainly directed by the Church, now he was to follow a special course of instruction mainly directed by the students themselves, for they had the power of electing their own teachers, and in these points lies the great difference between a University of Masters and a University of Students.

'In 1592 there were at Padua two Universities, that of the jurists, and that of the humanists—the *Universitas juristarum* and the *Universitas artistarum*. The jurists' University was the most important, both in numbers and in the rank of its students; the *artistarum Universitas* consisted of the faculties of divinity, medicine and philosophy. It was the poorer, and in some points it was actually under the control of the jurists. In each University the students were enrolled according to their nationality into a series of 'nations'. Each nation had the power of electing one, and in some cases two representatives—*conciliarii*—who formed with the Rectors the executive of the University. The *conciliarii*, with the consent of one Rector, had the power of convening the congregation or supreme governing body of the University, which consisted of all the students except those poor men who lived at other's expense.'

With regard to Harvey's career at Padua, D'Arcy Power noted that it has not been possible to find any record of his matriculation, although there are interesting references to some of his fellow-countrymen at the end of the 16th century. Although Harvey got to Padua in 1599, the first mention we find of him is dated in 1600. His name is slightly mis-spelled, although collateral evidence allows us to be certain that the entry does refer to William Harvey.

An article published in 1892 by a Dr. Andrich, and dealing with the English and Scottish 'nations' at Padua, mentions, says D'Arcy Power—'. . . a list of the various persons belonging to it. This register contains the entry "D. Gulielmus Ameius, Anglus", the first in the list of the English students in the Jurist University of Padua for the new century as it heads the year 1600–1, and a similar entry occurs in 1601–2. There are also entries about this person which show that at the usual time of election, that is to say, on the 1st of August in the years 1600, 1601 and 1602, he was elected a member of the council (*conciliarius*) of the English nation in the Jurist University of Padua. His predecessors, colleagues, and successors in the council usually held office for two years. He was therefore either elected earlier into the council, or he was resident in the University for a somewhat longer time than the majority of the students.'

Following on Andrich's publication, Professor Ferrari, then *Rector Magnificus* of Padua University, and Dr. Girardi certified after careful examination of this entry that '. . . there is no doubt that in the original the word is "Arveius" and not "Ameius" and that it refers to William Harvey'. They are confirmed in this idea by the discovery of his 'Stemma' as a councillor of the English nation for the year 1600. 'Stemmata' are certain tablets erected in the university cloisters and in the hall or 'Aula Magna' (which is on the first floor) to commemorate the residence in Padua of many doctors, professors and students. Harvey's stemma is reproduced in Fig. 3.

In 1893, Professor Ferrari, continuing the search (hitherto unfruitful) for Harvey's *stemma*, wrote:

'We have succeeded in our search for the arms of Harvey. We have discovered two in the courtyard in the lower cloister. The first is a good deal decayed and the inscription has disappeared; but the second is very well preserved and we have also discovered the inscription under a thin coating of whitewash which it was easy to remove.'

'The memorial consists,' wrote D'Arcy Power, 'of an oval shield with a florid indented border having a head carved at each end of the oval. The shield shows a right arm which issues from the sinister side of the oval and holds a lighted candle around which two serpents are twined. Traces of the original colouring (a red ground, a white-sleeved arm, and green serpents) remained on one of the monuments, and both have now been accurately restored by the Master and Fellows of Gonville and Caius College, Cambridge. A coloured drawing of the tablet has also been made at the expense

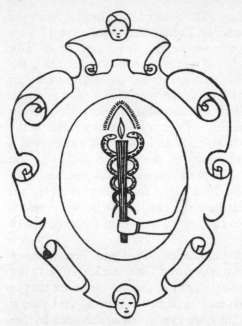

FIG. 3. The 'stemma' or symbol of William Harvey on the wall of the hall at the University of Padua.

of the Royal College of Physicians of London, and is now in their possession. A replica of this drawing was presented by the University Senate of Padua to Gonville and Caius College on the occasion of the dinner given in their hall in June, 1893, to commemorate the admission of Harvey to the college on 31st May, 1593.'

During a visit to Padua in April, 1955, I was able to note how well preserved this *stemma* is. It is on the capital of one of the columns of the interior peristyle and is almost directly opposite to the main gate as one enters.

D'Arcy Power draws the following conclusions:

'It appears, therefore, that Harvey was a member of the more aristocratic *Universitas Juristarum* at Padua, which admitted a few medical and divinity students into its ranks, and that he early attained to the position of *conciliarius* of his nation. As a *conciliarius* Harvey must have taken part more than once in one of the most magnificent ceremonials which the University could show—the installation of a new Rector. The office of Rector was biennial, the electors being the past rectors, the councillors, and a great body of special delegates. The voting was by ballot, a Dominican priest acting as the returning officer. The ceremony took place in the Cathedral in the presence of the whole University. Here the Rector elect was solemnly invested with the rectorial hood by one of the doctors, and he was then escorted home in triumph by the whole body of students, who expected to be regaled with a banquet, or at the least with wine and spices. Originally a tilt or tournament was held, at which the new rector was required to provide two hundred spears and two hundred pairs of gloves; but this practice had been discontinued for some time before Harvey came into residence. A remarkable custom, however,

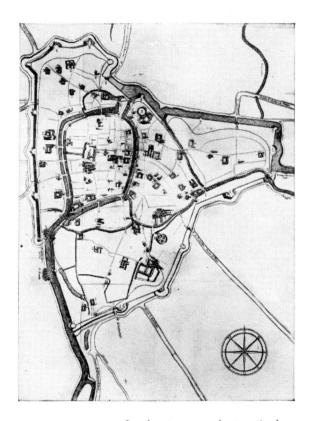

PLATE VI. Map of Padua in Harvey's time (early
seventeenth century). The river Bacchigliano flows
in from the south-west and, after encircling and
meandering through the town, which it divides into
the three islets described in the text, flows eastward
to the Adriatic Sea

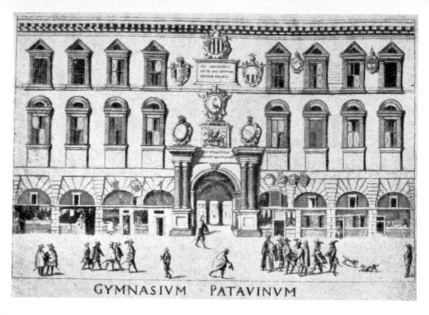

GYMNASIVM PATAVINVM

PLATE VII. The façade and gateway of the University of Padua, from a seventeenth-century engraving. They remain little changed today

PLATE VIII. The anatomy theatre designed by Fabricius at the University of Padua, preserved exactly as it was when Harvey attended lectures there

remained, which allowed the students to tear the clothes from the back of the newly elected rector, who was then called upon to redeem the pieces at an exorbitant rate. So much licence attended the ceremony that a statute was passed in 1552 to restrain "the too horrid and petulant mirth of these occasions", but it did not venture to abolish the time-honoured custom of the *vestium laceratio.*

'To make up for the magnificence of these scenes the Paduan student underwent great hardships. Food was scanty and bad, forms were rough, the windows were mere sheets of linen, which the landlord was bound to renew as occasion required; but to this Harvey was accustomed, for as late as 1598 the rooms of some of the junior fellows at King's College, Cambridge, were still unprovided with glass. Artificial light was ruinously expensive, and there was an entire absence of any kind of amusement.'

From this little picture of life at Padua University in those bygone days, and from the fact that Harvey came so soon to occupy such honourable positions, we must conclude that he must have been one of the most diligent and hard-working of the students of his time. What we shall later learn of his character and temperament also leads us to think that he must have made the best possible use of his opportunities. But this does not, of course, mean that we must regard Harvey as a dry-as-dust schoolman, working all day and all night and devouring books like a bookworm. We may be sure that he remained, essentially, the young Englishman we saw at Cambridge, and that he found, with others of his own nationality, frequent relaxation at tennis or some other game to keep his body as well as his mind vigorous and active. Not improbably, also, in his lusty and full-blooded young manhood he took part in some of those gigantic rags (often taking the form of ranged battles between different nations and corporations) of which the historians of Padua have left us descriptions.[1]

Many of these combats were provoked by the acrimony aroused by the action of the representative of Pope Gregory VIII and by the Society of Jesus by which, little by little, there had been organized in Padua another university rivalling the Bo, a university of religious surveillance. This was a monument of protest against the deplorable liberalism which, it was held, Venice and Padua exhibited by admitting to the Bo students without discrimination of religion— Protestants as well as Catholics. The two universities were always in conflict and one Rector of the Bo was even assassinated by masked

[1] See the work already referred to by Borgherini-Scarabellin and Luisa Acerbi.

individuals on the morrow of a decision taken against the Jesuits by the Venetian authorities. Also in the year 1600, while Harvey was at Padua, a former professor at the Bo, the famed ex-Dominican astronomer and philosopher, Giordano Bruno, was burned at the stake in Rome. He had been lured into an ambush by the servants of the Holy Inquisition which had then dealt with him.

Without doubt, it was at Padua that Harvey acquired the habit of always wearing a dagger at his side (as is reported by his friend and chronicler Aubrey), and also his trick of fingering the pommel while he talked.

But though Harvey may have taken his part in the disturbances that all undergraduates indulge in, he certainly knew how to absorb himself in his studies. His work was carried on with passionate curiosity and, if he had a number of friends in the different faculties, these were chosen by him from among those most fired by the desire to learn and to learn from each other. No doubt, in the fine season, he must have made any number of excursions with such friends into the most attractive countryside that lies around Padua. But then again, he must often have walked alone, absorbed in deep meditation. A man with such a strong personality, one with so great a power of concentration, with so logical a mind, could not consent to fritter away his life in unprofitable occupations, nor would he feel very strongly the temptations to waste his precious time in dissipation.

We cannot be far from the truth in thus assessing Harvey's character and temperament, and there is nothing, I think, in the following paragraphs that may not be supported by ample evidence of Harvey's reactions to the medical science of his day. There is nothing unlikely, nothing indeed that is not probable, in the conjectures in which I have indulged.

Such, then, was Harvey's temperament that he must have made a number of excursions into realms other than that of his chosen subject—into law, natural science, philosophy, arts and letters. These disciplines, in addition to his own of anatomy and medicine, must have encouraged his naturally critical turn of mind (that would never be satisfied with mere words and affirmations) to ponder on the attacks, admittedly timid and indirect, that were still being delivered from time to time on Galen's teaching, and to these attacks he must have contributed some of his own, due to his acute observations.

Most of all, he must have been often pulled up short by the contradictions exposed by the discovery that his master Fabricius had just made—or rather rediscovered—of the valves in the veins,[1] and by the teaching of Fabricius himself of a blood-stream in the veins flowing against these same valves! For, despite his discovery, Fabricius, then aged about sixty-three, did not deduce from it the right conclusions, namely that, in view of the disposition and arrangement of these valves in the veins, the blood-stream could only travel towards the heart. Moreover, Fabricius did not dare question or did not think of contesting the doctrine of Galen which made the venous blood to flow in an outward direction from the liver.

However, William Harvey, in the ardour and daring of his youth, hearkened eagerly to the objections raised by Vesalius to the new ideas of.Colombo, and certainly, also, to the theories of Caesalpinus (who was then teaching at Rome). The Englishman did not hesitate—albeit in the secret of his own mind—to free his spirit from the trammels of the official physiology derived from Galen's doctrines.

Frequently, when Harvey passed through the market-place his curiosity prompted him to buy from the stalls some of the newly caught fish, still squirming and flopping about. He would take them back to his rooms and there observe through an opened thorax the last spasms of these creatures' hearts. What he saw appeared to him to be in direct contradiction with the official teaching. During holidays and vacations he sometimes organized little expeditions into the Paduan countryside, taking with him a few chosen companions. They could, in a day or two's walk, reach the lazy lapping edges of the lagoon—a perfect place for catching small marine animals. These creatures Harvey studied carefully, seeking to understand the movements of their humours and their blood.

We may be fairly confident in attributing such activities to Harvey when they are so consistent with his character and temperament, and we may now, perhaps, be allowed to accompany him in our imagination on one of these meditative walks of his. We will

---

[1] The valves in the veins had, indeed, been described at the beginning of the 16th century in the writings of a master anatomist of Paris, Sylvius of Louvilly (1478-1555), 'that old miser, but prince of lecturers,' as D'Arcy Power described him, 'who warmed himself in the depth of a Parisian winter by playing ball against the wall of his room rather than be at the expense of a fire, and who threatened to close the doors of his class-room until two defaulting students either paid their fees or were expelled by their fellows. But the work of Sylvius had fallen into oblivion and Fabricius rediscovered the valves in 1574. His observations were not published until 1603 when they appeared as a small treatise *De Venarum Ostiolis.*'

suppose that, some days after he had been capped as Doctor of Medicine (on 25th April, 1602), Harvey set forth alone just before dawn with a well-furnished knapsack slung upon his back. In his hands he holds a stout staff. He is lively and happy, though absorbed in meditation, and he walks briskly in the fresh air which is still impregnated with the damp odours and perfumes of the night.

His mind is filled with his latest observations and his whole interest centred upon them. He puts to himself once again the question as to whether, in contradiction with all that he has been taught, there is not in all animals whatsoever a movement of humours that nourishes the body and follows a continuous *circulus* or circuit from veins to arteries, a movement that is for ever being renewed and repeated.

His meditative and generalizing spirit, animated with the energy of youth, recurs incessantly to the question as to whether all the movements of nature that he observed with such passion are not, in some way, patterned on that *circulus* which we find in all the realms of nature—for example, the water that goes to form clouds, the clouds that drop rain upon the hills, the snows that melt and seek the sea once more.[1] If it is the sun that causes the evaporation of sea-water and if it is the melting of this water's ice that gives back to the sea what the sun has drawn from it, have we not there something analogous to the action of that singular organ, the heart? Does not the heart receive the cold blood, warm it and then project it towards all the organs of the body, which the blood then revivifies before it returns once more to warm itself in the heart? Thus are his meditations aided by the horizons which, even from Padua, he can see stretching from the Alps to the Adriatic.

These matters are, however, as yet confused and imprecise in his mind. Little by little, the idea becomes fixed; it seems plausible— even probable; he is urged to follow up that hypothetical circulation of the blood suggested by a comparison of the heart with the sun.

Is not Galileo, who at this very time is teaching science in Padua itself,[2] inclined to accept the opinion of a certain Polish canon, one

---

[1] This idea is, indeed, explicitly expressed by Harvey—about thirty years later—in the *De Motu Cordis et Sanguinis.* We shall have occasion to refer to this again in Chapter VII when we come to analyse Harvey's great book.

[2] Galileo Galilei came from Pisa (where he had first taught) to occupy a chair at Padua in 1589, then being aged twenty-five. He was still at Padua in 1610, the date at which he invented his astronomical spy-glass, the ancestor of the telescope. No doubt, between 1598 and 1602, William Harvey must have had plenty of opportunities of meeting Galileo since the great astronomer was then at the zenith of his fame. We shall note again, in our analysis of the *De Motu Cordis et*

Copernicus, that the sun is fixed while the earth circles round it, and is the heart or centre of the universe towards which the vapours of the earth are drawn or from which they retire? By day the earth offers itself to the sun; at night it escapes the sun; but all the time our planet moves circularly around that centre of the universe. Well, why should not our hearts, fixed in the centre of *our* universe or organism, be to us what the sun is to the earth? Why should not the blood describe a circular course and then return to the heart, there to be warmed? A new and daring idea! But it is exciting and fascinating.

Then again, with the urge that the finest minds always feel to seek a unity of principle under a diversity of forms and expressions, he asks himself if a like order does not also control human societies —whether the prince or sovereign or oligarchy are not, in the State, like that central distributor that the heart seems to be—whether princes do not receive a current of riches in order to apportion it for

---

Sanguinis, that most probably Harvey accepted Galileo's ideas, for otherwise a passage in the *De Motu* cannot be readily explained. We do not know whether Harvey visited Galileo (who was at the end of 1633 authorized to return and live under supervision at his house in Arcetri near Florence) when the great physician came back to Italy in 1636 and certainly spent some time in Rome. Harvey parted company for a time, as we shall see, with Lord Arundel's embassy sent to the Court of the Emperor Ferdinand II at Vienna. But nothing allows us either to affirm or to deny that Harvey and Galileo met in 1636. John Milton was in another case, since we have proof positive that the poet visited the ageing Galileo. In his *Areopagitica* (1644) Milton, speaking of his sojourn in Italy in the years 1638-39, wrote:

> Thus it was that I found and visited Galileo, grown old a prisoner to the Inquisition, for thinking in astronomy otherwise than the Franciscan and Dominican licensers thought.

In *Paradise Lost* (first published in 1627) we read in lines 283 to 291:

> He scarce had ceas'd when the superior Fiend
> Was moving tow'ard the shore; his pond'rous shield,
> Ethereal temper, massy, large and round,
> Behind him cast; the broad circumference
> Hung on his shoulders like the moon, whose orb
> Through optic glass the Tuscan artist views
> At evening from the top of Fesole,
> Or in Valdarno, to descry new lands,
> Rivers or mountains in her spotty globe.

On the other hand, the English philosopher, Thomas Hobbes, waited upon Galileo in this same year, 1638, when Harvey was again in Italy. There is, then, some reason for thinking that the old Florentine master, once professor at Padua, was not forgotten by Harvey.

the good of the commonwealth. For our young counsellor at the Law faculty also meditates upon the mechanism of political and social institutions.

So in Harvey's mind there forms an image of a cycle incessantly renewed, a cycle from which, it seems to him now, no form of life can escape. It is true that in these matters, once more, everything is vague enough, but in a high intelligence a concept, however imprecise it may be, is a spur to further research.

Harvey has a day or so of solitude and communion with nature before him. What better opportunity to run over all that he has been taught, and to test it by the exciting new ideas that have haunted him for so long? He will review the whole subject in his mind while he walks towards Venice and the sea. If we are to follow him we must be prepared to lose ourselves, as he does, in the absorbing arguments of the subject. With him, we shall forget for a time that we are on a journey, forget the very road beneath our feet, the sky over our heads. The path is indeed familiar and makes no demands on our attention. (The reader, however, may find it helpful to refer from time to time to Figs. 8 and 9 on pages 184 and 185.)

Harvey's mind is running now on the known facts of anatomy, and he realizes that they are insufficient to support a final theory. He must, first of all, learn all that it is possible to find out about the intimate and precise action of the heart that beats so consistently and without interruption. He has been taught that when the heart appears most contracted and small in volume—that is to say, in systole, to use the classical term—it is then in process of admitting into its right cavities some drops of a 'first' and still quite 'coarse' blood which has come to it from the liver. This is the venous blood which that organ has manufactured as a 'first decoction' from mysterious elements brought by the *vena porta* from the stomach and the intestines.

This 'first decoction' blood (according to the traditional teaching) then pours into the *vena cava* by the hepatic vessels and rises in the ascending *vena cava* in order to undergo, in the heart, a 'second decoction' which purifies the blood by purging it of all 'fulginosities' and coarse matter. At the same time, Harvey had been taught, the right side of the heart undergoes a dilatation (because of the 'ebullition' of its contents). This enlargement—diastole—opens its upper 'exit-doors' and the venous blood of this second decoction rises to the lungs not only to nourish them but also, in them, to lose its impure vapours, while another blood-stream flows out of the heart by the superior and inferior *venae cavae* towards all the different parts of the body.

This ascent from the liver to the heart and the lungs, followed by the descent of warmer and purer blood from the heart to all parts of the organism, occurs (according to the teaching) like the ebb and flow of the tides in the Euboic Sea, so that for a time the flow sets in one direction, and then, after an interval, the blood-stream flows by the same channels in the opposite direction.[1]

While the right cavities of the heart, contracted and closed in upon themselves, are admitting venous blood from the liver, Harvey's masters have told him that the left cavities of the heart, likewise contracted, also admit a little venous blood through orifices in the muscular septum that separates the two ventricles. This blood, mixed with the *pneuma* that descends from the lungs into the left ventricle by means of the vessel known as the *arteria venosa*, is there, in its turn, subjected to a 'decoction' which, because of the mixture of blood and *pneuma*, produces 'arterial blood'—that is to say, blood charged with the 'vital principle'. This is then poured (by the apertures that the dilated receptacle had been forced to open) into the *aorta* which, like all the other arteries, 'sucks it up'. This blood is thus distributed to all the organs and reinforces the action of the venous blood, but the arterial blood, like the venous blood, retreats after its mission is accomplished, so that there is no passage of blood from the arterial system into the venous system, and no passage of the venous stream into the arterial stream. Here and there, however, there might be some anastomosis from arteries to veins but such a phenomenon has not been well explained and its existence, indeed, is held to be far from proved.

All this does not seem either very clear or very logical to young William Harvey. For, he says to himself, if the 'heated' blood simultaneously dilates both the right heart and the left heart, such blood must be in both at precisely the same moment, but there is between the two a thick, fleshy wall, or septum, in which there is no sign at all of any visible aperture. If there are only tiny and invisible apertures, how can the left heart receive its drops of blood

[1] The Euboic Sea is the long strait that separates the island of Euboea from the Attic coast, where the ebb and flow of the tide (generally so insignificant in the Mediterranean) is very noticeable because of the narrowness of this arm of the sea. This phenomenon so struck the Ancients that when they wanted to express their idea of the blood rising by veins and arteries to permeate the organism, and then returning to the heart by the same passages to be rewarmed, but only to start again on an endless repetition of its motions, they cited by way of illustration the ebb and flow of the tides in the Euboic Sea.

from the right heart in time to produce (after their mixture with air) a dilatation at the same time as the right heart and empty itself at precisely the same moment? There is something in all this that does not work out, he thinks; surely the difficulty of passage from the one side of the heart to the other must delay the action of the left heart, and so the two ventricles cannot possibly empty themselves at one and the same time.

Furthermore, no one has yet been able to see these supposed channels of intercommunication; no one can say exactly where they are to be sought. While Vesalius, in his first edition of *De Humani Corporis Fabrica* (Basle, 1543), still seemed to believe in the existence of these 'channels',[1] in the second edition (1555) he expressed his doubts, though without going as far as his former colleague, Servetus, who had perished tragically at the stake in Geneva on 27th October, 1553. (Prudence, indeed, commanded Vesalius to make no mention of Servetus's name.[2])

---

[1] André Vesale (1514–64) was the son of an apothecary at Brussels and came of a long line of physicians. From an early age he showed great curiosity in the workings of the human body, and after he had satisfied the Schools of Louvain, Paris and Montpellier he was nominated Professor of Anatomy at Louvain in 1532. In 1535 he enlisted in the army of the German Emperor, but returned to teaching at Bologna in 1538 and at Padua in 1540. He later went back to Bologna and from there moved to Pisa. In 1543, the first edition of his *De Humani Corporis Fabrica libri septem* appeared at Basle, but a second edition was published in 1555, two years after the death of Servetus, and in this Vesalius took a much firmer stand against the doctrines of Galen. He went to Madrid in 1561, where he wrote his *Anatomicarum Gabrielli Fallopii observationum Examen*, but was charged by the Inquisition with having dissected a living man and his enemies had him sentenced to death. He was saved by the intervention of Philip II, who had his death sentence commuted into 'a voyage of atonement to Jerusalem'. He lost his life in a shipwreck off the island of Zante, at the age of fifty, when he was returning at the invitation of the Venetian Senate to resume the Chair of Anatomy at Padua.

[2] I quote below the relevant passage from the *Christianissimi Restitutio*, in which Servetus anticipated Colombo by six years. In the *Bibliothèque Nationale* there is a copy of this book which bears traces of the fire from which it was rescued, but the text is clear:

> *Fit autem communicatio haec non per parietem cordis medium ut vulgo creditur. Sed magno artificio a dextro cordis ventriculo, longo per pulmone ductu, agitatur sanguis subtilis: a pulmonibus praeparetur, flavus efficitur, et a veina arteriosa in arteriam venosam transfunditur. Deinde, in ipsa arteria venosa inspirato aeri miscetur, expiratione a fuligine repurgatur. Atque ita tandem a sinistro cordis ventriculo totum mixtum per diastolem attrahitur apta supellex, ut fiat spiritus vitalis. Quod ita per pulmones fiat communicatio et praeparatio, docet. . . .*

Now this communication (i.e. of the blood from the right ventricle to the left) does not take place through the median wall of the heart, as is commonly thought. But by an admirable artifice the subtle blood makes its way, mingled,

We may here digress a little to remark that during that age of transition between the 16th and 17th centuries there must have come to the young Harvey's ears while he was at Padua some echoes of Servetus's work. Although the volume was burned whenever copies were found, still many clandestine copies of the book passed from hand to hand after the drama at Geneva. Although no one dared to speak of the heretic Servetus—heretic to Catholic and Protestant alike—we cannot think that the great Spaniard's work was not known among the cosmopolitan throng of students at Padua, men by their nature and condition impressionable, irreverent and ever open to new and subversive ideas.

Moreover, if Vesalius did not go so far as to reproduce (in the 1555 edition of his *Anatomy*) the revolutionary theory of his former fellow-student at the dissections carried on in Paris by the anatomist and surgeon, Master Gonthier of Andernach, nevertheless in 1559 the Italian anatomist Realdo Colombo, the famed professor of Padua who died in that same year but whose reputation long remained considerable, certainly did adopt Servetus's hypothesis in his *De Re Anatomica*. Colombo, however, added the prudent rider that 'no one has seen or described this before me'. And Colombo's text, we know, made a great impression upon young Harvey's mind.

The reader is asked to believe that we have not forgotten that we are still accompanying Harvey on his road to Venice, but there are many miles to go and plenty of time for cogitation and digression. We may picture Harvey here as taking a note-book from his pack in order to refresh his memory of some small detail, though he certainly has the outlines of the traditional teaching at his fingertips. In order to follow him we must be more explicit than he needs to be, and this the sympathetic reader will readily understand.

The doctrines of Servetus were better known in Harvey's time than they are today, and to provide a historic background to Harvey's meditations so that we may view them in a true perspective I shall give here brief summaries of ten relevant points which I

---

from the right ventricle by the long way round through the lungs. By the lungs this blood is changed, becomes yellowish and passes from the *vena arteriosa* into the venous artery. Then, in this same venous artery, the blood becomes mixed with the air breathed in and is freed of impurities by exhalation. And then all the mixture is drawn into the left ventricle of the heart at the moment of diastole, and is matter ready to be transformed into vital spirit. That it is by the lungs that the communication and the preparation are effected is shown. . . .

elaborated in the French press in 1955,[1] the occasion being the 4th centenary of the judicial murder of Servetus at Geneva on 27th October, 1555. These points are as follows:

1. That contrary to certain groundless allegations, Servetus was a learned anatomist and a man deeply versed in medicine, besides being an amateur theologian.

2. That Servetus's theology was based upon his anatomical knowledge and that it was upon this knowledge that he fully intended to take his stand. On this, and on what he had observed of the human blood, he considered that he was qualified, later on, to discuss the 'soul'—possibly because of the Old Testament phrase 'for the blood is the life' (or *anima*, that is, 'soul', in the Vulgate).

3. That, in consequence, Servetus wished, first of all, to tell what he knew of the blood and of its circulation; and this was not at all what Galen had maintained and what had been taught consistently for fourteen hundred years, as anyone may observe by autopsies (as Servetus himself put it).

4. That it was Servetus's anatomical observations that led him to contradict the teaching of Galen concerning the supposed direct passage of the blood from the right ventricle to the left through the supposedly perforated muscular wall which separates them. This wall is not, at least after birth, perforated at all.

5. That, in these conditions, at birth the amount of venous blood which is in the lungs and in the left heart must become arterial, and in order to pass from one ventricle to the other must take a long passage through the lungs, all of which is contrary to Galen's opinion that the blood rises to the lungs only to 'nourish' them and that it there lies stagnant, becomes exhausted, and does not pass right through the lungs.

6. That this new thesis of an unperforated cardiac septum and of the transpulmonary passage of the blood, set forth in 1553 by Servetus, could not possibly have been borrowed from Colombo, who does not mention this idea until 1559 in his *De Re Anatomica*. Most probably Servetus had discovered his theory while he was (together with Vesalius) acting as prosecutor for the surgeon and anatomist, Master Gonthier of Andernach, and Servetus, being by nature more daring than Vesalius, had made bold to declare these facts in the face of all his contemporaries.

7. That those who are obliged to give up the Colombo trail as

[1] In several articles in *Presse Médicale, Revue de l'Histoire des Sciences, Bulletin de l'Union Médicale Latine,* and the newspaper *Franc-Tireur.* My aim was to sketch a portrait of Servetus as a great, if largely forgotten, scientist.

hopeless, but who, nevertheless, are determined to deprive Servetus of the merit and glory of his discovery, maintain that he got his idea from a Moslem physician of the 13th century, one Ibn-en-Nafis, who did, indeed, write a commentary in Arabic on Avicenna in which he mentions what Servetus later on was to observe and describe. But there is no sort of evidence that Servetus knew of Ibn-en-Nafis's work, which remained unnoticed in Europe. The theory would imply that Servetus, by some extraordinary chance, was the only man to have known the Moslem physician's work and to have utilized it.

8. That since Servetus was himself a very skilful dissector (as Gonthier of Andernach states in the diploma granted to the Spanish scientist) it is most reasonable to assume that he had discovered for himself that the median septum of the heart is not perforated and that the blood must traverse the lungs. This is, I think, far more probable than that Servetus discovered the doctrine mentioned in an Arabic commentary of the 13th century. Why indeed should we refuse to Servetus, an anatomist of the first rank, the intelligence and the perspicacity we may be willing to ascribe to Ibn-en-Nafis?

9. That, admitting the bare possibility that Servetus may have been put on the right track by Ibn-en-Nafis, the fact that Servetus defended and proclaimed his discovery, through thick and thin, against the whole consensus of opinion of his epoch, proves that he must have reached his conclusions through direct observation and dissection, since, had he not been certain that he had seen the real state of things with his own eyes, even he would hardly have dared to publish abroad so startling a theory.

10. That, after Servetus's martyrdom and the destruction, at the same time, of almost all the copies of *Christianissimi Restitutio* (three only escaped the fire of the common hangman) still, not a few MS. copies of the book circulated in secret (as has been well pointed out and proved by E. F. Podach in the *Bulletin de la Société d'Histoire du Protestantisme français*: October–December, 1952), and that these came, without much difficulty, into the hands of the anatomists as well as of the 'theologians' who wanted them, so that it was by Servetus's book that the idea of the transpulmonary passage of the blood reached Italy.

However, though William Harvey would have been perfectly familiar with Servetus he would have had no need to refer directly to his text since Colombo had become a recognized authority by the end of the 16th century. Harvey would, for example, be well acquainted with the following passage from Colombo's *De Re Anatomica*:

> *Inter hos ventriculos septum adest, per quod fere omnes existimant sanguini, a dextro ventriculo ad sinistrum, aditum paterfieri . . . sed longa errent via: nam sanguis per arteriosam venam ad pulmonem fertur, ibique attenuatur: deinde, cum aere una, per arteriam venalem ad sinistrum cordis ventriculum defertur: quod nemo hactenus aut animadvertit, aut scriptum reliquit, licet maxime sit omnibus animadvertendum.*[1]

Between these ventricles there exists a wall through which almost everyone believes that there are passages from the right ventricle to the left . . . but this is a profound error, for the blood is carried by the *vena arteriosa* to the lungs where it is tempered. After that, and with some air, the blood descends by the *arteria venosa* to the left ventricle, which no one, up to now, has seen or described, although anyone can observe the fact for himself.

Further, there were certain other texts that also excited the imagination of the young student of Padua, such as that written (some years after Colombo) by Caesalpinus who was, when Harvey left Padua, eighty years of age though still delivering his brilliant lectures in Rome itself. (A portrait of Caesalpinus is given in Plate X.) We are now with Harvey in 1602, but in 1595 Caesalpinus had republished at Venice (in the edition known as the 'Junta') both his *Quaestiones Peripateticarum Libri V* and his *Quaestiones Medicarum Libri II.*[2] Certainly, young Harvey knew that Caesalpinus did not

---

[1] Realdo Columbo, *De Re Anatomica*, 1572 edition, p. 325.

[2] Because Harvey (who mentions Colombo) does not refer to Caesalpinus as among the authors who influenced him, it has been too hastily assumed that Harvey knew nothing of this anatomist. This is highly improbable, for as we have seen above, not only was Caesalpinus still lecturing at Rome, but his works had been reprinted at Venice only a year or so before Harvey took up his residence at Padua. Without wishing to exaggerate the influence which Caesalpinus's views on the general circulation of the blood may have had on Harvey, we cannot imagine that he was not well acquainted with the great anatomist's works. If, however, Harvey does not mention or quote from Caesalpinus's writings that was probably because he had come to consider that the Italian's arguments were rather feeble guesses than the proofs that must be forthcoming concerning the circulation of the blood, proofs that Harvey himself was to spend twenty years of his life in amassing and in testing. In this connection it is interesting to remark that the British film produced in 1928 (for the Royal College of Physicians) to celebrate the tercentenary of him 'who was its most illustrious member' did not hesitate to show Caesalpinus as one of Harvey's precursors. The scenario presented, first of all, the celebrated portrait of Harvey (executed in 1655) and then hands

share all Colombo's views since he wrote these words: 'The blood flows from the right ventricle of the heart, *partly* by the median wall' (no doubt this statement was a graceful tribute to the great reputation of Galen) 'and *partly*, for reasons of cooling, through the lungs.'

But Harvey knew, also, that Caesalpinus, in other passages of his works, went much farther than Colombo. So the young Englishman may have repeated to himself this quotation from the *Quaestiones Peripateticarum*:

> *Idcirco pulmo, per venam arteriis similem, ex dextro cordis ventriculo fervidum hauriens sanguinem, eumque per anastomosim arteriae venali reddens, quae in sinistrum cordis ventriculum tendit, transmisso interim aere frigido per asperae arteriae qui juxta arteriam venalem protenduntur non tamen osculis communicantes, ut putavit Galenus, solo tactu temporat. Huic sanguinis circulationi, ex dextro cordis ventriculo per pulmones in sinistrum ejusdem ventriculum, optime respondent ea, quae ex dissectione apparent. Nam duo sunt vasa in dextrum ventriculum desinentia, duo etiam in ministrum; duorum autem uno intromittit tantum alterum educit, membranis eo ingenio constitutis. Vas igitur intromittens vena est magna quidem in dextro, quae cava appellatur, parva autem in sinistro, ex pulmone introducens, cujus unica est tunica ut caeterarum venarum. Vas autem educens arteria est magna quidem in sinistro, quae aorta appellatur, parva autem*

---

moving to take hold of an ancient treatise; next they finger a few pages of Galen's *De Venarum et Arteriarum Sectione*, the *De Usu Partium* of Vesalius's *Fabrica*, and the *Quaestiones Peripateticae* of Caesalpinus. I know, of course, that quite different opinions have been expressed by other authors and I am acquainted with the remarkable articles in the *Annals of Science* (January, 1938, to October, 1939) in which the late Dr. Bayon set them forth. But since these opinions have not taken into account the texts of Caesalpinus which I have produced here, I am not convinced and I stand by the passages in the Latin text that I have cited above.

This does not, of course, mean that I see in these passages anything but a rather faint light, though one indicating a path different from that trodden by Galen. Caesalpinus's guesses, and his argument that there is a return of the venous blood by an opposite direction to that taken by the arterial blood in its flow, are founded only upon vague considerations and nothing is scientifically demonstrated. From all this all that Harvey could have derived would have been that sort of pregnant doubt which incites men of his mettle to go back and to start examining a problem from the very beginning—in fact to commence all over again and to reach conclusions only after every possible kind of observation and lengthy experiment. The genius and the work of Harvey are so immensely superior to all the inchoate mutterings he must have heard as a student, that it is in no way derogatory of his fame—quite the contrary in fact—to show how he and he alone overcame all the difficulties presented by a most arduous and delicate exploration. Once again we see that he must be acclaimed as the one and only true discoverer of the circulation of the blood.

*indextro ad pulmones derivans, cujus similiter duae sunt tunicae ut in
caeteris arteriis.*[1]

And it is why the lungs draw from the right ventricle, by a
vein like unto an artery [the *vena arteriosa* that we now call the
pulmonary artery], the blood in a state of ebullition, so that it
passes by anastomosis into the *arteria venosa* [that is our pulmonary
vein], whence it finds its way into the left ventricle of the heart,
while the channels of the *aspera arteria* (which are situated close to the
channels of the *arteria venosa* but which have no communication
with them, contrary to what Galen thought) carry cool air and
temper the blood by simple contact. The facts observed in dissection
agree best with this circulation from the right ventricle of the heart,
through the lungs, into the left ventricle. For there are two vessels
which terminate in the right ventricle, and also two in the left ventricle.
Of these two vessels one conducts blood and the other removes it,
thanks to valves so disposed as to aid in this movement. In the right
ventricle the vessel which brings in the blood is the great vein called
the *vena cava* and that which conducts the blood into the left ventricle, coming from the lungs [our pulmonary vein, which in those
days was called the *arteria venosa*], is a smaller vessel and which has,
like all veins, but one tunic. But in the left ventricle the vessel that
carries off the blood is the great artery called the aorta and in the right
ventricle a little artery that communicates with the lungs a vessel
whose walls have, like all arteries, two tunics. [That is, our pulmonary
artery, then called the *vena arteriosa*.]

From all this Harvey is driven to reflect that there is, through the
lungs, a continuous passage by the *vas intromittens vena cava* into the
right ventricle and by the *vas intromittens arteria venosa* into the left
ventricle. Caesalpinus conceived also of an uninterrupted passage
through the organs from the *vas educens aorta* (issuing from the left
heart) to the *vas educens vena arteriosa* (leaving the right heart). These
two systems, 'transpulmonary' and 'transorganic', do constitute such
a circuit or circulation as Caesalpinus was the first to describe.

So well had the Italian anatomist defined his conception, and
further, in his *Quaestionum Medicarum Libri II*, he had endeavoured
to explain the states of walking and sleeping by the different and
contrasting conditions of the veins and arteries to be observed in the
two phases of human existence. Caesalpinus thus expressed himself,
first of all making some observations about a ligature placed upon
the neck:

[1] *Quaest. Perip. Libri V.–Quaest. IV* (p. 123).

*Sed illud speculatione dignum videtur, propter quid ex vinculo intumes-
cunt venae ultra locum apprehensum, non citra: quod experimento sciunt qui
venam secant, vinculum enim adhibent citra locum sectionis non ultra: quia
tument venae ultra vinculum non citra ... Debuisset opposito modo contingere
... si motus sanguinis et spiritus a visceribus fit in totum corpus—intercepto
suo meatu non ultra datur progressus, tumor igitur venarum citra vinculum
debuisset fieri.*

What is most worthy of remark is that by the fact and act of the
ligature it is the veins above it that swell out and not those below it
and this those well know by experience who perform a blood-
letting, since they place the ligature on this side of the place selected
for the puncture because the veins swell above the ligature and not
below it. If the blood and the vital spirit moved from the viscera to
the uttermost parts of the body just an opposite effect would be
produced, for then, by the interruption of the blood's course, the
swelling of the veins should take place between the ligature and the
heart.

We shall see that, later on, Harvey repeats in his *Exercitatio* (1628),
almost word for word, this argument derived from experiment.
But to continue Caesalpinus's exposition:

*Ac solvitur ex eo quod scribit Aristoteles De Som. Cap. III, ubi inquit
necesse enim quod evaporatur aliquo usque impelli, deinde converti et
permutari sicut Euripi, calidum enim cujusque animalium ad superiora
natum est ferri, cum autem in superioribus locis fuerit, multo simul iterum
revertitur, ferturque deorsum. Haec Aristoteles.*

Thus are solved our doubts about what Aristotle wrote concerning
sleep when he says that it is necessary that what blood remains must be
continuously driven forward and then return again to be transformed
and renewed, in the same way that the tides ebb and flow in the
Euboic Sea, for the heat of every animal is so constituted by nature
that it moves towards the remoter parts of the body and when it has
reached them it returns again once more to the inner parts. Thus
Aristotle.[1]

---

[1] Aristotle, who flourished in the 4th century B.C., possessed the greatest
understanding and the most encyclopaedic mind of his age. He dealt with all the
problems presented by nature. In the 2nd century A.D. Galen, so far as his anatomical and physiological ideas were concerned, founded his teaching upon that
of Aristotle and his successor Erasistratus of Smyrna (3rd century B.C.). Throughout the Middle Ages anatomists, theologians and philosophers constantly refer
to these two Greek philosophers.

But, the young Harvey recalls, Caesalpinus refuses to accept the idea of a 'flux' and 'reflux' of the blood through the same channels, and interprets the movement of the blood much more judiciously as an outward movement through the arteries and a return movement through the veins at certain physiological times of the day.

Pro cujus loci explicatione illud sciendum est, cordis meatus ita a natura paratos esse, ut ex vena cava intromissio fiat in cordis ventriculum dextrum, unde patet exitus in pulmonem. Ex pulmone praeterea alium ingressum esse in cordis ventriculum sinistrum ex quo tandem patet exitus in arteriam Aortam, membranis quibusdam ad ostia vasorum appositis, ut impediant, retrocessum; sic enim perpetuus quidam motus est ex vena cava per cor et pulmones in arteriam aortam, ut in Quaestionibus Peripateticis explicavimus. Cum autem in vigilia motus caloris nativi fiat extra, scilicet ad sensoria, in somno autem intra, scilicet ad cor, putandum est in vigilia multum spiritus et sanguinis ferri ad arterias, inde enim in nervos est iter. In somno autem eumdem calorem per venas reverti ad cor, non per arteriam, ingressus enim naturalis per venam cavam datur in cor, non per arterum.

In order to understand this, we must know that the orifices of the heart have been so disposed by nature that blood is admitted from the *vena cava* into the right ventricle whence there is a way out through the lungs. Moreover, there exists another way of access for the blood from the lungs to the left ventricle, from which also there is an exit through the artery called the *aorta*. As certain valves are disposed at the entry and orifices of these vessels, it comes about that there is a perpetual displacement of blood from the *vena cava* through the heart and lungs to the *aorta*, as I have explained in my *Peripatetic Questions*. If we take into account that in the waking state there is a movement of natural heat towards the exterior, that is to say towards the organs of sense, while in the sleeping state there is, on the contrary, a movement towards the interior, that is towards the heart, we must judge that in the waking state much of the spirit and blood become engaged in the arteries, since it is by them that access is had to the nerves, while, on the other hand, in sleep the animal heat comes back through the veins to the heart, but not by the arteries since the access provided by nature to the heart is through the *vena cava* and not through the *aorta*.

Thus, notes young Harvey, there is set forth quite clearly a circulation from arteries to veins and then from veins to arteries. He recollects how the passage continues:

Indicio sunt pulsus qui ex pergiscentibus sunt magni, vehementes celeres, et cum quodam vibratione, in somno autem parvi, languidi, tardi et

rari (De Cau. Pul. IX et X) nam in somno calor nativus minus vergit in
arterias, in eosdem erumpit vehementius cum expergiscuntur. Venae autem
contrario modo se habent, nam in somno sunt tumidiores, in vigilia exiliores,
ut patet intuenti eas quae in manu sunt. Transit enim in somno calor nativus
ex arteriis in venas per osculorum communionem quam anastomosim vocant,
et inde, ad cor, ut autem sanguinis exundatio ad superiora et retrocessus ad
inferiora instar Euripi manifesta est in somno et vigilia.

As a proof of this we have the pulsations which, in those awake,
are strong, rapid and marked by a certain vibration, whereas in
sleep the pulsations are slight, languishing, slow and fewer (*De Cau.*
Pul. IX et X). This is because, in sleep, the native animal warmth
enters less into the arteries, whereas when we are awake it courses
through them more abundantly. The contrary takes place in the veins,
for while we are asleep they become more marked, in waking more
effaced, as we may observe from those of the hand. For in sleep the
native heat passes from the arteries into the veins through the process
of communication called anastomosis and thence to the heart. In like
manner, the flow of blood to the more remote parts of the body and
its return to the more central parts, takes place as does the ebb and
flow in the Euboic Sea, and thus manifests itself in sleeping and
waking.

But, thinks young Harvey, interrupting the train of his reasoning, if we still have to take the Euboic Sea as a model, it is not now
held to refer to the same movements as before. 'Thus Aristotle'—
Haec Aristoteles—wrote Caesalpinus but now we have the flux and
reflux of the Euboic Sea interpreted by this same Caesalpinus as the
image of a progress of the blood through the arteries and of its return
through the veins. So Caesalpinus writes:

Sic non obscurus est hujus modi notus in quacumque parte corporis
vinculum adhibeatur aut alia ratione occludantur venae. Cum enim tollitur
permeatio, intumescunt rivuli qua parte fluere solent, forte recurrit eo
tempore sanguis ad principium ne intercisus estinguatur.

Just as the flux of the blood towards the exterior parts of the
body and of its reflux towards the more interior parts occurs, so, in
the same way, can be explained the displacement of the blood when we
apply a ligature to any given part of the body or employ any other
means of compressing the veins. When indeed the flow of blood is
stopped, we see the small vessels swell which, before, had carried along
the blood with ease, while at the same time what is on the other side
of the ligature rapidly drains towards the heart, its source, so that it
may not become annihilated as it would were the blood not to reach
the heart.

Caesalpinus thus proposes a circular course: arterial flow from the left ventricle and the blood returning to the right ventricle after having bathed the organs. At the same time, the blood 'in preparation' moves through the lungs from the right ventricle to the left, thus completing the circuit. And the rhythm of this movement would be modified, says Caesalpinus, according to the states of sleeping or waking, the stream of blood passing through the arteries to the organs of thought and movement being much more considerable in the waking state, while during sleep the blood-stream is appeased and it is then that the venous system is the more charged with blood.

All this, mostly founded upon observation of the valvular orifices of the heart (which impose movements in one direction without any possibility of return by the same channel), is not so badly reasoned and thought out, Harvey considers. All the same, the whole question remains vague and disjointed in not a few respects. We cannot deduce a general, normal and constant flow of blood throughout the whole organism merely from some particular observations about two intermittent states such as those of sleeping and waking. We cannot even postulate such a current from examining such accidental and local occurrences as a stricture of the neck or the arm, a stricture which causes the vein to swell always on the same side of the ligature.

Then again, what are the rhythm and the speed of this circulation —supposing we can observe it everywhere in the body? To pierce this mystery we must, indeed, know what is the quantity of blood that fills and empties from the heart at each one of its movements. We must know what comes in by the *vena cava* and what goes out on the other side by the *aorta*. If one drained off this blood, how long would the body then take to become bloodless? So many experiments must be made if the general circulation and continuous movement of the blood are to be demonstrated and proved. Obscurity and doubt shroud all these matters and Harvey promises himself that when he gets back to England he will, in some way or other, find the answers to all these questions.[1]

[1] From what I write here it may be seen how little I think of Caesalpinus's explanations. They did not amount, indeed, to much more than a flash of intuition, uncertain and not really very illuminating. They were, however, to excite in a mind as brilliant as Harvey's a prospect that the Italian anatomist was certainly very far from having glimpsed: the prospect of a rapid, constant circulation of the blood. Caesalpinus was very far from having any idea of this sort of circulation and we should err indeed in seeing in a suggestion thrown out, so to speak, at hazard something comparable with the colossal discovery made by Harvey. To

He is, however, fully alive to the difficulties of the task, and he heaves a sigh as he unshoulders his knapsack and looks about him for a place to rest. He has loitered longer than he had intended, for the sun is already on the meridian. He realizes that he is hungry and unpacks his little parcel of food, but he gives scant attention to his eating for his mind is still buzzing with the profusion of new ideas that are the fruit of his meditations. The sun grows hot and, the meal over, Harvey feels a little sleepy—a state to which his strenuous mental exertion has contributed not a little. After all, his time is his own, and in the shade of a tree he takes his siesta.

While he rests I take the opportunity of referring to a scientist then lecturing at Padua, one Eustachio Rudio, who is said (by Zecchinelli—who himself lived in Padua at about 1848—and others) to have 'inspired' Harvey. Rudio is the author of the two treatises *De virtutibus et vitiis cordis* (1587) and *De naturale atque morbosa cordis constitutione* (1600), but Harvey does not refer to either of them, nor does he mention Rudio.

The titles of these works are certainly striking, but upon examination they prove to be lengthy compilations of the ancient doctrines to which are added a few notes on later observations. They contain no new categorical affirmations, nor do they make up a body of doctrine such as may be found in the books of Colombo or of Caesalpinus, whose work must have impressed Harvey much more than the verbose treatises of Rudio.

Again, we may dismiss out of hand the supposition that Serpi's writings may have 'inspired' Harvey. Father Paolo Serpi (1552–1623), of the Servite Order, composed a MS. which became known only long after his death—and also after the publication of Harvey's *Exercitatio*. Fulgencio, who had succeeded to Serpi's ecclesiastical benefice, published his predecessor's writings in the hope that they would prove that Serpi had discovered the existence of the venous valves before Fabricius. But if this had been the case, then Serpi must have made his discovery before 1574 and before he was twenty-two years of age, since from that year Fabricius taught

---

do that would be like comparing the Château of Versailles with the woodman's hut that was once half-hidden in the scrub and brush that covered the site of Louis XIV's magnificent edifice. We might, of course, say that both hut and palace were dwellings, though that would not mean much. All the same, there can be no doubt that all the contradictions he heard about the blood and the heart while he was at Padua (and many of them enunciated by Caesalpinus himself) certainly did induce Harvey to tackle the whole problem anew, starting at the very beginning.

openly about his discovery of the valves for thirty-five years. During this long period neither his teaching nor his book had aroused Serpi himself to make any claim to priority. (Fabricius dates his discovery at 1574 in his book, *De venarum osteolis*.) Fulgencio also endeavoured to prove that the youthful Serpi had deduced from his discovery of the venous valves the circulation of the blood—an idea which does not seem to have occurred to Fabricius at all. But this is obviously special pleading on the part of Fulgencio the apologist.

We may remember that there have not been wanting writers to affirm that Harvey had predecessors as far back as the 15th century. These alleged pioneers flourished in Italy, Spain or France (according to the taste and fancy of the author) well before the really eminent researchers, such as Servetus, Colombo and Caesalpinus, who lived in or near Padua in the second half of the 16th century. Among the alleged 'precursors' we find no less a person than Leonardo da Vinci, a man of great and many-sided genius but one who left nothing to warrant the suggestion that he held the doctrine of the circulation of the blood as against the dogma of Galen universally accepted in his time. It is true that Leonardo was a skilled anatomist (it is said that he dissected more than seventy bodies) and that he added greatly to the anatomical knowledge of his day, but his anatomical work was descriptive, not explanatory. (To realize how remarkable were the services he rendered to this discipline we have only to examine the collections of his drawings at Windsor Castle, in the Ambrosiana in Milan, or at the *Institut de France* in Paris.) Nowhere in Leonardo's drawings or writings is there evidence that he had considered the physiology of the heart or the movement of the blood in any way other than in strict accordance with the doctrines of Galen. None of Leonardo's drawings goes to disprove the theory of a porous wall between the right heart and the left, and some of the drawings actually look as if they were intended to give an indication of the existence of such a wall, yet it was the conviction that the septum was non-porous that provided the starting-point for the campaign to overthrow Galen's doctrine.

As with Serpi and Leonardo, so with Rabelais (1485–1553). Despite all that has been said of this author as a precursor of Harvey, there is nothing to be found in any of his writings that would lead us to suppose that he in any way anticipated Harvey's discovery. In fact, I have actually quoted[1] texts from the *Tiers-Livre* of Rabelais's *Pantagruel* in order to illustrate Galen's classical system.

To resume our chronicle, we find young Harvey refreshed and

[1] In my *Circulation du sang, schema nouveau*, nearly thirty years ago.

on the road again, as energetic as ever. As he makes his way across the country he is excited to find that his ideas are beginning to crystallize themselves in his mind. They are much less hazy and he is getting a firmer grip of them. But ideas, which are suggested by observation and experiment, must be tested by observation and experiment, and new knowledge must be acquired. Taking up this thread again, he rapidly reviews the evidence of his own observations at Padua. What has he actually seen with his own eyes?

He has observed most carefully the hearts of large animals such as birds and mammals while they were in their death agonies and their heart's movements so slowed down that they could be easily studied. He has also watched the naturally slower-moving hearts of eels and other fish bought in the Padua market—and even the hearts of chicken embryos after he had broken their shells. What he has seen is that the auricles and ventricles do not dilate and contract simultaneously, but that there is a phase during which the auricle appears to be the more full and, if it is transparent, red or pink in colour. This is followed by a phase in which the auricle grows pale and collapsed while, at that same moment, the ventricle seems to be the more filled and highly coloured. Then the ventricle becomes contracted and collapses while a similar movement to the first is begun by the auricle. All this seems to fit in very well with the theory of a passage or flow of blood from the auricle (when it becomes contracted) into the ventricle, which then becomes coloured and dilated.

However, the movements of contraction and of expansion of the auricle and the ventricle are not simultaneous, as Harvey has been taught, but successive. How could it be possible that such an error has persisted? Is it probable that, after so many centuries, men can still be so deceived as not to see that the movements of the ventricles are not simultaneous with those of the auricles, and that for both the filling corresponds to the diastole and not the systole, as Harvey's masters have taught him? This, Harvey finds it hard to believe. It is surely impossible that men like Galen, Mondino, Chauliac, Vesalius, Colombo, Fallopius, Fabricius and Caesalpinus, can have made erroneous observations! It must therefore be William Harvey himself who is in error.

Nonetheless, his observations and his experiments on fish and other animals have been made and they cry aloud their evidence. Furthermore, are not his new conclusions in accord with those contained in a recently published veterinary work printed at Venice in 1598, hardly four years before Harvey got to Padua—a book entitled *Anatomia del Cavallo, Infermità e sui Remedii etc.*, and written in the vulgar tongue by one Carlo Ruini, a Senator of Bologna?

After a really remarkable description of the heart, Ruini has declared that, contrary to all classical and official teaching, it is in diastole that the heart fills with blood, and in systole that it empties. This man of Bologna has described the sequence of these two movements, auricular first of all, ventricular afterwards. Speaking of the two great valves shaped like tongues that descend from the left auricle into the left ventricle, Ruini has written:

> *L'officio suo è, quando il cuora s'allarga, apprendosi, di lasciare intrare il sangue, e gli spiriti dall'arteria venale nel ventricolo manco ed interiore, quando si ritira il cuore, che il sangue e gli spiriti non ritornino di nuovo nell'arteria venale.*

Their function is to allow, when the heart dilates and they open, the admission of blood and spirit from the venous artery into the left ventricle and to prevent, when the heart contracts, the blood and spirit from returning to the venous artery.

And, when mentioning, later on, the three small crescentric valves that exist between the left ventricle and the great artery of the *aorta*, Ruini says:

> *Queste tele quando il cuore si ritira, apprendosi, lasciano uscire lo spirito vitale con sangue, che va con empito nell'arteria grande, e quando s'allarga il cuore, vietano, chiudendo il buco, che lo spirito ed il sangue non rientri di nuovo nel ventricolo.*

These membranes, by opening when the heart contracts, allow the vital spirit to flow out with the blood which gushes with great impetuosity into the great artery, and when the heart dilates they prevent, by the shutting of the aperture, the spirit and the blood from flowing back into the ventricle.

Exactly the same thing takes place, according to Ruini, in the right ventricle, where two similar little valves exist.

But, then, all this—both what Harvey himself has observed in the still living and palpitating hearts of small animals and what Ruini has described concerning the arrangement of the little valves in the hearts of the horses he has dissected—all this surely provides further reasons for admitting that each time blood arrives simultaneously at the auricles (on the right side from the *vena cava* and on the left side from the *arteria venosa*) it is projected by the contraction of the auricles into the two ventricles, which are dilated in their turn, but only to contract again simultaneously and send the venous blood to the lungs and the arterial blood to the other organs.

In this fashion there must be a one-way circulation which tends to confirm that the lungs are certainly involved in the passage not only of part of the blood but of the whole blood-stream, from the right heart to the left heart. Moreover, if there were, in this manner, an unceasing flow of the whole blood-stream—traversing the right heart, the lungs and then the left heart, and then entering the *aorta*— we must furthermore admit that the organs, if they are not to burst, must continually drain off the surplus of blood that remains after they have been nourished—a surplus of blood that is constantly driven forward by new blood that incessantly arrives. Again, there must be in the organs, of necessity, a continuous flow of arterial blood arriving and of venous blood leaving, thus achieving the cycle that is to begin again through the right heart, the lungs, the left heart, etc.

But where, and how, the young physician now ponders, does this venous blood (that he considers to be impoverished and exhausted on its return) become once more nutritive and profitable to the body—that is to say, turned into arterial blood? Somewhere, we must grant, the venous blood is recharged with all its necessary and beneficent principles—the warmth and the vital spirit that are the essence of arterial blood. But where does this regeneration, this renovation, take place? In the heart? But that will hardly do, for the venous blood must be delivered warm and ebullient into the right auricle. It is because of this warmth and of the volume already acquired by the blood that the right auricle becomes dilated, and the blood, reacting to contraction, is then communicated—still very warm—to the right ventricle. Therefore, the blood's warmth must be renewed before it reaches the right auricle—in the *vena cava* itself.

What if there takes place here a 'fermentation of the blood' somewhat comparable with the fermentation of young wine when it receives its warmth and vital spirit? *Calorem et spiritum vini?* What if the blood passes from the right heart to the lungs in order that there this blood, too warm and in too great a condition of fermentation, may be tempered, clarified and transmitted, less warm but purer, to the left auricle? And what if this, in its turn, swells up with the blood from the lungs and then reacts by forcing the blood into the left ventricle, whose main function must be to distribute the blood to all the organs of the body? Yes, indeed, that would be a state of things fairly logical and coherent!

Still, so much of all this is in direct opposition to what is taught in the University of Padua. How much of the new theory stands in need of verification! How many risks and dangers must be avoided before such revolutionary ideas can be established! How much hard work, indeed, remains to be done! Harvey becomes so engrossed in his plans for future investigations that he does not realize how far he has walked—or even that the sun has set. He goes on mechanically—across this by-way—when suddenly he is awakened from his dream. His feet are in water! His meditations have led him right down to one of the lagoons (a few miles distant from the real sea-lagoons) that merge into the maritime marshes by a sort of no man's land—half dry soil and half fen, criss-crossed with mysterious rivulets and runnels of water hidden in the tufted grass.[1]

Above him, the deep blue vault of night is already spangled with stars, while towards the east there rises majestically the full, golden moon. The soft radiance bathes the landscape and casts a pale iridescence over the sluggish sea of the lagoons far away. From one point a brilliant glow spreads along between sea and sky: Venice. On this particular evening the Mistress of the Adriatic is illuminated for a great festival. To the light of torches and lanterns there is dancing and the gondolas, like black swans, glide along the canals. It is not difficult to imagine the enchantment of such a night in Venice, or . . . but here the dreamer starts from his reveries to realize that he is lost! He looks about him in the moonlight for the path by which he may retrace his steps and find refreshment and shelter for the night. Far off he descries the sombre outline of a town that must surely be Mestre. That serves him as a guide and lends him courage and hope, and he soon makes out a path that leads roughly in the right direction, and presently he finds himself upon a road.

Not far upon his way he finds an *albergo* at whose portal is a country carriage that seems to await its owner's arrival. On enquiry he learns that this man, a market-gardener, plans to be at Padua for the morrow's market. He makes a proposal and is eventually given

[1] I have composed this imaginary excursion of Harvey's at the instance of and with the advice of my friend Dr. Terray of Aix-les-Bains, who is better fitted than I am to judge the time necessary to walk so far (for I have done the journey only by rail). I have spared no pains to make my description—as far as it goes—trustworthy, though the episode was introduced partly to serve as a vehicle for the authentic Latin texts of Servetus, Colombo and Caesalpinus, which must be noted if we are to get a clear idea of the new anatomical theories which were beginning to make their appearance at the end of the 16th century.

some food and wine and promised a lift back to Padua for a fair price. He has, however, not brought enough money for this un-expected adventure, but on his declaration that he is a 'Counsellor of the University of Padua' a small deposit is accepted and he is allowed to take his seat in the cart. By jogging on through most of the night Harvey may expect to get to Padua early in the morning, when the town-gates are opened. He is, in fact, taken by the shrewd driver right to the door of his lodging, where he pays the balance of his fare. He has hardly had time to tidy himself for the day when he remembers that Fabricius da Aquapendente is to lecture early that very morning. So, with a young man's indefatigable energy, he sets off again on foot for the Bo.

Fabricius is to lecture on the valves of the veins, which he has observed and described with peculiar care, and Harvey is anxious to hear if the Master has anything to add to his earlier texts. In particular, will Fabricius have anything to say about the *direction* of the flow of venous blood? The valves with which he is so familiar are shaped to compel unidirectional flow, yet Fabricius has not hitherto drawn attention to this. Can he possibly have failed to realize the implications of his own discovery?

William Harvey finds this hard to believe and wonders.

Thinking over his spiritual adventure on the road to Venice the day before, he asks himself if he should dare, now, to confess to his professor the doubts which have begun to assail him regarding Galen's teaching. What would the celebrated anatomist, whose mind was so permeated with veneration for the Ancients, say and think? No, he will not inflict such certain pain upon his Master, to whom any questioning of the dogmas of Galen, the Master of Pergamum, must seem sacrilegious.

As a candidate for the doctor's degree he has, a week or so since, replied impeccably and in the most classical language to Fabricius's questions, and to those of the other eminent professors on the jury before which he was called to defend his thesis for the doctorate of medicine. And has he not been solemnly capped as a Doctor of the University of Padua? As he nears his destination Harvey muses once more upon the ceremony that took place only a week ago when, as is set forth in his finely-illuminated Diploma, the Magnificent and most Excellent Rector, D. Johannis Thomas Mildous, handed to him as a sign of approval and praise a number of books on philosophy and medicine, 'at first shut and then opened', placed a golden ring upon his finger and, putting upon his head the Doctor's cap, kissed him and gave him the magisterial blessing.

He has indeed received the greatest praise from his examiners, and this is generously recorded in the Diploma. This is no mean 'certificate', but a magnificent quarto booklet of six sheets of vellum bordered with elegant arabesques, in the centre of which is inscribed the flattering text in large golden letters, the rest of the writing being in sepia with golden capitals.[1] On the back of the first sheet, the face of which is blank, there is set in a rich and elaborate illumination a large central oval bearing the words:

IN
CHRISTI
NOMINE
AMEN

The *stemma* of the young English *conciliarius* is displayed above the oval, while below there is a rustic medallion to which two further medallions symbolizing sylvan and marine inspiration, respectively, serve as pendants. The last sheet of the vellum is certainly, for Harvey, the most precious, for it is signed by all the masters and officials of the University. Most notable of these signatures is that of Fabricius da Aquapendente.

As he reflects upon the honours bestowed upon him Harvey cannot help feeling somewhat embarrassed. He is seized with the uneasiness of a sincere and scrupulous young man who puts to himself the question, 'Do I really believe what I replied to the questions of the jury?' For Harvey is more than merely conscientious, he is passionate in his quest for truth and for exact truth. Still, he is young and inexperienced and thinks to himself, 'Did I not rather recite my answers by rote and without the necessity of real conviction?' But how can he express his doubts? No, he cannot. He must take them with him from Padua and trust that the coming years will dissipate his misgivings. Thus deciding, he makes his way to his place and there, for a time, we must leave him.

It will be evident from the manner in which I have described Harvey's residence at Padua, and from the deliberate fiction I have employed (without departing in any way from probability), to call to the reader's attention the authentic texts of this fiercely contested debate, that I have myself arrived independently at a con-

[1] A magnificent coloured facsimile reproduction of this Diploma was published by the Royal College of Physicians in 1928 to commemorate the tercentenary of the publication of the *Exercitatio*. I have based my description closely upon this facsimile, and I was able to examine the original during my Harveian pilgrimage in England in October, 1955.

clusion intermediate between the denial that Harvey owed anything to Italy and the claim that both the idea and the proof of the circulation of the blood were already current there and that Harvey had only to reap their fruit.

That Harvey always cherished his Italian memories is certain. For instance, in the fine portrait that was painted of him sixteen or seventeen years after this visit (that is to say when the physician was about seventy-five years of age) we can see that the sitter was desirous of being shown looking towards the Eternal City. A similar preoccupation may be noted in another portrait of the same period, namely that of Harvey's faithful and devoted disciple, Dr.—afterwards Sir George—Ent. The two met, as we shall see, in Rome in 1636. Ent's picture also shows a background view of Rome. Harvey, as I pointed out in my lectures at Rome and Padua in April, 1955,[1] by thus insisting upon an Italian setting for his portrait, seems to have desired to indicate that he had kept alive and fresh the memories of the time he had spent in Italy, and of the scientific and humanistic education he had there received.

If we reflect upon the refined culture of which the young student was able to partake at Padua, we must conclude that Harvey, during his time at the Bo, was not merely a *bos suetus labore* with his head——so to speak—lowered into his own furrow, but that he often displayed interest in those manifestations of the arts and sciences by which he was surrounded. He must have enjoyed the company of some of those youthful and universal minds which had contributed to the blossoming of the Renaissance in an atmosphere like that of spring-time, when the sap rises and bursts the buds into bloom. We know that he loved the arts and had an understanding of them, and we may be sure that he passionately admired fine literature and the clarity of splendid expression in language. We know that he was devoted to Virgil. We find the Roman poet's name mentioned many times and we can discover quotations from Virgil's works in Harvey's writings—a witness to his good taste and his liking for what is noble and beautiful in the art of letters.[2] Moreover, Mantua was

[1] *Harvey et l'Italie.*

[2] For instance, at the head of one of Harvey's notes for his Lumleian Lectures is this motto, taken with but slight modification from the Third Eclogue of Virgil:

> *Stat Iove principium, Musae; Iovis omnia plena.*
> Everything begins in Jupiter, O Muses; by Jupiter are all things filled.

The Third Eclogue, of course, reads:

> *Ab Jove principium, Musae; Iovis omnia plena.*
> Begin with Jupiter, O Muses . . . etc.

not so far from Padua that Harvey could not easily have made a pilgrimage to the birth-place of the poet in the enchanting country watered by the Mincio.

The time came when Harvey had to pay his farewells to his friends and masters at the university and set out on his journey back to England. It was undoubtedly a sad day for the young doctor, eager though he must have been to see his own country again. There is little doubt that he left Padua towards the end of 1602 (old style), *i.e.* before the 24th March, 1603 (new style). Harvey had received his doctorate on 25th April, 1602, but it is not known why he postponed his return to England until the end of the year. That he did so is evident from the fact that Harvey is inscribed once more in the registers at Padua in August, 1602, as *Anglus Conciliarius*. But he is also found inscribed in 1602, without further precision of date, as present at Cambridge to take his 'licence'. This must have been at the end of 1602, but we should remember that at this period the year ended on 24th March, Lady Day (25th March) being the first day of the new year, so that Harvey could have arrived at Cambridge at any time until early March, 1603 (new style), and still have been registered in the year 1602.

The reasons for the delay in his departure for England are a matter for conjecture. He possibly prolonged his stay in order to travel, to visit neighbouring universities and see what was being done in them, or perhaps to pursue that *enquiry of doubt* which was to lead him little by little to recast entirely the traditional opinions on the circulation of the blood. Certainly he could have learned there nothing more than we have already indicated, but if he only found himself fortified in that precious doubt which is so great a stimulant to research, then his stay was indeed profitable.

It is, then, with such things as these in his mind that Harvey finally set out for the mists of the North. To his great joy, he was to have his youthful vision perpetually before his eyes for the rest of his life, for had not the sacred fire—that *ignis ardens* which only the gods can give—been kindled in his breast?

Chapter V

Physician and Scientist

I. *The Years of Ascent* (*1602–1639*)

Residence in London—Licence from the University of Cambridge—Candidate of the College of Physicians, 1604—Marriage—Fellow of the College of Physicians, 1607—Physician at St. Bartholomew's Hospital, 1609—Origins of the College of Physicians and the Lumleian Lectures—The offices of Censor, Elect and Treasurer—Physicians, Surgeons, Barber-surgeons and Apothecaries—Anatomy lessons founded by the Lumley Bequest—Harvey's teaching as shown by his notes—Public dissections—The publication of Harvey's *Exercitatio* at Frankfurt—Harvey's reaction to criticism—His observations on insects and animals—Harvey at the Courts of James I and Charles I—His relations with Bacon and Shakespeare—The Lennox Mission, 1630-32—Harvey's journey to Scotland with the King—His observations on natural history—Harvey's improvement of the management and efficiency of St. Bartholomew's Hospital—The case of the Lancashire Witches—The extent and variety of Harvey's medical work—The autopsy on Old Parr—Lord Arundel's Mission to the Continent, 1636—Harvey's commission to buy pictures in Italy for Charles I—The route and incidents of the journey—Dr. Ent—Back in London, 1637-38

O N his return to England Harvey is considered by D'Arcy Power to have taken up his residence in the parish of St. Martin's-extra-Ludgate. With his Padua Diploma he should have been able, forthwith, to practise in his own country, since the wording of the document ran as follows:

Authorisation and liberty to ascend the magisterial chair in all countries and in all places and there to deliver lectures, to rehearse, to consult, to teach, to cherish, to discuss, to interpret, to decide questions, to direct schools, to create bachelors, to use and to enjoy each and every one of the privileges, the prerogatives, the liberties, the preeminences, the honours, the favours, the graces and other indulgences, by whatsoever name called, enjoyed by the Doctors and Masters of the Roman Curia, of the Schools of Paris, Cambridge, Oxford, Pavia, Bologna, Perugia, Basle, Vienna and Ingolstadt and of all other places whatsoever, using and enjoying and authorised to use and enjoy in the future everything that is in accord with the tenor and contents of the Privilege above recited, without let or hindrance from any laws, decrees, constitutions, statutes or other ordinances, under whatsoever clauses and terms by which derogation is accorded by virtue of the Imperial authority to all and everyone, even not expressed by these presents.

It is clear that Padua was rich in jurists! However, despite this imposing rigmarole, Harvey very soon sought and obtained from the University of Cambridge a licence to practise. No doubt this was because he already had it in mind to join the College of Physicians in London, and knew that while admission to the College was practically confined to graduates in medicine of the English Universities, those who held a diploma from a foreign university were allowed to enrol themselves if they produced letters testimonial of admission *ad eundem* at Oxford or Cambridge.[1]

Thus it was that, with his licence from Cambridge, Harvey was admitted on 5th October, 1604, as a candidate at the College of Physicians, which was then situated in Knightrider Street, and was lodged in a house built of stone that had formerly belonged to Linacre. The candidates were the members or commonalty of the College from which the Fellows were chosen. Their functions and privileges we shall discuss later on. Less than three years after having been accepted as a candidate, namely on 5th June, 1607, Harvey was to be admitted to the coveted position of a Fellow and, almost at once, to apply for the appointment of physician at St. Bartholomew's Hospital.

Before we follow him through the different phases of his professional career, we must note that on 24th November in this same year, 1604—that is to say, but little more than a month after he had been accepted as a candidate at the College of Physicians—William Harvey, aged twenty-six years, married at St. Sepulchre's Church in London Elizabeth Browne, daughter of a physician named Lancelot Browne, who (so D'Arcy Power tells us) practised medicine under both Elizabeth I and James I but died in the same year as his daughter's marriage. As we mentioned in Chapter I, the union was

[1] D'Arcy Power.

childless. It would seem to have lasted until 1645 or a little later, that is to say until the middle of the Civil War, though we have no precise evidence of the exact date of Mrs. Harvey's death.

In the discourse he delivered at St. Bartholomew's Hospital in 1928, on the occasion of the tercentenary of the publication of the *Exercitatio de Motu Cordis et Sanguinis*, Sir W. Herringham, then a consultant at the hospital, said that 'she was a kind-hearted lady whose charitable dispositions Harvey continued after her death, and in his Will where she is mentioned with great affection'.

But to return to Harvey's membership of the College of Physicians and his application for a post at St. Bartholomew's Hospital, we should first of all say something of the origin and organization of the famous College of Physicians of London, which already enjoyed much of the great prestige and reputation which it so justifiably enjoys today. We shall then show what were the prerequisites for obtaining the position of practising physician at the hospital on the occurrence of a vacancy.

The College of Physicians was founded in 1518, in the reign of King Henry VIII, at the instance of and under the first presidency of Thomas Linacre. Linacre, who was physician in ordinary to Henry VIII, obtained from the sovereign letters patent conferring upon the College the sole right to issue licences for the practise of medicine in London. This privilege was afterwards extended to the whole realm. For the meetings of the new body, Linacre put at its disposal two rooms in his Knightrider Street house and, indeed, bequeathed these to the College at his death in 1524. The rest of the dwelling he left, by his will, to Merton College, Oxford.

In 1582 there occurred an important event in the history of the College of Physicians. This was the creation (as a perpetual foundation) of the lectures on anatomy and surgery that were to be called the 'Lumleian Lectures' after Lord Lumley, one of the two benefactors. Thereupon, the Fellows decided to take from their common fund the sum of one hundred pounds (which must have been almost all the money the College possessed) and to devote it to the enlargement of their quarters so as to make them suitable for meetings; the additions to the house were, indeed, dictated by the necessity for providing room for those who attended the lectures. Two years later, during the years 1583–84, it was decided to add a spacious hall to the existing building.

So it was in Harvey's time, but the subsequent history of the College was one of steady development. In 1614 a move was made to more commodious accommodation at Amen Corner, Paternoster

Row, on land belonging to the Dean and Chapter of St. Paul's Cathedral. This edifice, which had, owing to Harvey's liberality, acquired (in 1653) a new meeting room and a new library, was destroyed during the Great Fire of London in 1666. Only a few books and some valuable souvenirs—among them, Harvey's portrait—were saved from the flames. Another new home now had to be found and the College removed to Warwick Lane, where Christopher Wren and Robert Hooke constructed for the Fellows a large octagonal edifice surmounted by a dome decorated with a gilded globe, which caused the irreverent to refer to the place as the 'pill-box'. It was here that the College had its headquarters from 1669 to 1823. In that latter year, in view of the changes and embellishments inflicted or conferred upon London by George IV and his architects, and also because fashionable London was now situated farther west, the President and Fellows of the College left the jumbled and, indeed, somewhat grubby purlieus of Warwick Lane and purchased from the Crown for £6,000 a site at the north-west corner of Trafalgar Square, which was just then being laid out. Robert Smirke designed the new edifice, which we shall have occasion to refer to later on. This present (and fourth) home of the College has a majestic and graceful façade of tall Ionic columns and is situated at the junction of Pall Mall East and Trafalgar Square, just opposite the National Gallery (*see* Plate IX).

However, what concerns us now is the old Knightrider Street home of the College. From the time of the foundation of the Lumleian Lectures the infant College was provided with a professor, chosen from among the Fellows, who taught anatomy and surgery. Those elected to this post were much envied by their peers since the position of Lumleian Lecturer carried with it not a little prestige. Harvey became Lumleian Lecturer in 1615. We shall, later on, deal with his teaching and with the regulations laid down by the Lecture's founders—regulations that the College was most careful to respect in all their details.

We may now consider Harvey's official appointment on 14th October, 1609, to succeed Dr. Wilkinson at St. Bartholomew's Hospital. Harvey had been appointed by the Governors as Dr. Wilkinson's assistant on 25th February of the same year, with the express purpose of becoming his successor. Dr. Wilkinson died in the summer of 1609, and on the following 14th October Harvey officially took over the position he was to retain until sometime during the Civil War. We cannot say exactly what that date was, for in the turmoil of civil strife many records were lost or indeed

PLATE IX. Portico of the present—and fourth—premises of the Royal College of Physicians, at the junction of Trafalgar Square and Pall Mall East, London

PLATE X
Andreas Cæsalpinus

PLATE XI. Jean Riolan

were never established. However, some documents lead us to believe that it may well have been during the year 1644 that Harvey was superseded. He was then residing at Oxford and had been there for two years at least, with the Court and the King's Army, awaiting the outcome of the critical struggle between King and Parliament. The defeat at Naseby (14th June, 1645) was followed by the siege of Oxford, the flight of the King in disguise on 27th April, 1646, and finally Fairfax's triumphant entry into the old university town on 11th May that same year.

Harvey's name appears for the last time in the Hospital's accounts for the year 1643. The following years were, like all those of the Civil War, uncertain and vacillating. The hospital organization seems to have been considerably upset and the work to have been carried on by makeshift *locum tenentes*. D'Arcy Power mentions that the *Journals of the House of Commons* contain the following significant note:

'Feb. 12, an. 1643–4. A motion this day made for Dr. Micklethwayte to be recommended to the Warden and Masters of St. Bartholomew's Hospital, to be physician in the place of Dr. Harvey, who hath withdrawn himself from his charge and is retired to the party in arms against the Parliament.'

In fact, John Micklethwayte was appointed physician in reversion to St. Bartholomew's Hospital on 26th May, 1648, and he succeeded to the post of full physician on 13th May, 1653. Micklethwayte, who was later knighted, was one of the physicians in ordinary to Charles II and died in 1682.

When Harvey was received a Fellow of the College of Physicians in 1607 he was twenty-five years of age. Quite soon he was to be elected to a number of administrative posts in the institution. He was made a Censor in 1613 and again in 1625 and 1629. The Censors were four Fellows nominated annually and charged with the duty of supervising, admonishing and controlling those who practised medicine in London and within a radius of seven miles thereof, whether they were Fellows of the College of Physicians or not.

'They had the power,' writes D'Arcy Power, 'to punish by fine and summary imprisonment in the Wood Street Counter, and the name of Harvey occurs more than once about this time in connection with the proceedings taken by the College against quacks or "Empirics", as they were then called.

'The Censors, attended by representatives of the Society of Apothecaries, were empowered to visit the shops of the apothecaries in London to "search, survey, and prove whether the medicines, wares, drugs, or any thing or things whatsoever in such shops or shops contained and belonging to the art and mystery of an apothecary be wholesome, meet and fit for the cure, health, and ease of his Majesty's subjects". These inquisitorial visits were made at irregular times every summer and autumn. The procession, consisting of the Censors with the Wardens and the Beadle of the Society of Apothecaries, started at one o'clock, and before six in the afternoon from twenty to thirty shops had been visited. At each shop the visitors entered and asked for a few drugs selected at random. They then examined the stock from which the supply was taken, as well as the individual sample offered. A few rough tests were applied and if the drugs were found to be bad or adulterated they were at once destroyed by the simple but effective method of throwing them out into the street. The records of each visitation were kept in a book belonging to the College of Physicians.'

After giving several picturesque examples of these visits to the apothecaries' shops—examples drawn from the book of reports compiled in the time of Dr. Robert Pitt (Censor in 1687 and in 1702)—D'Arcy Power continues:

'A part of Harvey's time was employed in duties of this nature, but on the 3rd of December, 1627, he was appointed to the still more important office of "Elect". The "Elects" were eight in number. They were chosen from the most cunning and expert men of the faculty in London. It was their duty once in a year to select one of their number to fill the office of President, whilst as a Board with a quorum of three they formed the examiners of those who desired to exercise or practise physic throughout England, whose fitness they certified by letters testimonial. These examinations were conducted at the house of the President, where on the 9th December, 1629, Harvey examined and approved that Dr. James Primerose who soon became the most malignant opponent of his teaching. Primerose was the pupil of Riolanus, Professor of Anatomy in Paris, and was well described as the quibbling advocate of exploded teaching.

'Harvey seems to have comported himself well even in the high position of an elect, for in 1628 he was made Treasurer of the College, an office to which he was re-elected in 1629, so that he must have shown some of the business capacity which was so marked a feature in the other members of his family.'

Such were the promotion and the administrative functions enjoyed by Harvey in the College of Physicians, but his real teaching was done after he had been appointed Lumleian Lecturer in August, 1615 (a post that was held for life). Before we see how he acquitted himself as a teacher we must obtain some idea of medical practice in his day, and in particular of the relations between the physicians and the surgeons and apothecaries.

Both instruction in and supervision of the practice of physic and surgery were vested in two separate and often openly rival organizations, each jealous of its rights and prerogatives. Medicine, as it was then conceived, was concerned with diagnosis and with the treatment of patients (except those suffering from wounds) by means of prescriptions and drugs mentioned in the Codex, which had gradually been compiled by the various Schools of Medicine. 'Internal' prescriptions only were considered worthy of the physician, who held that manual acts of any sort were degrading and unworthy of his dignity. Surgery, on the other hand, if not derived from was at least annexed to the profession of barber, and surgeons had the right to intervene in all cases needing 'external' treatment of maladies themselves thought of as 'external'. Finally, as a sort of after-thought, there came the apothecaries, who took part in such external treatment as the administrators of douches and enemas as prescribed by the physicians.

As a result of these distinctions there grew up during the Middle Ages the guilds of surgeons and barber-surgeons on the one hand, and that of the physicians on the other. Members of both guilds, when they were not simply 'empirics' or quacks, or when they felt it necessary to be in possession of diplomas and what we should now call 'degrees', obtained their qualifications in towns where there were organizations of barber-surgeons and physicians with officially appointed masters whose duty it was to examine candidates and issue licences and diplomas.

The two corporations had, through the Middle Ages, gradually accumulated prerogatives, just as did other schools derived from the early ecclesiastical foundations of theology, law, etc., established by the Church in certain cities of the Frankish and, later, the Carolingian realms. But as a knowledge of the human body must necessarily play a part in the physicians' and barber-surgeons' professional activities, the two corporations had come to acquire (to the complete exclusion of all other organizations) the right to receive each year a few bodies of felons hanged for crime. The exercise of this privilege was hedged about with a number of conditions and stipulations, and very few bodies were actually placed at the disposal of the physicians and surgeons. Each year they were able to conduct three or four dissections *in mortuo* and hold demonstrations lasting a few days each. Furthermore, as there existed then no known means of keeping dead bodies fresh and uncorrupted, the demonstrations had to be made so short that only a few main points of anatomy could be mentioned; there was no time to spend upon details.

Any private demonstrations made upon bodies procured clandestinely were severely punished. In 1540, the Act of Parliament by which the hitherto distinct corporations of Barber-Surgeons and Surgeons were merged into one, specifically authorized the masters of the unified guild to take each year the bodies of four felons condemned and put to death 'for their further and better knowledge, instruction, insight, learning and experience in the science and faculty of surgery'.

In 1565 the College of Physicians obtained from Elizabeth I a similar privilege, the grant authorizing the President of the College to receive each year one, two, three or four bodies for dissection. At the same time the source of supply, so to speak, was enlarged so as to include persons executed in London and its neighbourhood, in Middlesex and in any county within sixteen miles thereof. The bodies of such persons might be taken by the College servants.

The lectures given at the College of Physicians gained much in reputation and prestige when in 1581 Lord Lumley and Dr. Caldwell made their foundation and established for their lectures conditions and regulations which, by the terms of the donation, must be rigorously observed. We shall see what happened later on, but in 1579, that is, two years before the foundation of the Lumleian Lecture, Caldwell had made a proposal for a similar lecture to the corporation of Barber-Surgeons, but with no result. These latter, no doubt, considered that the ten pounds sterling then offered annually would not even meet the cost of the numerous and copious repasts which it was the custom to offer between the morning and afternoon sessions on each occasion of an anatomical dissection.

In 1581, Caldwell's donation, considerably increased by Lord Lumley's benefaction, was placed at the disposal of the College of Physicians, while the anatomical teaching of the Barber-Surgeons in the Hall in Monkwell Street went on as before, many of the lecturers being, like Dr. Andrewes (who died in 1628) and his successor Dr. Alexander Reid, Fellows of the College of Physicians. We shall have occasion to refer again to Dr. Alexander Reid, who was eight years Harvey's junior and for ever his most obstinate opponent in the most obdurate Galen tradition.

To return to the foundation of the Lumleian Lectures, 'the design of the benefaction,' says D'Arcy Power, 'was a noble one. It was the institution of a lecture on Surgery to be continued perpetually for the common benefit of London and consequently of all England, the like whereof had not been established in any University of Christendom (Bologna and Padua excepted). An attempt had been made to establish such a lectureship at Paris, but the project failed when François I died on the last day of March, 1547.

'The reader of the Lumleian lecture was to be a Doctor of Physic, of good practice and knowledge who was to be paid an honest stipend, no less in amount than that received by the Regius Professors of law, divinity and physic, in the Universities of Oxford and Cambridge. The lecturer was enjoined to lecture twice a week throughout the year, to wit on Wednesdays and Fridays, at ten of the clock till eleven. He was to read for three-quarters of an hour in Latin and the other quarter in English "wherein that shall be plainly declared for those that understand not Latin".

'The lecturer was appointed for life and his subjects were so arranged that they recurred in cycles. The first year he was to read the tables of Horatius Morus, an epitome or brief handling of all the art of surgery, that is, of swellings, wounds, ulcers, bone-setting, and the healing of broken bones commonly called fractures. He was also to lecture upon certain prescribed works of Galen and Oribasius, and at the end of the year in winter he was directed "to dissect openly in the reading place all the body of man, especially the inward parts for five days together, as well before as after dinner; if the bodies may last so long without annoy".

'The second year he was to read somewhat more advanced works upon surgery and in the winter "to dissect the trunk only of the body, namely, from the head to the lowest part where the members are to handle the muscles especially. The third year to read of wounds, and in winter to make public dissections of the head only. The fourth year to read of ulcers and to anatomize [or dissect] a leg and an arm for the knowledge of muscles, sinews, arteries, veins, gristles, ligaments, and tendons. The fifth year to read the sixth book of Paulus Aegineta, and in winter to make an anatomy of a skeleton and therewithall to show the use of certain instruments for the setting of bones. The sixth year to read Holerius of the matter of surgery as well as of the medicines for surgeons to use. And the seventh year to begin again and to continue still".

'The College of Physicians made every effort to fulfil its trust adequately. . . . Dr. Richard Foster was appointed the first Lumleian lecturer, and when he died in 1602, William Dunne took his place. Dunne, however, did not live to complete a single cycle of lectures for Thomas Davies was elected in May, 1607. The College then again began to outgrow its accommodation, and as the site did not allow of any further additions to the buildings, a suitable house and premises were bought of the Dean and Chapter of St. Paul's in Amen Corner, at the end of Paternoster Row. The last meeting of the College in Linacre's old house in Knightrider Street, took place on the 25th of June, 1614. Dr. Davies died in the following year, and on the 4th of August, 1615, William Harvey was appointed to the office of Lumleian lecturer, though his predecessor was not buried until August 20th. He continued to occupy this post until his resignation in 1656, when his place was taken by (Sir) Charles Scarborough. . . .

'Harvey, in all probability, began to lecture at once upon surgery as the more theoretical portion of his subject, but it was not until April, 1616, that he gave his first anatomical lecture. It was a visceral lecture for the terms of the bequest required that it should be upon the inward parts. At this time Harvey was thirty-seven years of age. A man of the lowest stature, round faced, with a complexion like the wainscot; his eyes small, round, very black and full of spirit; his hair as black as a raven and curling; rapid in his utterance, choleric, given to gesture, and used when in discourse with any one, to play unconsciously with the handle of a small dagger he wore by his side.

'The MS. notes of his first course of lectures are now in the British Museum. They formed a part of the library of Dr. (afterwards Sir Hans) Sloane, which was acquired under the terms of his will by the nation in 1754. For a time the book was well known and extracts were made from it, then it disappeared and for many years it was mourned as irretrievably lost. But in 1876 it was found again amongst some duplicate printed books which had been set aside, and in the following year it was restored to its place in the Manuscript Department. The notes were reproduced by an autotype process, at the instigation of Sir E. H. Sieveking, and under the supervision of a Committee of the Royal College of Physicians. This facsimile reproduction was published in 1886 with a transcript by Mr. Scott, and an interesting introduction from the pen of Dr. Norman Moore.

'The original notes are written on both sides of about a hundred pages of foolscap, which had been reduced to a uniform size of six inches by eight, though the creases on the paper show that they have been further folded so as to occupy a space of about eight inches by two. These leaves have been carefully bound together in leather which presents some pretensions to elegance, but it is clear that the pages were left loose for some years after they were written. There seems to be no doubt that Harvey used the volume in its present form whilst he was lecturing, for three small threads of twine have been attached by sealing wax, to the inner side of the cover so that additional notes could be slipped in as they were required. It must be assumed that Harvey did this himself, for he wrote so badly and the notes are so full of abbreviations, interlineations, and alterations, as to render them useless to anyone but the author.

'The title-page, which is almost illegible, is written in red ink. It runs *Stat Jove principium, Musae, Jovis omnia plena. Prelectiones Anatomiae Universalis per me Gulielmum Harveium Medicum Londinensem Anatomie et Chirurgie Professorem. Anno Domini 1616. Anno aetatis 37 prelectae Aprili 16, 17, 18. Aristoteles Historia Animalium, lib. i. cap. 16. Hominum partes interiores incertae et incognitae quam ob rem ad caeterorum Animalium partes quarum similes humanae referentes eas contemplare.*'[1]

Perhaps what is most striking in this inscription is the phrase *Anatomiae Universalis*. It seems to express that generalizing and universal trend of Harvey's mind which was, indeed, evident in many sides of his personality. This was one of great sweep and range. Harvey was not circumscribed, not confined to the sole interests of one line of enquiry and exploration. He could, at all times, cast his glance towards far horizons and embrace any subject which might throw light upon the arduous task that was his main study in life. That is to say, he was interested in comparative anatomy in its widest possible sense. The opening passages of these Praelectiones should be compared with what, thirty years later—in 1649, when he was seventy-one—he wrote at the beginning of his two Letters addressed to Jean Riolan, the celebrated Parisian anatomist —*ad Iohannem Riolanum, filium, Parisiensem*. Here he expresses his surprise that Riolan had not better understood the *Exercitatio* of 1628. (A portrait of Riolan is given in Plate XI.)

Until the year 1649, that is, for a period of no less than two decades, Harvey had treated with silent contempt all the insults and intrigues of the pamphleteers who had attacked him. But on the publication in 1648 of Riolan's *Manual of Anatomy*—the *Enchiridion*

[1] This begins, as we have already shown (p. 91), with a verse from the Third Eclogue of Virgil, slightly modified, and runs thus: 'Everything begins in Jupiter, O Muses, by Jupiter are all things filled. Preparatory Notes for the Universal Anatomy by me William Harvey, Physician in London, Professor of Anatomy and Surgery. In the Year of Our Lord, 1616, and of my age the 37th. For my lectures, 16, 17, 18 April: Aristotle, *History of Animals*, Book I, Chapter 16. Of the interior organs of Man, ill-defined and little known and that because it is desirable to examine the organs in animals to which the human organs correspond.'

—Harvey, faced by an adversary for whom he felt respect, sought the opportunity of engaging in courteous controversy and of explaining to Riolan what he had evidently not understood in the *Exercitatio* of 1628. Then it was that Harvey, in reply to those who ridiculed him for seeking in inferior animals fresh evidence for the understanding of human anatomy, made this magnificent declaration:

'If you will but consent to examine the inferior animals—as did Heraclitus who, as Aristotle remarks, entered for that reason into a bake-house—I would say this to you, enter therein also for the immortal gods are not absent. It is in the little things that the Creator seems most great and in inferior beings that, sometimes, he reveals himself most clearly.'

To return to the notebook, we see that the notes were jotted down in connection with Harvey's lessons at the public dissections which began on 16th, 17th, and 18th April, 1616. We may remark, however, that Harvey's 'theoretical' teaching had begun in the August of the preceding year, immediately after his appointment, the dissections not being held until the end of the winter or in the beginning of spring. The rules of the Lumley foundation laid down that these autopsies must (at the beginning of the teaching cycle of six full years) be devoted during the first twelve months to the viscera ('especially the inward parts') 'as well before as after dinner'. The second year was devoted to the trunk and muscles, the third to the head, the fourth to the arms and legs, the fifth to the skeleton and the sixth to the practical medical and surgical applications of the ideas expounded in the lectures.

The programme and plan for the visceral lectures in April, 1616, as set forth at the beginning of the 98 MS. pages, opens with the general rules of the method Harvey intended to follow, namely:

'1. To show as much as may be at a glance, the whole belly for instance, and afterwards to subdivide the parts according to their position and relations.

'2. To point out what is peculiar to the actual body which is being dissected.

'3. To supply only by speech what cannot be shown on your own credit and by authority.

'4. To cut up as much as may be in the sight of the audience.

'5. To enforce the right opinion by remarks drawn from far and near, and to illustrate Man by the structure of animals according to the Socratic rule. To bring in points beyond mere anatomy in relation to the causes of diseases, and the general study of nature with the object of correcting mistakes and of elucidating the uses and actions of parts; for the use of anatomy to the physician is to explain what should be done in disease.

'6. Not to praise or dispraise other anatomists, for all did well and there was some excuse even for those who are in error.

'7. Not to dispute with others, or attempt to confute them, except by the most obvious retort, for three days is all too short a time.

'8. To state things briefly and plainly, yet not letting anything pass unmentioned which can be seen.

'9. Not to speak of anything which can be as well explained without the body or can be read at home.

'10. Not to enter into too much detail, or into too minute a dissection, for the time does not permit.

'11. To serve in their three courses according to the glass. In the first day's lectures the abdomen, nasty, yet recompensed by its infinite variety. In the second day's lecture, the parlour. In the third day's lecture the divine banquet of the brain.'

D'Arcy Power suggests that the word 'parlour' here means 'thorax', and he further comments that:

'Harvey adheres pretty closely in his visceral lecture to the programme which he had thus laid down for his own guidance.

'The first set of notes deal with the outside of the body, and the abdomen and its contents. The second portion contains an account of the chest and its contents; whilst the third portion is devoted to a consideration of the head with the brain and its nerves. Only nine pages of the ninety-eight which the book contains are allotted to the heart. The scheme of the lectures is first to give a general introduction in which the subject is arranged under different headings, and then to consider each part under a variety of sub-headings. Harvey's playfulness is shown even in the introduction. Each main division is indicated by a roughly drawn hand, and each hand is made to point with a different finger. The first hand points with its little finger, and has the other fingers bent, though the thumb is outstretched as if applied to the nose of the lecturer. The next heading is indicated by an extended ring finger, the next by the middle finger, whilst the later ones are mere "bunches of fives" or single amputated digits. In his description of the abdomen Harvey shows himself fully alive to the evils of tight-lacing, for, in speaking of the causes of difficult respiration he says, "young girls by lacing: undercut their laces."[1]

[1] This remark by Harvey concerning what may be called 'aesthetic physiology' I find very pleasing. Aesthetics, indeed, has no sure basis but in physiology.

After a full discussion of the situation and functions of the various parts of the abdominal viscera, he passes on to the thorax and enunciates his memorable discovery in these remarkable words, which are initialled to show that he thought the idea was peculiarly his own:

' "It is plain from the structure of the heart that the blood is passed continuously through the lungs to the aorta as by the two clacks of a water bellows to raise water.

' "It is shown by the application of a ligature that the passage of the blood is from the arteries into the veins.

' "Whence it follows that the movement of the blood is constantly in a circle, and is brought about by the beat of the heart. It is a question therefore whether this is for the sake of nourishment or rather for the preservation of the blood and the limbs by the communication of heat, the blood cooled by warming the limbs being in turn warmed by the heart."

'Here the notes on the heart end abruptly, and Harvey passes on to consider the lungs. These few sentences show, however, that he had discovered the circulation, and that although he delayed for twelve years to make his results public he was unable to add any important fact in the interval.

'The College of Physicians still preserve some interesting memorials of this portion of Harvey's Lumleian lectures. They consist of a series of six dissections of the blood vessels and nerves of the human body, which are traditionally reported to have been made by Harvey himself. The dissections are displayed upon six boards of the size of the human body, and they exhibit the complete system of the blood vessels separated from the other parts so as to form diagrams of the circulatory apparatus. They have been made with such care that one of the series still shows the semilunar valves at the beginning of the aorta. . . .

'Harvey continued his Lumleian lectures year by year, but we know nothing more of them until 1627, when he delivered a series of lectures upon the anatomy and physiology of the human body, more especially of the arm and leg, with a description of the veins, arteries, and nerves of these parts. This was clearly the Muscular lecture, and if he had followed the course prescribed by the founders of the lecture it should have been given in the years 1619 and 1625, for the years 1621 and 1627 should not have embraced an anatomical course. The notes of the Muscular lecture are in the Sloane collection at the British Museum, where they have been preserved by as happy an accident as those of the much more important Visceral lecture. The volume consists of 121 leaves with writing upon both sides of each page. The notes are as rough and as concise as those of the Visceral lecture, and the language is again a mixture of Latin and homely English.'

Regarding this remark of D'Arcy Power's about the style of the *Praelectiones*, we may note that Harvey, in the rapid movement of his thought and of his hand, often used indifferently both Latin or English—whichever of the two came first into his mind. And this is quite understandable if we think of the rapid images demanded by his mental processes, images illustrated by the representations of fingers which have been referred to above. We find, for instance, in the *Praelectiones* such jumbles of Latin and English as this:

'Exempto corde, frogg, scripp' (for ship), 'eel, crawle, dogg ambulat.' (That is, 'with the heart removed, the frog jumps, the eel crawls, the dog walks'.)

Or again:

'Snayles cornubus tactu pro visu utuntur, unde oculi as a Centinell to the Army locis editis anterioribus.' ('Snails use their horns to feel instead of seeing, hence those eyes placed like sentinels of an army in commanding advanced points.')

This 'shorthand' for expressing his thoughts is also marked from time to time with the initials 'W.H.' in the margin opposite the statements Harvey thought most important or most peculiar to himself. Initialling seems to have been a common habit with him, for he also used it in books as we may see in those read and annotated by him (*see* Fig. 4). In other places in the notes there occurs the Greek letter delta, Δ. Here is an example of such annotations:

'An W. H. potius.'

'Cor, imperator, rex.' ('Should not the heart be rather considered as emperor or king?')

'Cerebrum Iudex, sergeant major praepositi.' ('Is not the brain the judge, the sergeant major, the assistant?')

These words, with the letters 'W.H.' and the 'potius' express, then, Harvey's real views about the heart—the master, the sovereign—and have been substituted for previous images such as these:

'An cerebrum rex.' ('Should not the brain be considered as king?')

'Nervi magistratus.' ('The nerves as his ministers?')

'Ramuli nervorum, officiales.' ('The branches of the nerves as assistants?')

'Musculi cives, populus.' ('The muscles: the citizens and workmen?')

So much for Harvey's jottings. We have kept until last a description of the few days devoted annually, at the end of the winter,
to the public and solemn dissection of those bodies which had been
claimed from the common hangman. The phrase 'public demonstrations' must be understood in two ways. First of all, the word
'public' in this connection means that the body utilized was, so to
speak, with the full knowledge of all delivered for general use after
the execution of a capital sentence, and so these 'public demonstrations' were contrasted with private and unauthorized dissections
performed in secret and in contravention of the then existing laws.
'Public dissections' meant also, naturally enough, 'official and
general demonstrations' for the general body of students—but not
for members of the public. Invitations to attend the demonstration
(both for those who taught and those who formed the audience at
these dissections) were conveyed by letter and conformed to rules
minutely laid down with due observation of precedence, rules which
it would have been unthinkable to have contravened. Thus was set
in motion for a few days each year a carefully ordered ceremonial
whose most minute details were always carried out.

Let us see what D'Arcy Power tells us in an account based upon
the records of the Barber-Surgeons' Company—for the ritual at
the College of Physicians must have been much the same.

'The *Manual of Anatomy* published by Alexander Reid in 1634,
has a frontispiece showing that the method of lecturing adopted in
England was the same as that in use throughout Europe. The body
lay upon a table, and as the dissections were done in the sight of the
audience, the dissecting instruments were close to it. The lecturer,
wearing the cap of his doctor's degree, sate opposite the centre of
the table holding in his hand a little wand[1] to indicate the part he
mentions, though in many cases the demonstration was made by a
second doctor of medicine known as the demonstrator, whilst the
lecturer read his remarks. At either end of the table was an assistant
—the Master of the Anatomy—with scalpel in hand ready to expose
the different structures, and to clear up any points of difficulty. The
audience grouped themselves in the most advantageous positions for
seeing and hearing, though in some cases places were assigned to
them according to age and rank.

'The lecturer upon Anatomy, apart from the fact that he was a
Doctor of Physic was a person of considerable importance in the

---

[1] The College of Physicians still possess a little whalebone rod tipped with
silver which Harvey is said to have used in demonstrating his Lumleian Lectures.
(*D'Arcy Power's note.*)

sixteenth century. The greatest care was taken of him, as may be
understood from the directions which the Barber Surgeons gave to
their Stewards in Anatomy or those members of the Company who
were appointed to supervise the arrangements for the lectures. They
were ordered "to see and provide that there be every year a mat
about the hearth in the Hall that Mr. Doctor be made not to take
cold upon his feet, nor other gentlemen that do come and mark the
Anatomy to learn knowledge. And further that there be two fine

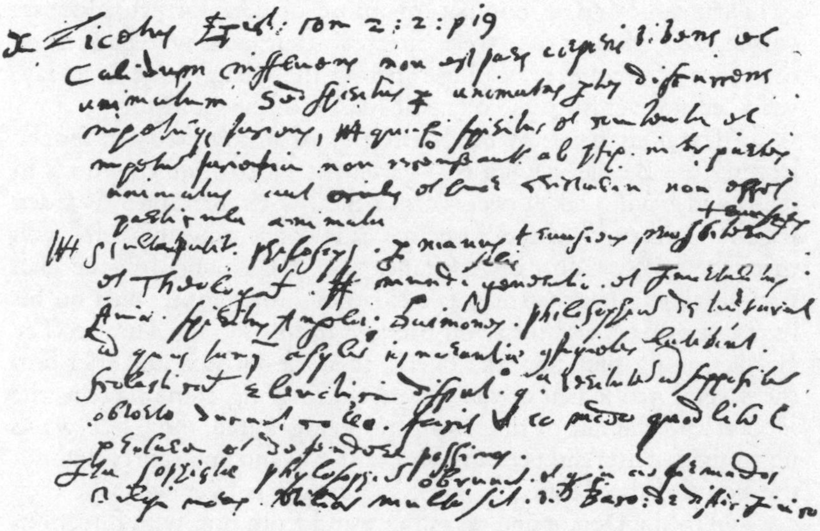

FIG. 4. Specimen of Harvey's handwriting, from a copy of *De generatione
animalium* which he presented to his brother Eliab. The symbol annexed
may be seen introducing the second paragraph and was often used by
Harvey to indicate his sole responsibility for the adjoining statement.

white rods appointed for the Doctor to touch the body where it
shall please him; and a wax candle to look into the body, and that
there be always for the doctor two aprons to be from the shoulder
downwards and two pairs of sleeves for his whole arm with tapes,
for change for the said Doctor, and not to occupy one Apron and
one pair of sleeves every day which is unseemly. And the Masters
of the Anatomy that be about the body to have like aprons and
sleeves every day both white and clean. That if the Masters of the
Anatomy that be about the Doctor do not see these things ordered
and that their knives, probes, and other instruments be fair and clean
accordingly with Aprons and sleeves, if they do lack any of the said

things afore rehearsed he shall forfeit for a fine to the Hall forty shillings."

'The whole business of a public anatomy was conducted with much ceremony, and every detail was regulated by precedent. The exact routine in the Barber Surgeons' Company is laid down in another series of directions. The clerk or secretary is instructed in his duties in the following words: "So soon as the body is brought in deliver out your tickets which must be first filled up as followeth four sorts. . . ." '

Then followed a number of more or less formal addresses varying according as they were directed to surgeons who had served the office of Master or to those 'below the Chair'—that is to say, who had not yet filled the office of Master of the Company.

' "The body being by the Masters of Anatomy prepared for the lecture (the Beadles having first given the Doctor notice who is to read) and having taken orders from the Master or Upper Warden [of the Company] of the Surgeons' side concerning the same, you meet the whole Court of Assistance [i.e., the Council] in the Hall Parlour where every gentleman cloathes himself [i.e., puts on his livery or gown], and then you proceed in form to the Theatre. The Beadles going first, next the Clerk, then the Doctor, and after him the several gentlemen of the Court; and having come therein, the Doctor and the rest of the Company being seated, the Clerk walks up to the Doctor and presents him with a wand and retires without the body of the Court . . . until the lecture is over when he then goes up to the Doctor and takes the wand from him with directions when to give notice for the reading in the afternoon which is usually at five precisely, and at one of the clock at noon, which he pronounces with a distinct and audible voice by saying, This Lecture, Gentlemen, will be continued at five of the clock precisely. Having so said he walks out before the Doctor, the rest of the Company following down to the Hall parlour where they all dine, the Doctor pulling off his own robes and putting on the Clerk's Gown first, which it has always been usual for him to dine in. And after being plentifully regaled they proceed as before until the end of the third day, which being over . . . he attends the Doctor in the clothing room where he presents him folded up in a piece of paper the sum of ten pounds, and where afterwards he waits upon the Masters of Anatomy and presents each of them in like manner with the sum of three pounds, which concludes the duty of the Clerk on this account." '

There is every reason to think that Harvey did full justice to the fare at these banquets and that he did nothing to cast any gloom upon the assembled company. Everything we know about him, indeed, makes us think that he liked good wine, good food and the cheerful presence of pleasant companions. His repeated attacks of gout suggest this as well as his copious use of coffee which he found, no doubt, both relaxing and also stimulating for the immense intellectual effort he demanded of his brain. In fact, in the years of his prime, at any rate, Harvey belonged to the company of those who hold that a sad scientist is a bad scientist. At Court, when he accompanied the King, and on those official missions in which he took part, Harvey certainly did not let slip an opportunity to enjoy the pleasure of gay parties and festivities. Sometimes, indeed, he aided in their preparation, and no doubt his highly strung nature demanded such relaxation even if he never lost sight of his main intellectual preoccupation. In short, we must think of Harvey as a full man—as an active man in every sense of the word.

If, indeed, some of his biographers have represented him as sad and depressed that is because they have depicted him as he was during the last years of his life, years that had been troubled with so many political and social upheavals. He had himself suffered so directly from reversals of fortune that we can well understand his reply to Ent, who asked the aged physician in his retreat if all were well with him. 'How can it be whilst the Commonwealth is full of distractions, and I myself am still in the open sea? And truly did I not find solace in my studies, and a balm for my spirit in the memory of my observations of former years, I should feel little desire for longer life.'

But if we have there an expression of Harvey's disillusionment after great efforts and long-drawn-out trials—an attitude intensified by the increasing burden of old age—the middle years of his life show a quite different tone. Then the man was energetic, enterprising, as ready for action as in the time of his youth, and always pursuing some scientific problem with intense interest.

It was, then, in his full maturity of thought and deed—he was fifty years old in 1628—that he published in Frankfurt his immortal *Exercitatio Anatomica de Motu Cordis et Sanguinis in Animalibus*, to whose finishing touches we referred in the first chapter of this book. This was the first 'Essay'—that is, the sense and meaning of the Latin word *Exercitatio*—to which, twenty years later, he was to add a sequel in his *Exercitationes duae Anatomicae de Circulatione Sanguinis ad Johannem Riolanum Filium*. They were twenty years of contemptuous silence observed by a man sure of himself, feeling himself above attack, expecting justification only from the passage of time and from the truth which he knew he possessed. A man, indeed, who considered that he had better to do than waste his time in penning fruitless answers to his opponents' attacks. Moreover, he had set himself a task of unending labour devoted to his studies of human and comparative anatomy, of physiology and general pathology, the results of which labours he was to embody in his MSS. *On Insects* and *Of Generation in Animals*. Of these two MSS. only the second was preserved—it was published in 1651—for the other was destroyed by the revolutionary soldiery during the sack of his apartments about 1643.

Although we find nowhere before 1649 any trace of Harvey's reactions in the face of the furious attacks his novel and sensational teachings excited, it seems clear that he continued these teachings during his Lumleian Lectures. It was at these lectures that he defended, by word of mouth, his views, his ideas and his discoveries.

The year 1628, the year of the publication of the *Exercitatio*, was also the year of political dramas which showed clearly enough how serious and how widespread was the opposition in men's minds to the methods of government pursued by James I and continued by his son Charles. They were methods which may be strikingly illustrated in the career of the celebrated royal favourite, George Villiers, who in the space of no more than five years (after 1619) was promoted from commoner to Duke of Buckingham and Lord High Admiral of England. In this year, 1628, however, Villiers was assassinated at Portsmouth by a naval officer, one John Felton, just as he (Villiers) was preparing to lead an expedition to the Isle of Ré in order to succour the Protestants besieged in La Rochelle by Richelieu.

In 1628 also there appears upon the political stage another figure that was to play a sinister role in the history of the British monarchy, though for the moment he was but a leader of the opposition in Parliament and an instigator of the Petition of Right presented to the King. This man was Thomas Wentworth, later Earl of Strafford, whom Charles I was to win over to his cause, and so to compromise, right up to the time that Strafford was condemned by Parliament and executed in 1641—eight years before the King himself.

Indeed, by 1628 an attentive ear could already hear the unmistakable rumblings which preceded the grave events that were to sweep up into Civil War and shake the whole fabric of the State from 1639 to 1649.

But before we come to consider the Civil War years, in which Harvey played his part, we may glance at another aspect of his activities during his maturity, activities that he pursued in addition to his work at the College of Physicians and at St. Bartholomew's Hospital. We refer to his professional practice in the City of London and also to the official missions which, at the command of the King, he undertook on several occasions.

Let us step back, for a moment, into the past; thus we may be the better enabled to see how events unfolded. When he took up his residence in London in 1604, at the age of twenty-six, Harvey was not only in excellent health and fired with youthful ardour, but he possessed also a knowledge of medicine as complete as was possible at the time. He was therefore admirably fitted to treat the variety of patients who consulted him and to answer all the demands made upon his skill.

No doubt it was his consciousness of his high calling and of his competence that gave Harvey that self-assurance which is so invaluable at the bedside of the sick. Confidence is inspired by a physician whose speech is unfaltering, forthright and firm. As a consequence, Harvey early achieved a considerable reputation; he attracted many patients and was soon in easy circumstances. Thus, he was not only able to execute in satisfactory conditions what he regarded as his 'mission', but he was able to devote some time each day to meditation upon the many problems, obscurities and uncertainties which he met with in his profession. His lofty conception of his calling, his enthusiasm and his ambitions, kept him far away from the ignorance and slothful dilettantism into which so many slip during the time which should be devoted to preparation for their life-work. Too many students are more concerned with vague sentimentality, gratification of the senses and with fashionable fads, than with the hard and exacting apprenticeship to a profession that is full of grave responsibilities.

In his private practice, we may think of Harvey as we pictured him at the beginning of this book, going and coming on the hack with the footcloth, making his way through the roads and streets of the City, and then after dinner receiving at his house a long list of patients. There was never any lack of these, especially after Harvey had been appointed (on 3rd February, 1618) Physician Extraordinary to the King, for James I, as a mark of his great esteem, nominated Harvey as 'Extraordinary' in addition to the Physicians in Ordinary. He was to hold this position until, in 1630, Charles I appointed him Physician in Ordinary.

Harvey also treated a number of other illustrious personages of his time, among others Sir Francis Bacon, who had fallen into disgrace after 1621 and who died in 1626 at the age of sixty-five. Bacon, not a little acrimonious, melancholy and even psychopathic, had nevertheless retained his great reputation as a writer and as a philosopher. However, it may be mentioned in passing that Harvey does not seem to have held a very high opinion of Bacon. The physician was a man of action, a man who proceeded directly upon the straight path to his goal. He despised long-drawn-out speculations and more or less metaphysical discussions—in fact, all that did not repose upon the clear evidence of the senses. He who constantly, and as a matter of course, applied the experimental method, no doubt thought that disquisitions upon experiment were unnecessary and superfluous.

Harvey was possibly less than just to Bacon's philosophy, which was in opposition to the still prevailing Scholasticism and which did attach great importance to the fact of experiment. In any case, if we may believe Aubrey (who is not, however, always very reliable), Harvey said of Bacon that he talked philosophy like a Lord Chancellor, and by that he meant as a man of fashion, as a dilettante, one who did not really come to grips with things. Nevertheless, Bacon did dabble in experiments and caught the chill from which he died while making one.[1]

This is not the place to discuss Bacon, whose character and career have excited so many—and often hair-splitting and disingenuous—comments, nor to attempt to follow those historians who have uttered the most contradictory suppositions regarding the man's origins, some not hesitating to declare them 'royal' while others express a quite opposite opinion. Each protagonist brings to his thesis, or hypothesis, arguments so subtle that they often seem designed to conciliate the opinions of both parties to the discussion.

However, here are a few facts. 1, Francis Bacon certainly existed. 2, He was just as certainly for a time Lord High Chancellor of England. 3, He was certainly the author of the works signed by him. 4, He certainly met William Harvey, and indeed knew the physician well. Some cranks have gone so far as to attribute Harvey's works to Bacon—in addition to all the plays and poetry of Shakespeare! 5, It is clear that Harvey spontaneously, instinctively and logically, all at once, discovered and applied that real experimental method whose necessity Bacon had demonstrated by means of 'philosophy'.

[1] He was stuffing a fowl with snow to test the idea of cold storage.

What also appears to be pretty sure is that Harvey, among his many meetings with men of all sorts and conditions, must have met Shakespeare somewhere in London, although it must be admitted that there are no documents of the time to prove that the two men were acquainted. Nevertheless, all the evidence we have does tend to suggest contacts between the physician and the poet. Harvey set up in practice in 1604. He resided in the parish of St. Martin's-extra-Ludgate, about half-way between St. Bartholomew's Hospital to the north and Blackfriars Bridge to the south and at a comparatively short distance from both. Harvey lived, then, fairly close to the two principal theatres where Shakespeare's plays were produced. The first of these playhouses was near Blackfriars Bridge and was made famous by the great actor Burbage; the second theatre was near London Bridge, on Bankside. This was the celebrated Globe Theatre, burned down in 1613.

Bankside was, in Harvey's early London years, a sort of beach and patch of waste ground on the south bank of the Thames opposite to (but not upon the territory of) the City, which was built exclusively upon the north bank. Bankside became, little by little, a 'transpontine' suburb where humble pleasure-gardens, inns, and what we should now call 'fun-fairs', grew up and flourished unhampered without the City boundaries. However, in addition to soldiers, sailors and the populace generally, the fashionable folk of the town did not disdain to go and drink and play while listening, more or less distractedly, to the latest novelties and comic pieces of the playwrights and actors. The players, who had begun by acting upon trestle tables in the courtyards of the inns, had gradually risen in social rank with the improved quality of their plays, so that in Shakespeare's time two proper theatres were flourishing in this district. We have all seen a picture of the Globe, a circular hut-like structure with a flag flying above it.

Shakespeare, no doubt, presented several of his pieces elsewhere than at the Bankside theatres, for we know that he acted himself in his own plays at the Courts of Elizabeth I and of James I. For example, *The Tempest* was played before the Court in 1611 and 1612, as is witnessed by two MSS. of the time, the *Booke of Revells* and *Vertue*. However, there is no warrant for the claim, sometimes made, that these occasions provided opportunities for Shakespeare, the dramatist, to meet Harvey, the King's physician. Such a meeting would have been quite impossible, for Harvey, still a young and comparatively unknown physician between 1604 and 1612 (the last year that Shakespeare appeared before the Court) was not appointed

Physician Extraordinary to the King until 1616, the year of Shakespeare's death.

Nonetheless, Harvey, interested in arts and letters as he was, and being a near neighbour to the theatres where Shakespeare's plays (many of them such as *The Merchant of Venice*, *Romeo and Juliet* and *Julius Caesar*, of Italian or classical inspiration) were acted, must often have attended at Blackfriars or the Globe. We cannot be far wrong in supposing that the profundity of the philosophical ideas and the loftiness of the moral and social principles of the dramatist[1] greatly attracted a man of the quality and temper and culture of William Harvey.

There is also the fact that a young physician interested in research, one Dr. John Hall (1575–1635), author of a medical work *Select Observations* and only three years older than Harvey, married Shakespeare's elder daughter, Susanna, at Stratford-on-Avon where he practised, in 1607. Possibly we have here another reason for believing that Harvey may have met the poet.

It has also been argued from a passage in *Hamlet* that the physician's works had some influence upon Shakespeare. The argument is, in my opinion, rather far-fetched. The passage in question occurs in Act I, Scene 5, where the ghost of the murdered king appears to his son:

> Sleeping in mine orchard,
> My custom always in the afternoon,
> Upon my secure hour thy uncle stole
> With juice of cursed hebenon in a vial,
> And in the porches of mine ears did pour
> The leperous distilment; whose effect
> Holds such an enmity with blood of man
> That, swift as quicksilver, it courses through
> The natural gates and alleys of the body;
> And, with a sudden vigour, it doth posset
> And curd, like eager droppings into milk,
> The thin and wholesome blood: so did it mine . . .

Some have deduced from this passage that Shakespeare had some inkling of Harvey's doctrine of the circulation of the blood. But, apart from the vagueness of the wording of the text—which may just as well be interpreted in the light of Galen's doctrines— *Hamlet* was played for the first time in 1603 and at that time it was quite impossible that Shakespeare should have had any knowledge

---

[1] Sentiments which contrast with the burlesque attitudes and speech of certain 'comic' characters inserted to amuse the general public.

of Harvey's ideas. Indeed, in 1603 the physician had not long finished his studies at Padua and had not as yet advanced anything publicly against the old scholastic tradition; he was hardly yet established in London. The date of *Hamlet* alone, then, destroys the fine fancy of such a connection between the dramatist and Harvey. There is nothing in any of Shakespeare's later works that can be seen as an acceptance of Harvey's ideas, and indeed, Harvey was still in the early stages of his investigations when Shakespeare's last play, *The Tempest*, appeared in 1611. Harvey did not, as we have seen, begin to deliver his Lumleian Lectures until 1616, the year of Shakespeare's death.

As far as Harvey's later influence upon the theatre is concerned, the situation was quite different when, seventy years after the appearance of *Hamlet*, i.e. in 1673, Molière wrote his *Malade Imaginaire*. Molière well knew about the doctrines of the English physician and he was also well aware of the decision taken by Louis XIV (judiciously advised by the young surgeon, Pierre Dionis) to have Harvey's doctrine taught in his *Jardin du Roy*, the present *Jardin des Plantes* at Paris and the ancestor of the *Museum d'Histoire Naturelle*. Molière, then, was the first, or one of the first, to conduct an offensive in favour of Harvey's teaching, an offensive that was taken up and continued by many of the eminent French writers of the *Grand Siècle*. Molière, we may remember, ridiculed the inept and ignorant Thomas Diafoirus and his great booby of a son, who refused 'to understand anything or to listen to . . . the supposed discoveries of our age touching the circulation of the blood and other opinions of the like kind'. And, after Molière, we have Boileau and La Fontaine. But we shall have occasion to refer to these matters at greater length later on.

To return to the story of Harvey's own career, a perusal of the *Exercitatio* and of other chronicles of the time shows that the great physician had, both at Court and elsewhere, a number of highly placed patients by whom he was often called into consultation, and upon whose bodies he was sometimes required to conduct postmortem examinations.

It has been said that after a period of great celebrity, and after the publication of his *Exercitatio*, Harvey lost much of his reputation and many of his patients owing to the attacks of his colleagues, who spread it abroad that he was little better than crack-brained. D'Arcy Power was not of this way of thinking, however, for he wrote concerning Harvey's own references to the widespread hostility he had had to meet:

'Such ideas probably occurred to him in his later years when he was depressed by repeated attacks of gout. But party feeling ran high, and was even greater than professional jealousy at a time when Harvey was very closely connected with the losing side. Some of his contemporaries took advantage of the double meaning attached to the word Circulator which Celsus applies to a Merry Andrew. It was also said about him that "though all of his profession would allow him to be an excellent anatomist, I never heard of many that admired his therapeutic way. I knew several practitioners in this town that would not have given threepence for one of his bills, as a man can hardly tell by his bills what he did aim at".

'The apothecaries at this time,' continues D'Arcy Power, 'were accustomed to buy up the bills or prescriptions of the leading physicians in much the same manner and for the same purpose that a clinical clerk or a dresser in a hospital now treasures up the prescriptions of his physician or surgeon. We can afford to smile at these pieces of contemporary criticism by empirics, for we remember that as the apothecaries objected to the practice of Harvey the attorneys led by Coke[1] sneered at the legal knowledge of Bacon, but in neither case has the verdict of posterity ratified that of contemporary opinion.' The many eminent positions and the important functions held by Harvey are proof enough that he was held in honour and respect, and the number of his patients must rather have increased than decreased.

In 1629, the year following the publication of the *Exercitatio*, Harvey was commanded by King Charles I to accompany James Stuart, Duke of Lennox (born in 1612 and therefore aged only seventeen years), who had been despatched on a mission to the continent. No doubt this 'mission' was in reality a Grand Tour designed to round off the young man's education, rather than an embassy with any real political or diplomatic significance.

Harvey had, however, to attend to some private business before he could leave England. On 3rd December, 1629, he invited the seven Elects of the College of Physicians to his house, and after an

---

[1] The reference is to the celebrated jurist, Edward Coke, who, in 1594, in the reign of Elizabeth I, obtained as against Bacon (then aged thirty-three) the post of Solicitor-General, which the latter, devoured as always by ambition, had sought to gain by all the means at his disposal. Bacon, who under James I rose much higher and became, as Lord Chancellor, the head of all the judiciary, revenged himself upon Coke by abasing him to the lowest rank that he could. But Coke, in his turn, got his revenge during the trial of Bacon in 1621 for misappropriation of public funds, malversation and corruption—a trial that resulted in the exclusion from public life of the favourite both of the King and the Duke of Buckingham.

excellent repast, asked their permission to resign his position as Treasurer of the College, a request that was immediately granted. On 21st January of the following year he petitioned for leave of absence from St. Bartholomew's Hospital, as witness this entry in the Minutes:

Curia tent. Sabti. xxi die Januarii 1629–30

In the presence of Sir Robt. Ducy Knight & Barronet,
President (and others).

DR. HARVEY

This day Dr. Harvey Physician to this hospital declares to this court that he is commanded by the Kings most excellent majesty . . .

(Then follows an account of the meeting and of the leave granted.)

After that, in a letter addressed to Mr. Secretary Dorchester to protect himself against a rival, one Dr. Adam Moesler (who, apparently, was endeavouring to secure Harvey's salary paid by the King), appointed as his *locum tenentes* three of his intimates, Drs. Chambers and Bethune, Physicians in Ordinary to the Sovereign, and Harvey's great friend Dr. Smith of London, whom he also recommended to the Governors of St. Bartholomew's Hospital.

However, Harvey does not seem to have started upon his journey until the spring following, that of 1631, when he joined the other members of the mission who had left for France in June, 1630. On 10th August of that year, indeed, the documents of the time show us that Lennox was at Dieppe and preparing to visit other towns in the north of France. At the end of September the duke was reported to be in Paris to spend the winter, with the intention of undertaking a tour of France in the spring of 1631, after which he was to proceed to Italy at the end of the summer 'unless' (as his correspondent Edward Dacres wrote to Lord Dorchester) 'the continuance of the war or the plague hinder him'.

Indeed, at this time the French were engaged in a war started by Richelieu with the intention of preventing the Court of Spain from seizing the Duchy of Mantua, and also of attaching this State to the French cause by making it over to the Duke of Nevers.

The Duke of Lennox was still at Paris at the beginning of April and it was probably at the French capital that Harvey joined him during the spring or early summer of 1631. In August of that same year Dacres wrote to Dorchester that 'Blois proved a place not long to be endured by my Lord because of the plague which grew hot there, as Tours likewise, where we made little stay, so that we came down to Saumurs there to pass the dog days from whence we are now parting they being at an end'.

It was doubtless during this same part of the tour that Harvey wrote to Dorchester of 'the miseries of the countries we have passed. . . . I can only complain that by the way we could scarce see a dog, crow, kite, raven or any other bird, or any thing to anatomise, only some few miserable people, the relics of the war and the plague where famine had made anatomies before I came.'

And Harvey added this note of commiseration:

'I interprete it well that it will be a great motive for all here to have and procure assurance of settled peace. It is time to leave fighting when there is nothing to eat, nothing to be kept, and nothing to be gotten.' Shortly afterwards, indeed, the Mantua war came to an end through the mediation of Pope Urban VIII, and Charles of Nevers was allowed to enjoy the Duchy of Mantua.

At this time, too, the pest was raging in northern Italy and in those lands the mission must traverse to reach Venice. No less than thirty-five thousand persons died at Verona alone. Because of this— and perhaps also from some political considerations—the travellers took their way *via* Bordeaux to Spain rather than to Italy. In any case, in February 1632 Lennox was created a Grandee in Spain before setting out for home. By the end of March, 1632, Harvey was back in England, since on the 26th of that month he drew up a new series of rules for the Library of the College of Physicians. This measure was doubtless induced by the legacy of six hundred and thirty volumes bequeathed by a Dr. Holsboch, a German who had for some fifty years practised surgery and medicine in England. The new rules were designed the better to protect the library from thefts. In May, 1632, we also find Harvey's signature at the foot of a petition addressed by the College of Physicians to the King, the object of which was to obtain control over the sale of certain poisons by obliging the purchaser to give his name.

To glance back for a moment, we may note that it was very probably in the quarter of 1630 that ended on Lady Day, the 25th of March, that Harvey was appointed Physician in Ordinary to the King, since the State Papers contain a note for the following payment:

'3 July 1635. To William Harvey, one of his Majesty's physicians in ordinary, his annuity for a year ending at Our Lady Day 1631 £300.' Further proof of Harvey's appointment is furnished by other annuities paid later, in instalments and with considerable delay indicative of the negligence and disorder common in those troubled times.

'Harvey's appointment as personal physician to the King seems,' writes D'Arcy Power, 'to have brought him into close connection with his master, and it was no doubt at this time that Charles allowed him to obtain the intimate knowledge of the habits and structure of the deer which was afterwards turned to such good use in the treatise on Development. Harvey, in fact, became the personal friend of his king, he accompanied him everywhere, and consequently took a share in the hunting excursions to which his Majesty was so devoted.' These activities are also reflected in the little jealousies and complaints expressed by the Governors of St. Bartholomew's Hospital regarding Harvey's frequent absences from his work.

At the beginning of 1633, Harvey was commanded by the King to accompany him to Scotland. Once more Harvey had to ask the Governors for leave of absence, and suggested as his interim Dr. Smith, his close friend (who only survived a fortnight the opening of the Harveian Museum of which he was the most active promoter). But the Governors were also solicited by Dr. Andrewes, who was strongly backed by certain political and commercial interests in the City. The rivalry between Smith and Andrewes lasted until the latter's death in July the following year.

'Charles' tour in Scotland,' says D'Arcy Power, 'was fraught with the most momentous consequences both to himself and his kingdom. He was crowned with great pomp in the Abbey Church at Holyrood, and the rochet worn by the Bishop of Moray when he preached before the assembled Court on this occasion was an innovation which gave the greatest offence to the people. This discontent was further increased by an order from the King enjoining the ministers to wear surplices and the Bishops vestments instead of the Geneva gown to which they had been accustomed since the Reformation. The dissatisfaction thus aroused culminated in the Liturgy tumults of 1637, when Jenny Deans launched her stool at the head of the Bishop of St. Giles whilst he was preaching in Edinburgh. The tumults in turn led to the formation of "the Tables" and to the taking of "the Covenant", which are so familiar to every student of the history of the Civil War.'[1]

[1] The first Covenant had been concluded in 1588 (at the time of the Armada's threat to both England and the Reformation) and was a coalition of Scots determined to protect their national Church from the attacks of both Anglicanism and Catholicism. In 1640, when Charles I sought to impose the Anglican liturgy upon the Scots, a parliament met together at Edinburgh, renewed the 1588 Covenant and raised an army that defeated the royal troops at Newburn-on-Tyne. We shall see something more of these happenings when we deal with the Civil War years.

Harvey does not seem to have been much perturbed by these events nor by the rather acrimonious discussions which they excited both at Court and among the rival sects that gravitated about it. During his stay in Scotland he was much more preoccupied with the way chickens develop in eggs, and it was to throw light upon this problem that he went to Bass Rock, of which he gives an interesting and entertaining account in the eleventh essay of his *Treatise on Generation* (*Exer. XI, De Ovi Cortice*).

After having referred to the desolate islets swept by the tempests off the east coast of Scotland, and to the incredibly great swarms and flocks of birds of all sorts that occupy them, Harvey gives a description of the Bass Rock:

'There is a small island, Scotsmen call it the Bass (let it serve as a type of all the rest), lying near the shore, but in deep water. It is so rugged and precipitous that it might rather be called a huge stone or rock than an island, for it is not more than a mile in circumference. The whole surface of the island in the months of May and June is almost completely carpeted with nests, birds, and fledgelings. There are so many that you can scarcely avoid stepping upon them, and when they fly the crowd is so great that it hides the sun and the sky like a cloud. The screaming and din too are so great that you can hardly hear anyone speaking close to you. If you look down upon the sea, as if from a tower or tall precipice, whichever way you turn you will see an enormous number of different kinds of birds skimming about and gaping for their prey, so that the sea looks like a pond which is swarming with frogs in springtime, or like those sunny hills looked at from below when they are covered with numerous flocks of sheep and goats. If you sail round the island and look up you see on every ledge, shelf, and recess innumerable flocks of birds of every sort and size, more numerous than the stars seen at night in the unclouded moonless sky, and if you watch the flights that come and go incessantly, you might imagine that it was a mighty swarm of bees. I should hardly be believed if I said what a large revenue was obtained annually from the feathers and from the old nests (used for firing) and from the eggs, which are boiled and then sold, though the owner told me himself. There is one feature too, which seems to be especially worthy of note because it bears closely upon my argument and is clear proof of what I have just said about the crowd of birds. The whole island shines brilliantly white to those who approach it, and the cliffs are as bright as if they were made of the whitest chalk; yet the natural colour of the rock is dusky and black. It is due to a brittle crust of the whitest colour that is spread over all and gives the island its whiteness and brilliancy, a crust of the same consistence, colour, and nature as the shell of an egg.'

The art, the poetry even, of Harvey's description show well his mastery of the expression of thought in words. His general style, the shortness and balance of his sentences, the aptness of his similes, testify to that clearness of thinking which is the foundation of all good writing.

In the autumn of 1633 Harvey was once more back in London, for in October he was summoned by the Governors of the hospital to an important meeting at which were to be established rules for a more satisfactory management and for the 'good of the poor of this house'. A number of the resolutions adopted are of great interest as showing the development of hospital administration and organization, but we cannot linger over these things here, and must refer readers to D'Arcy Power's work where they will gain a clear account of the high estimation in which Harvey's services were held at this time. It was he, indeed, who procured the additional rules and stipulations subjecting the surgeons, apothecaries and midwives and nurses to the entire control of the chief physician. In these regulations we may see reflected Harvey's definition of the privileges and the superiority of the physicians, a point of view that he had not ceased to advocate since 1620 when he was charged by the College of Physicians, together with Drs. Mayerne and William Clement, to watch carefully the activities of those surgeons who were endeavouring to influence Parliament in their interests.

At the meeting of 15th November, 1634, the hospital's Council decided that, owing to the increase in the number of patients treated and because of the additional expense to Dr. Harvey occasioned by his position as Physician in Ordinary to the King, a second physician should be appointed for as long as seemed desirable to the Governors. Dr. Andrewes, physician in reversion, was to be admitted as immediate physician to the hospital.

This arrangement did not last long, for, as we have seen already, Dr. Andrewes died eight months later. In August, 1634, his position was given to Dr. Clarke with the stipulation that after the death or the resignation of Dr. Harvey, Dr. Clarke should remain sole physician to the hospital. As a matter of fact, Clarke himself died in 1653, that is, four years before Harvey, but as the latter left the hospital in 1643 owing to the turmoil of the Civil War, Dr. Clarke was for some ten years the physician to St. Bartholomew's Hospital.

It was in the year 1634 that Harvey was called to give an expert opinion in the famous case of the Lancashire witches. A boy of ten, one Edward Robinson, the son of a Lancashire wood-cutter, made accusations out of spite against a neighbour, Mother Dickenson. It seems that she had reproached the lad with playing truant from school. In what we might today call a mythomania complex young Robinson concocted such a convincing tale of sorcery against Mother Dickenson that the magistrates who examined him accepted it as true.

One day, he said, as he was wandering about in one of the clearings of the woods, gathering blackberries, he saw two grey-hounds which he thought belonged to the local landowners. Then a hare darted across the path and he tried to set the dogs on it, but neither of them would follow. So, the lad averred, furious at the dog's behaviour, he picked up a stick and was about to belabour them when one of them turned into a woman and the other into a boy. The woman, who was none other than Mother Dickenson, then offered Robinson money if he would sell his soul to the devil —which he refused to do. Thereupon, the woman took a bridle out of her pocket and touched the head of the other boy with it, and he instantly became a horse. Snatching up Robinson, Mother Dickenson jumped with him upon the horse and after a wild ride through woods, fields, swamps and streams they reached a huge barn. The witch got down from the horse, took Robinson by the hand and dragged him into the building. There he saw seven old women pulling at seven halters that hung down from the roof, and while they pulled he saw fall from the halters on to the floor some large pieces of meat, lumps of butter, loaves of bread, basins of milk, hot puddings and black puddings. Supper was spread, and when it was ready the other witches came to share it.

As a consequence of this highly imaginative recital many women were arrested, for the boy was sent from parish to parish in order to identify the 'witches' he had seen in the barn. The story spread through the country and made so great a stir that Sir William Pelham wrote to Lord Conway that he had sensational news of a round-up of witches in Lancashire where, it was said, nineteen had been condemned and at least sixty more implicated. 'It is suspected,' he added, 'that they had a hand in raising the great storm wherein his Majesty was in so great danger at sea in Scotland.'

Of course, the number of arrests had been magnified by popular rumour, but seven of the accused were condemned and Bishop Bridgeman of Chester was requested to examine them. When the prelate visited the gaol he found that three had died and that a fourth, Janet Hargreaves, lay in a hopeless condition. Of the three

remaining who were interrogated by Bridgeman, two declared that
they had no knowledge at all of witchcraft, but the third, a widow
of sixty named Margaret Johnson (whose over-excited imagination
and feeble wits the bishop at once recognized) said she had been a
witch for six years. She added that 'there appeared to her a man in
black attire, who said, if she would give him her soul she should
have power to hurt whom she would. He called himself Mamilion,
and appeared in the shape of a brown-coloured dog, a white cat, and
a hare, and in these shapes sucked her blood.'

The report of the bishop to Mr. Secretary Coke was communicated to the King, and he commanded the Earl of Manchester,
the Lord Privy Seal, to report on the affair to his two surgeons,
Alexander Baker and Clowes. Manchester's letter reads thus:

To Alexander Baker, Esq. and Sarjeant Clowes his
Majesty's Chirurgions.

These shall be to will and require you forthwith to make choice
of such midwives as you shall think fit to inspect and search the bodies
of those women that were lately brought by the sheriff of the County
of Lancaster indicted for witchcraft and to report unto you whether
they find about them any such marks as are pretended: wherein the
said midwives are to receive instructions from Mr. Dr. Harvey his
Majesty's Physician and yourselves.

Dated at Whitehall the 29 June 1634.

H. Manchester.

The prisoners, who were then at the Ship Tavern in Greenwich,
were brought to London as soon as the King's commands were
received. After the women had been examined the following report
was drawn up:

Surgeons Hall in Monkwell Street, London.

2 July a.d. 1634.

We in humble obedience to your Lordship's command have this
day called unto us the Chirurgeons and midwives whose names are
hereunder written who have by the direction of Mr. Dr. Harvey
(in our presence and his) made diligent search and inspection on
those women which were lately brought up from Lancaster and find
as followeth, viz.:—

On the bodies of Jennett Hargreaves, ffrances Dicconson and
Mary-Spencer nothing unnatural nor anything like a teat or mark
or any sign that such a thing hath ever been.

On the body of Margaret Johnson we find two things which may be called teats. The first in shape like to the teat of a bitch but in our judgement nothing but the skin as it will be drawn out after the application of leeches. The second is like the nipple or teat of a woman's breast, but of the same colour with the rest of the skin without any hollowness or issue for any blood or juice to come from thence.

The report was signed by ten midwives, by Alexander Reid, M.D., lecturer in anatomy at the Barber-Surgeons' Hall (whom Harvey seems to have deputed to take his place) and by six surgeons evidently chosen from among the most noted in London. As a result, the four women who had survived of the original seven convicted were pardoned, an act of justice which, says Mr. Aveling, 'may have been due to the enlightened views and prompt and energetic action of Dr. Harvey'.

Harvey, then, found himself consulted in important cases of pathology which occurred in the society of his time. Since, in his days, specialization (which increased as it became ever more necessary to enquire more and more deeply into any given subject) had not restricted the field of enquiry, Harvey's activities were very extensive and varied. Specialization, indeed, is not seldom a bane, if too soon and too exclusively it circumscribes the mind and confines it within too narrow limits.

Harvey applied himself to medicine, of course, but also to surgery, as witness the 'silver instruments of surgery' which he bequeathed to Dr. Scarborough, and the great physician's own notes on the cure he made of 'enormous sarcoceles by the simple means of dividing or tying the little artery that supplied them and so preventing all access of nourishment or spirit to the part affected, by which it came to pass that tumour on the verge of mortification was afterwards easily extirpated with the knife or searing iron'.

The searing-iron was, of course, used to prevent the haemorrhages incident to all operations on healthy and well-nourished tissues, for, despite the early efforts of Ambroise Paré, there did not as yet exist any effective apparatus or means for staying the flow of blood.

As may be seen from many passages in his *Treatise on Generation*, Harvey was also an expert gynaecologist and as well versed in such practical midwifery as that with which the prejudices and habits of his time allowed him to familiarize himself.

In 1635 Harvey was accused before the Court of the Barber-Surgeons' Company by one William Kellett, who 'being called here in Court for not making presentation of one of Mr. Kinnersley's maids that died in his charge, he said here in Court that Mr. Dr. Harvey being called to the patient did upon his view of the patient say that by means of a boulster, the tumour on the temporal muscle could be discussed and his opinion was that there was no fracture but the vomiting came by reason of the foulness of the stomach and to that purpose prescribed physic by Briscoe the Apothecary so the patient died by ill practice, the fracture being neglected and the Company not called to the view'. It was the sort of complaint that jealousy and a sense of grievance have ever thrown out against physicians.

In this same year, 1635, Harvey was commanded by the King to examine the body of Thomas Parr, who had died at the reputed age of no less than a hundred and fifty-two years and nine months, after having lived during the reigns of nine sovereigns. Parr was passing his declining years frugally in Shropshire when, a little time before his death, he was induced by Thomas Howard, Lord Arundel, to go to London to be shown to the King. After a post-mortem Harvey concluded that all the internal organs seemed to be in excellent condition so that it might be thought that the patriarch would have still had some time to live had he not been disturbed in his habits and way of life. His death must be attributed to the change from the pure air of Shropshire to that of London, and to the unaccustomed food to which he had been subjected in the household of so great a personage as Arundel.[1]

It may have been a common interest in Old Parr that served as a starting-point for the friendship between Arundel and Harvey that lasted until Arundel's death at Padua in 1646. No doubt Arundel found in Harvey a man interested in the arts, for Thomas Howard was a prince of collectors and his gallery of marbles was famous. In any case, in early April of the following year, i.e. 1636, when Arundel was despatched as Ambassador Extraordinary to the Emperor Ferdinand II at Vienna (after the Peace which the Protestant States had just concluded with the Emperor), Harvey was appointed a member of the mission, concerning which D'Arcy Power gave a very interesting account in the *Proceedings of the Royal Society of Medicine*, 1916–17, under the title of 'A Revised Chapter in the Life of Dr. William Harvey, 1636'.

The mission set sail from Margate on 8th April, 1636, and

[1] The notes of the autopsy came into the possession of Harvey's nephew Michael, who presented them to Dr. Bett, and they were not printed until 1669, when they were published in Dr. Bett's work *On the Source and Quality of the Blood*.

reached the Dutch coast on the 10th. Then, travelling by Delft, The Hague and Leyden, Arundel and his party reached the Rhine where they embarked for Wesel, Duisburg and Düsseldorf. On 21st April the embassy was at Cologne and a first mention of Harvey is made in a letter from Lord Arundel, who had just visited the Jesuit college. 'I found,' he says humorously, 'in the College little Dr. Harvey, who means to convert them.' After passing through Coblenz, Mainz, Frankfurt and Würzburg the party arrived on 20th May at Nuremberg, from which town Harvey wrote a letter to Caspar Hofmann in which he offered to demonstrate the circulation of the blood, since he had, he said, learned that Hofmann complained of the theory and that 'he impeached and condemned Nature of folly and error, and that he had imputed to her the character of a most clumsy and inefficient artificer in suffering the blood to become recrudescent, and making it return again and again to the heart in order to be reconcocted only to grow effete again in the arterial system'.[1]

It is recorded, indeed, that Harvey did make a public demonstration of his doctrines and convinced everyone present with the exception of Hofmann who, then aged and enjoying the reputation of a kind of medical pontiff, stayed sceptical and badgered the demonstrator with so many objections that finally Harvey lost his temper, threw his scalpel upon the floor and left the theatre.

Regarding this journey, Aubrey relates an anecdote which, because it accords much better with what we know of Harvey's character than do many of Aubrey's stories, we may perhaps accept. He says that he learned from another member of the mission, William Hollar, the celebrated painter, that, 'Dr. Harvey would still be making observations of strange trees and plants, earths, etc. and sometimes like to be lost. So that my Lord Ambassador would be really angry with him, for there was not only a danger of thieves but also of wild beasts.' We may realize how real these dangers were when we remember that the party had to pass through the country devastated by the Thirty Years' War, which was to continue to spread ruin and destruction until it was ended in 1648 by the Treaties of Westphalia.[2]

---

[1] This letter is reproduced in the article by D'Arcy Power referred to above.

[2] After having been confronted with the Mantua war in 1632, Harvey now found himself in the middle of the Thirty Years' War (1618–48), the result of the incessant quarrels which had occurred between German Catholics and Protestants since the illusory Peace of Augsburg had been concluded. Ferdinand II aimed at re-establishing the hegemony of the Catholic House of Austria, while the chief of

From Nuremberg, Harvey accompanied the embassy (*see* map in Fig. 5) through Ratisbon (24th May, 1636), Passau (2nd June), Linz (5th June) to Vienna, which was not reached until 24th June. Arundel and his suite stayed at Vienna only until 1st July, for he had met the Emperor and Empress at Linz and as there had been several audiences with Ferdinand II the embassy spent twenty days in that town. During the stay at Linz Harvey began a correspondence (of eleven letters in all) addressed to Lord Feilding, the British envoy at Venice. The first is dated from Linz, 9th June (19th in the Gregorian calendar). The second letter was also written at Linz in June, 1636, the third at Baden on 29th June (9th July, New Style).[1] Harvey had taken advantage of his stay in Vienna to make an excursion to Baden, some seventeen miles distant from the Austrian capital. We shall have occasion to refer, later on, to the remaining eight letters.

The mission left Vienna on 1st July and set off for Bohemia (the Queen of Bohemia being Charles I's younger sister) by way of Iglau, Prague and Pilsen. Ratisbon was again reached on 17th July. A few days later the mission moved to Augsburg 'to fill in time'. Then, when Arundel and his party moved back to Ratisbon where they remained until the beginning of November, Harvey went down to Italy with two companions, there to purchase pictures for Charles I. In a letter dated from Ratisbon in the middle of July mention is made of 'honnest little Harvey whom the Earl is sending to Italy about some pictures for His Majesty'.

D'Arcy Power stated that the distance from Augsburg to Venice was about four hundred and sixty miles and that the journey was undertaken on horseback with two 'attendants'. We have no information about the route taken from Augsburg to Villach, but

the Protestant faction, the Elector Palatine Frederick V, was by them recognized as Holy Roman Emperor. After a thousand vicissitudes and three main phases, often called the Palatine, the Danish and the Franco-Swedish, the latter marked by the victorious campaigns of Condé and Turenne, the war was ended by the Treaties of Westphalia in 1648 by which was established a number of religious and political arrangements defining the position of the main German principalities as against a diminished Austria, as well as the cession to France of the Three Bishoprics of Verdun, Toul and Metz, as well as of Alsace.

[1] It was only in 1752 that the English (then finding themselves eleven days behind the calendar adopted elsewhere) conformed to the Gregorian calendar, published in 1582 after the corrections made in the astronomical computations at the instance of Pope Gregory XII. In the States of the Church the New Style was promulgated in October, 1582; in France and the Low Countries in December of the same year.

FIG. 5. Map of Harvey's travels across Europe in 1636 with Thomas Howard, second Earl of Arundel and Ambassador Extraordinary of Charles I to the Emperor, Ferdinand II. From Augsburg to Rome (and back) Harvey travelled alone.

it may have been through Munich (67 miles), thence to Innsbrück (105 miles), to Franzensfeste on the Brenner Pass (49 miles) and to Villach (13 miles). From that point onwards Harvey's letters show that he went from Villach to Pontebba (30 miles), thence to Sacile and Conegliano (9 miles) and to Treviso (17 miles). At Treviso he was only eighteen miles from Venice and might have considered that he had reached his goal, but he was to be greatly disappointed. His first letter, written from Treviso to Lord Feilding, the British envoy to the *Serenissima*, is dated Friday, 3rd August, so that if he left Augsburg as soon as Arundel got there (that is to say on the 23rd of July) Harvey would have covered the distance from Augsburg to Treviso at an average of forty miles a day.[1] The only news we have of him during these ten days of travel is contained in a letter addressed by Sir Thomas Roe to the Queen of Hungary, in which it is said that Dr. Harvey assured his personal friends that much was to be expected from the sense of justice and equity of the Emperor, but that he (Roe) considered Harvey's opinion to be based, like that of a physician, upon nothing more than symptoms.

But at Treviso, Harvey met with a serious obstacle to his plans and, for a time, was affected both in his health and in his peace of mind. His letters show all that clearly enough.

D'Arcy Power published letters Nos. 4 to 9, written by Harvey from Treviso to Feilding at Venice. In them the physician complains of the quarantine inflicted upon him on his arrival at Treviso, but by another letter to the same Feilding (No. 10 of the collection), dated at Florence, 7th–17th September, Harvey thanks the envoy for the welcome he gave him when he passed through Venice, and then tells Feilding what has been happening at the Court of Florence. From this we must conclude that Harvey arrived in Venice about the end of August and reached Florence during the first days of September.

[1] I would not like to guarantee the correctness of the figures printed by D'Arcy Power in the *Proceedings*, for if we add up 67, 105, 49, 13, 30, 9 and 17 (the figures given for the distances between the various laps of the journey) we get 290 miles, and even if we add the 18 on to Venice that gives us only 308 miles of the 460 mentioned as being the mileage from Augsburg to Venice. It is true that the distance from Pontebba to Sacile is not mentioned. Furthermore, 290 miles covered in 10 days (really at least 11) give at the most 30 and not 40 miles a day. If we look at the map we shall be surprised to find only 13 miles given for the stretch from Franzensfeste to Villach, while 49 miles are recorded for the lap from Innsbrück to Franzensfeste. All these figures need checking, but it is perhaps hardly worth while doing this as what is of importance is the general account of the trip and not its minor details.

After this letter there is again a gap in our information on Harvey's whereabouts until 5th October, when we find him at Rome. The guest-book of the English College in Rome shows that Harvey dined there on 5th October, 1636. Dr. Ent was present on this occasion and probably the two travellers had arranged to meet at the College, for Ent was almost a fellow-townsman of Harvey's, since he had been born at Sandwich and had received his doctor's diploma at Padua on 28th April, 1636.[1]

If we compare the dates of Harvey's arrival in Florence and that of his presence in Rome, we may infer that he spent most of the month of September in the former town. But he makes no mention of Galileo, whom he could hardly have failed to have met. This silence is as difficult to explain as his not referring to Padua, his old university town which he almost certainly passed through twice on this tour, the first time on his way from Treviso to Venice and the second time on his way from Venice to Florence. Maybe, indeed, Harvey passed no less than four times through Padua, if he returned northwards by the same road that he came.

Perhaps we may attempt some explanation of Harvey's silence regarding Padua, and also of his conduct at Florence, where it is almost impossible to believe that he could have remained a whole month without visiting, at least in private, the aged man of genius who was there finishing his days under close surveillance after his condemnation by the Inquisition, on 22nd June, 1632, for his 'heretical' teaching that the earth moved round the sun. From 1589 to 1610 Galileo had been a professor at Padua, so that during his university days there Harvey must often have attended Galileo's celebrated lectures.

It is rather curious that D'Arcy Power makes no mention at all of these two reticences on the part of Harvey—no reference to Padua or to the famed astronomer. Here are my conjectures:

It does not seem likely that Harvey had no desire to see Padua once more, though it is just possible that he might have made his visit *incognito* and was therefore disinclined to talk about it afterwards. If this is what happened we may explain his conduct in

---

[1] Ent had also been up at Cambridge (Sidney Sussex College). With so many ties between them it is not surprising that Ent and Harvey were destined to remain firm friends until the latter's death. It was, indeed, Ent's affection for Harvey that led him to defend, against Parisanus, Harvey's doctrine of the circulation of the blood. Harvey's affection for Ent led him to entrust his fellow-physician with the publication of *De Generatione Animalium* 'in any fashion that he thought best'—as we shall see later on.

several ways. He might have wanted to view the old scenes without being recognized or even seen, possibly from fear of being embarrassed by new faces, and maybe hostile ones. Then, again, he may have desired to avoid attention as a 'heretical' scientist, for the new generations of students were thus taught to regard him, since they were still fed upon the doctrines of Aristotle and Galen.

Harvey was in many quarters regarded as a 'traitor', and indeed was so termed by Parisanus, who did not cease to spew forth against the English physician an uninterrupted flow of insult and abuse. Again, doubtless, Harvey's experience at Nuremberg did not encourage him to attempt another public demonstration of his doctrine in the amphitheatre where he had so often sat as a student. I think that it is in such considerations that we must seek for an understanding of why he must have passed *incognito* through Padua and why he does not mention the city in his correspondence. At Venice, on the other hand, no one knew or cared whether a man called Harvey, attached to Lord Arundel's diplomatic mission and charged with the purchase of pictures for the King of England, was the same person who, eight years before, had published that *Exercitatio de Motu Cordis et Sanguinis* which had aroused the violent hostility of professors and practisers of medicine. The prestige that Harvey must have enjoyed as an emissary of Charles I would prevent most people from making any such identification, and we may suppose that Harvey chose to preserve the secret of his identity.

Things must have been much the same at Florence as at Venice and Padua. Why, at Medici's Court, should Harvey, the revolutionary scientist, reveal himself and run the risk of undergoing once more an experience as unpleasant as that of Nuremberg? It was far more prudent to remain the confidential servant of the King of England and to enjoy the deference that such a position must have guaranteed to him. Hence, in his letter to Lord Feilding what Harvey speaks of is receptions at Court, and the whole contents of the communication are merely diplomatic.

Concerning Galileo, his old and now persecuted master, it is possible—even probable—that he went in secret to see him at Arcetri. It is certainly pleasing to think of Harvey acting thus, for we know that he was a warm-hearted man, faithful in his friendships. We may imagine this representative of Charles I, then, as standing a little upon his dignity, as possibly rather stiff and reserved during the day, but at night setting off to sit and talk with his old master, and possibly to scrutinize the limpid night of Florence through the telescope that Galileo had devised to search the heavens.

We have seen that Harvey must have reached Rome at the beginning of October, for he met Dr. Ent there on the 5th of that month. However, we have no information as to the length of his stay in Rome, nor do we know the exact date on which Harvey left the city. Lord Arundel received the royal command to return to England at the end of September, 1636, and he must have informed Harvey. The latter may have left Rome hurriedly, since he was back at Ratisbon at the beginning of November. On his way to Germany he again passed through Venice, for there is in existence a letter from Harvey addressed to Feilding (the 11th Letter) dated at Ratisbon, 5th–15th November, 1636, in which the writer informs the envoy that he had rejoined the mission and thanks Feilding for all he had done for Harvey in Venice.

The return journey to England began on Tuesday, 8th November, when the mission left Ratisbon in the morning. Nuremberg was reached three days later. D'Arcy Power's account of this journey (based on the official reports) contains interesting observations upon the purchase of art objects made at different stages on the road home, and upon a variety of incidents; sometimes there were ceremonious welcomes in the towns, sometimes dangers were encountered in traversing a country that was ravaged by war, and where there was no sort of security for the traveller. Leyden was reached on 14th December.

Arundel hastened to visit the main sights of the Dutch university city, especially the academy itself and the School of Anatomy. After dinner, the party pushed on to The Hague. Here is the account written by William Crowne, who was a member of the mission and, in a pamphlet of seventy pages printed in London in 1637, narrated in detail the whole journey from the departure from Greenwich on 7th April, 1636, to the arrival at Hampton Court Palace on 30th December.[1] Utrecht was reached on 13th December, and from Leyden the embassy travelled to The Hague. He says:

'Here we stayed until December 21st and then left for Rotterdam. On Saturday being the 24th December (and Christmas Eve by our style) at 11 of the clocke in the night tooke boates and went to our ship called the Garland and about 3 in the afternoon set sayle and

---

[1] *A true Relation of all the remarkable Places and Passages observed in the Travels of the Right Honourable Thomas Lord Howard, Earle of Arundell and Surrey, Premier Earle and Earle Marshal of England, Ambassadour Extraordinary to His Sacred Majesty Ferdinando the Second, Emperour of Germanie. Anno Domini 1636 by William Crowne, Gentleman.*

sayled over the barre, having a Pilot sayling before us with a lan-
thorne on the top of his mast sounding for the depth all the way.
And the next day at twelue of the clocke cast anchor in the Downs
and there rode and could not land for the roughnesse of the sea until
Tuesday morning the 27th December and then landed at Deale and
from thence by poast to Canterbury and so to Sittingbourne
to bed.

'The next day in the morning earely to Gravesend and there
tooke water to London, where on the way my Right Honourable
Lady met his Excellence, who exchanged barges and there she
entertained him with a banquet and earely the next morning went
to Hampton Court to His Majesty.'

In connection with this banquet we may note that during the
whole journey the embassy seems to have enjoyed fine fare and a
copious supply of wines in all the towns, where a welcome was
extended to Arundel and his suite. As D'Arcy Power suggests, the
fact that Harvey at the age of fifty-eight supported such an expedition through lands devastated by war, shows that he had lost
nothing of his enterprising spirit and of his taste for travel. Harvey
appears to have been used to fairly heavy drinking, for without
previous training he would hardly have been able to hold his own
at a 17th-century *Kneipe*. Moreover, Harvey would have been no
true Englishman had he not, when on the Continent, done justice
to good wine—Chianti, Asti, Claret or Burgundy—though we
should hasten to add that, like many of his fellow-countrymen of
today, he also found that atmosphere of intellectualism very much
to his taste.

Thus we find Harvey back in London again at the end of
December, 1636, and able to resume his professional duties. During
the two ensuing years there is, however, no mention of him except
in a certificate dated 2nd December, 1637: 'Having had experience
of the disposition and weakness of the body of Sir Thomas Thynne,
Knight (who hath been and still is our patient) we testify that we are
of the opinion that it will be dangerous for the health of his body to
travel this winter into the country and place of his usual abode
until he hath better recovered his health and strength.—*Will.
Harvey.*'

I have called this period of Harvey's life that of the rise to full
maturity of his scientific and professional activities and influence,
but before we move on to consider the dark days of the Civil War
I should like to add a few words concerning the part Harvey played
in what might be called the Public Health regulations of his time. I

refer to his participation in the drawing up of the Deontological Code which was designed to regulate the acts of all those physicians, surgeons and apothecaries who were called upon to attend the bedside of the sick and to work together for the greatest possible good and care of their patients.

Harvey's part stands out clearly if we compare the new rules and regulations which he introduced at the College of Physicians and at St. Bartholomew's Hospital. Indeed, at the College Harvey exercised control and asserted his authority over all those who were concerned in Public Health matters throughout England, while at the hospital he had secured the adoption of an organization which became a model for that of all similar charitable institutions throughout the realm. Harvey, as we have seen, added to the existing regulations other much more precise rules and statutes by which the functions and attributions of each one were clearly defined and by which was established the rigorous discipline necessary for the maintenance of good order and high moral standards in the three professions.

We may also note that, in Harvey's day, St. Bartholomew's Hospital was under the administrative control of the Governors appointed by the King, who met regularly to serve as the supreme authority in all matters of supervision and of general policy, and a Physician in Chief under whom were placed all the medical staff, namely the surgeons, apothecaries and nurses. The Physician in Chief was assisted by a 'Physician in Reversion', whose duties included deputizing for the Physician in Chief when necessary, and who became his successor when he died or resigned. For some time, indeed, there were two assistant physicians appointed by the Board to help Harvey, who was much occupied by his duties as Physician in Ordinary to the King.

On the surgical side, the chief physician had under his orders and command three surgeons, over all of whose professional activities the physician had command. One of the surgeons at the hospital during the time that Harvey was Physician in Chief was the celebrated Master John Woodall (1556-1643). We find him as surgeon at St. Bartholomew's from 1616 until the year of his death, and also (from 1612 to 1642) as surgeon-general to the Honourable East India Company. Woodall was the author of a treatise famous in its day: *Military and Domestique Surgery*, dedicated to Charles I and published in the same year as Harvey's *Exercitatio de Motu Cordis et Sanguinis*—that is, in 1628. Master Woodall appears to have been highly esteemed by Harvey, with whom the surgeon was often called into consultation to decide whether or not an operation should be performed on a patient. These things have lately been recalled in an excellent article published in the review *Angiology*.[1]

The thirty-six years of Harvey's life which we have just been considering were a time of uninterrupted rise to posts and positions of importance. We now have to deal with the succeeding years—the years of vicissitude and civil war.

II. *The Years of Civil War* (1639-1649)

The approach of the revolutionary storm—Religious uprising in Scotland—Visit to London in 1638 of the French Queen-Mother, and the discontent caused by her Catholic propaganda—Her death at Cologne attended by Jean Riolan, 1641— The Pacification of Berwick, 1639—The Long Parliament—Second outbreak of hostilities, 1642; the King flees—Provision made by the King for his Physician in Attendance—Harvey's apartment at Whitehall pillaged—Harvey's ride from Nottingham to Derby to consult Dr. Percy Willoughby—Harvey at the Battle of Edgehill—Harvey at the Oxford headquarters of the Royal Army—The capitulation of Oxford—Harvey's medical and scientific activities at Oxford—His election as Warden of Merton College, 1645—Merton, the Queen's residence as headquarters of the Administration and the Royal resistance—Friendship between Harvey and Scarborough at Oxford—Scarborough joins Harvey in London— Harvey in embittered retirement after family losses and the execution of the King—Two letters dated from Cambridge, 1649, and addressed to Jean Riolan at Paris

With the year 1639 we enter upon a period of civil strife and commotion and we must consider their effect upon Harvey's existence.

The King's mind was obviously tending, more and more, towards the idea of personal power exempt from all control by his subjects and he set about to achieve his aim with the aid of two men whom he had been able to attach closely to his cause. One was Thomas Wentworth, whom we have already mentioned, a jurist who became a liberal parliamentarian and one of the promoters in 1628 of the Petition of Right, the charter of English liberties. Wentworth had gradually been won over to the King's side and came to play the part of a sort of 17th-century and English Mirabeau.

[1] 4th-5th October, 1954, pp. 391-413, under the title 'The Case of Ellin French', by Sigmund Epstein, M.D., of New York.

He was created Earl of Strafford and became Lord Deputy in Scotland and northern England before being sent to rule and to subdue the Irish. The other man in whom the King put his trust was the ecclesiastic Laud. Charles had appointed him Archbishop of Canterbury, for Laud was devoted to the Anglican and Royal causes, which he regarded as identical, and sought by all means— even the most violent—to impose the King's will and the discipline of the Established Church.

By 1639 discontent against the King and his counsellors and against their methods of coercion had become widespread not only in Ireland and Scotland but also in England itself, where Presbyterian and 'liberal' ideas were making great headway. The Scottish religious revolts in 1637 had resulted in the anti-episcopal league known as the 'Covenant', and there is no doubt that these insurrectionary movements were encouraged in secret by Cardinal Richelieu, who sought to avenge himself for Charles's opposition to French aims and ambitions in Flanders. We need not imagine, for a moment, that Richelieu's political activities would be in any way influenced by sentimental considerations, such as that the sister of his king (Henrietta Maria) was the wife of the King of England.

It was about this time that Marie de' Medici, the widow of Henri IV of France, paid her only visit to England to the Court of her daughter and son-in-law. The Queen-Mother's troubled and agitated life, made up of changes of fortune and of political vicissitudes, had reached a stage when she was once more on such bad terms with her son (Louis XIII of France) and with his all-powerful minister, the Cardinal-Duke of Richelieu, that she had to withdraw with those of her supporters who were the enemies of the Cardinal to Holland, whence (in October, 1638) she sailed for England with the intention of making a prolonged stay at her daughter's Court. But in England, Marie de' Medici's tactless behaviour and her ill-advised and very marked Catholic propaganda, soon so seriously disturbed the Anglicans and, indeed, the population as a whole, that complaints against the French Queen-Mother did not cease until she had been escorted out of the kingdom. As the Dutch would not have her back she and her suite left for Cologne, where they established themselves like forerunners of the later revolutionary *émigrés* of 1790. It was at Cologne that, on 22nd August, 1641, Marie de' Medici died, with her faithful physician, Jean Riolan, at her bedside. The Queen's death was due to various complications following ulceration of the varicose veins in her legs.

It was, then, during the period of the Queen-Mother's residence in England—that is to say from the end of 1638 until 1640—that Riolan came to London. He remained not only one of Marie de Medici's most faithful supporters but he retained his position as her physician and was able to visit England several times in order to see his royal patient. There can, therefore, be no doubt that Riolan had many opportunities for meeting Harvey, the Physician in Ordinary of Charles I. It must have been in memory of these meetings that, at the end of 1648, Riolan made up his mind to send his little manual of anatomy, *Enchiridion*, direct to Harvey. It was published at Paris in that same year and Harvey thanked Riolan for the gift at the beginning of the first letter to Riolan, dated from Cambridge in 1649.

We shall have occasion to refer again to the letters and we shall see by the two communications addressed to Riolan that Harvey, when in contact with the French physician in London, had not succeeded in converting him to the new ideas about the circulation of the blood. Each of these two strong-minded men kept to his own way of thinking. However, we must admit that Riolan, whose father was also a physician and who was firmly attached to the traditional teaching of Galen, was also a man of noble mind and kind heart. Although he could conceive of no deviation from the doctrine of the Ancients, Riolan's sense of duty and his fidelity to his friends inspired in Harvey a very real respect and esteem, although the English physician combated the Frenchman on the ground of scientific fact. But we shall elaborate upon these considerations when we come to deal with the sort of scientific duel that was engaged between the *Exercitationes Anatomicae* and the *Enchiridion*.

But let us resume our brief sketch of the great historical events which were to be so tragic for the King and his followers during the decade from 1639 to 1649.

In the summer of 1639 Charles put the Royal army under the command of the Earl of Arundel—the same who had led the mission to the Imperial Court a year or so before—and he invited the English peers to join him in a campaign against the Scots. Charles, accompanied by a brilliant suite, proceeded with twenty-five thousand men to occupy the border-town of Berwick. The Scots troops, with Leslie at their head, advanced southwards, took up their positions on the Duns Law and barred any further English advance towards the north. For some time neither side made any move, and the King, realizing that his troops were being won over to the Scots and that if he joined battle his defeat would be certain, suddenly decided to negotiate. So, after having signed an agreement known as the 'Pacification of Berwick' on 18th June, 1639, Charles returned to London. In the meantime a parliament had assembled in Scotland. Its sittings began on 2nd June, 1640, and each member was required under grave penalties to sign the Covenant. At the King's request the Scots sent representatives to London, but when they arrived Charles refused to receive them. The Scots parliament then appealed to the French. A new Scots army was raised, crossed the Tweed and entered English territory on 20th August, 1640. While the English-garrisoned fortresses of Edinburgh and Dumbarton fell into the hands of the insurgents, their army occupied in succession Newcastle, Durham, Tynemouth and North and South Shields. Finally, the royal troops of Charles I suffered a most grievous defeat at Newburn-on-Tyne.

Thereupon, on 24th September, the King called together his Council and the decision was adopted to open fresh negotiations with the Scots. The chiefs of the English Army met eight representatives of the Scots at Ripon, where the terms of the 'Treaty of Ripon' were settled, although the instruments were not actually signed and sealed until nearly a year later. The Scots got all they claimed and were promised a sum of £300,000 for their expenses—if one may so express it. The armies were thereupon disbanded and it looked as though peace had been restored. The King paid another visit to Scotland where a new parliament was in session, while the Long Parliament was opened in London on 2nd November, 1640, with Lenthall as Speaker.

Strafford was condemned to death for high treason and executed on 11th May, 1641, without Charles having made any apparent effort to save the life of his devoted servant, and the English parliament began openly to prepare for war. An army was being raised, and a thorough-going Puritan, one Isaac Pennington, was elected Lord Mayor of London. The King, after having failed to secure the arrest of the famous five Members, left London in August, 1642, and proceeded to Nottingham, where the Royal Standard was raised and preparations made to meet the Parliamentary attack. This was delivered on 23rd October at Edgehill and we shall see what part Harvey played on that occasion, for he had, since 1639, followed the King on his journeys and in his adventures. But before we deal with the events of Edgehill we must glance back a little and see what happened to Harvey during the early years of the civil struggle.

Documents exist which show that Dr. Bethune, the senior Physician in Ordinary in attendance upon the King, died in July, 1639, and that Harvey was appointed his successor with an increased salary which is stated, according to a note in Harvey's own handwriting, to have been £400 a year. In addition to this, Harvey had an apartment at Whitehall Palace and a number of other perquisites which are mentioned in the following letter copied from the Letter Book of the Lord Steward's office:

Charles R.

Whereas we have been graciously pleased to admit Doctor Harvey into the place of Physician in Ordinary to our Royal Person, our will and pleasure is that you give order for the settling a diet of three dishes of meat a meal, with all incidents thereunto belonging, upon him the said Doctor Harvey, and the same to begin from the seventeenth day of July last past and to continue during the time that the said Doctor Harvey shall hold and enjoy the said place of Physician in Ordinary to our Royal Person, for which this shall be your warrant.

Given at our Court of Whitehall the sixth of December, 1639.

To our trusty and well beloved Councillors Sir Henry Vane and Sir Thomas Jermyn, Knights, Treasurer and Comptroller of our Household or to either of them.

By a further warrant, dated 27th September while the King was at York, signed by his hand and addressed to the Comptroller of the Household, Dr. Harvey was adjudged an alimentary allowance of £200 a year, this, no doubt, in lieu of the three meals a day, which it may not have been easy to provide in those troubled times.

At the end of November, 1640, Harvey was in London, for on the 24th of that month he obtained from the College of Physicians authority to sue the heirs of Lord Lumley for payment of his fees as Lumleian lecturer in surgery and anatomy. But it seems that the grave general situation prevented Harvey from proceeding with his case. He took up the matter again in 1647 and spent a good deal of money in lawyer's fees, but it was not until after Harvey's death that his successor, as Lumleian lecturer, Sir Charles Scarborough, won the case.

We know nothing of Harvey's movements in 1641 and the only record of him is a dedication which he wrote on page thirty-eight of the album of one Philip de Glarges, a volume that is in the British Museum. The text reads thus:

'Dii laboribus omnia vendunt.'
Nobilissimo juveni Medico Phillipo de Glarges amicitiae ergo libenter scripsit
Gul Harveus.
Anglus Med. Reg. et Anatomie professor, Londin:
May 8 A.D. 1641.

'The Gods sell all for toil.'
This was willingly written as a mark of friendship
for the noble young Doctor Philip de Glarges by
William Harvey, the Englishman, Physician to the
King and Professor of Anatomy. At London 8 May
A.D. 1641.

By 1642 the conflict between King and Parliament had reached
a critical phase and Harvey accompanied the King when the Court
left for Nottingham in the middle of August. It was soon after this
departure, apparently, that Harvey's apartment in Whitehall was
sacked by the Parliamentary soldiery. These made no bones about
breaking into the dwellings of those suspected of royalist tendencies, or of seizing anything of value on which they could lay
their hands. Obviously Harvey's name must have stood high upon
the lists of suspects because of his official position, of his lodging in
the King's palace and of the frequent mention of his name in the
parliamentary debates of the time, for these (although theoretically
secret) were soon utilized by the leaders of the mob.

It was about this time that those precious papers containing
accounts of dissections, autopsies and observations made on patients
that Harvey had collected, as well as his notes on the development
of insects and on comparative anatomy, were scattered and lost. It
is referring to these papers that Aubrey wrote: 'He had made dissections of frogs, toads, and a number of animals, and had curious
observations upon them.' Harvey himself said bitterly:

'Let gentle minds forgive me, if recalling the irreparable injuries
I have suffered, I here give vent to a sigh. This is the cause of my
sorrow: Whilst in attendance on His Majesty the King during our
late troubles, and more than civil wars, not only with the permission
but by the command of the Parliament, certain rapacious hands not
only stripped my house of all its furniture, but, what is a subject
of far greater regret to me, my enemies abstracted from my museum
the fruits of many years of toil. Whence it has come to pass that
many observations, particularly on the generation of insects, have
perished with detriment, I venture to say, to the republic of letters.'

It was probably in the early days of September, 1642—before
the King left Nottingham on the 13th of that month—that Harvey
took the opportunity of riding over to Derby to see Percival
Willoughby who had been admitted an extra-licentiate at the
College of Physicians on 20th February, 1640–41. Willoughby says:
'There came to my house at Derby, my honoured good friend Dr.
Harvey. We were talking of several infirmities incident to the womb.

He added to my knowledge an infirmity which he had seen in women, and he gave it the name of a honey-comb[1] which he said would cause flooding in women.'

The battle of Edgehill was fought on 23rd October and D'Arcy Power relates Harvey's probable activities on that day in the following words:

'All the morning was spent in collecting the King's troops from their scattered quarters, and it was not until one o'clock that the royal army descended the steep hill leading to the wide plain in which stand the village of Radway and the little town of Kineton. Harvey took charge of the two Princes, boys of 12 and 10 years old, who afterwards became Charles II and James II, and in the course of the morning he probably walked along the brow of the hill from the inn at Sunrising to the Royalist headquarters which were placed about a mile further east. Weary with waiting he and the boys betook themselves to the wide ditch at the very edge of the hill, and to while away the time Harvey took a book out of his pocket and read. "But," says Aubrey, "he had not read very long before the bullet from a great gun grazed the ground near him, which made him remove his station." As soon as the battle had really begun, Harvey, we may be sure, was alive and interested, his book was pocketed and he devoted himself at once to assist the wounded. The very nature of the wounds would give additional zest to the work, for, unless he was present at the battle of Newburn-on-Tyne, this must have been his first opportunity of treating gunshot wounds. Anthony Wood in his account of Adrian Scrope shows that Harvey was no impassive spectator of the fight, for he says: "This most valiant person, who was son of Sir Jervais Scrope, did most loyally attend his Majesty at the fight of Edgehill, where receiving several wounds he was stripped and left among the dead, as a dead person there, but brought off by his son and recovered by the immortal Dr. Will. Harvey, who was there but withdrawn under a hedge with the Prince and the Duke while the battle was at its height." '

During the battle Harvey, like nearly all those attached to the King's person, must have experienced grave forebodings when he saw his sovereign throw himself into the thick of the conflict to encourage his troops, at the same time telling them to be merciful to those of the enemy who might fall into their hands.

When victory had been won the King decided to march on London. On 27th October he occupied Banbury and on 29th he

[1] That is, *epithelioma. (D'Arcy Power.)*

entered Oxford in triumph. Harvey was received at Oxford with many marks of esteem. His great reputation opened all doors before him. At Oxford he soon settled down to his accustomed pursuits,

FIG. 6.   The Civil War, 1642–52. Oxford was surrendered in 1646.

unmindful of the clatter of arms and the constant marching and countermarching around him, for the city remained the head-quarters of the royal army until its surrender in July, 1646. A map of the principal battlefields of the Civil War is given in Fig. 6.

Aubrey says that he first saw Harvey at Oxford 'in 1642, after the Edgehill fight, but I was then too young to be acquainted with so great a doctor. I remember that he came several times to our College to George Bathurst, B.D., who had a hen to hatch eggs in his chamber, which they opened daily to see the progress and way of generation.' This Bathurst was a distinguished Fellow of Trinity College. He was killed two years later defending Faringdon, and it was most probably the advice and aid of such friends as Bathurst that secured Harvey's incorporation as Doctor of Physic at Oxford on 7th December, 1642.

Young Thomas Sydenham—who was to become so distinguished a physician—was in 1642 only eighteen years of age, and though he had lately come up to Oxford to begin his medical studies he does not seem to have met Harvey (then aged sixty-four) at the University. As an ardent republican Sydenham left Oxford at the beginning of the summer when it declared for the King, while Harvey, as we have seen, did not reach Oxford until Charles got there on 29th October. When Sydenham returned to Oxford in 1646 the town had fallen to Fairfax's troops, while Harvey had left and had retired to London and into private life. Sydenham does not seem to have realized the importance and the greatness of his elder's work, for he makes no mention of it in his own books, at least in those that are known to us. Perhaps, however, this omission is due rather to the fact that Sydenham's writings are devoted more to clinical and therapeutic questions than to considerations of an anatomical or physiological nature.

We may now see how Harvey occupied himself at Oxford until the King fled in disguise from the town on 27th April, 1646. The great physician himself may have stayed until 23rd June, the eve of Fairfax's entry into the city, and if so he would have left with Prince Rupert, Prince Maurice and the rest of the lords and ladies of the old Court. But let us consider first of all the year 1643. Then it was that the last mention of Harvey's name was inscribed in the registers of St. Bartholomew's Hospital:

Item to Dr. Harvey, Physician, xxxiii li. vi s. viii d.

No mention is made in the registers of either Harvey's resignation or of his dismissal, although the severance of his long-standing connection with the hospital must have caused no little disturbance. The omission must undoubtedly be attributed to the state of disorganization produced by the Civil War. There is, however, a curious note to be found in the Journals of the House of Commons:

'Feb, 12, an. 1643-4. A motion this day made for Dr. Micklethwayte to be recommended to the Wardens and Masters of St. Bartholomew's Hospital, to be physician in the place of Dr. Harvey, who hath withdrawn himself from his charge and is retired to the party in arms against the Parliament.'

Micklethwayte was indeed appointed Physician in Reversion to the hospital in succession to Harvey on 26th May, 1648, and succeeded to the post of full Physician on May 13th, 1653. Later, he was knighted, became one of the Physicians in Ordinary to Charles II, and died in 1682.

But while these things were happening Harvey was quietly continuing his dissections at Oxford, and he also practised his profession among all classes of the population that filled the town. A memorial dated from Milton on 17th October, 1641, and addressed from Richard Cave to Prince Rupert, one of the leaders of the royal forces, is proof of the high esteem in which Harvey was held and of his being called in as a consultant in difficult cases. This communication relates to Rupert's brother, Prince Maurice, who had fallen sick. We also learn from the memorial that Harvey's friend from London, Dr. Smith, was at this time at Oxford:

May it please your Highness.

This last night arrived here at Milton, Dr. Harvey and Doctor Smyth and this morning they were with the other two Doctors having seen and spoken with his Highness your brother intreateth me to write as followeth.

That his sickness is the ordinary raging disease of the army, a slow fever with a great dejection of strength and since last Friday he hath talked idly and slept not but very unquietly, yet the last night he began to sleep of himself and took his rest so quietly that this present morning when Doctor Harvey came to him he knew him and welcomed Doctor Smith respectively and upon Doctor Harvey's expression of his Majesty's sorrow for and great care of him he showed an humble, thankful sense thereof. Doctor Harvey asking his highness how he did, he answered that he was very weak, and he seemed to be very glad to hear of and from your Highness as was delivered by Doctor Harvey.

Now the Doctors having conferred and computed the time have good hopes of his recovery yet by reason that the disease is very dangerous and fraudulent they dare not yet give credit to this alteration. And concluding the disease to be venomous they resolved to give very little physic only a regular diet and cordial antidotes. The

Doctors present their most humble services to your Highness and subscribe themselves
    Sir,
Your Highness' most humble servants,

                  WILL HARVEY.
                  ROBERT VILVAIN
                  EDMUND SMITH
                  THO. KING

MILTON, Oct. 17th, 1643.

That, on the other hand, Harvey found at Oxford men who understood his work and even collaborated with him in it is evident from Aubrey's note which we have already quoted, the veracity of which we have no reason to doubt. It was, indeed, at this time that there formed around Harvey at Oxford that gathering of men of science which was later to become the Royal Society.[1]

However, on 9th April, 1645, Harvey's connection with Oxford University became much closer for he was then elected Warden of Merton in succession to Sir Nathaniel Brent, who had left Oxford and joined the parliamentary party by whom he was appointed Judge Marshal. Brent signed the Covenant and became a Presbyterian, although he had formerly been a friend of Laud's. In view of Brent's conduct, the King had dismissed him from his charge and had ordered a board of seven Fellows to submit a list of three names from which he would himself choose Brent's successor as Warden. Harvey's name was at the head of the list and the King at once appointed him. This was, as we have seen, on 9th April, 1645. On the 11th of the same month the new Warden, on taking public possession of his post, addressed a short allocution in Latin to the Fellows. This is preserved in the College archives and may be translated:

'The Warden, before the Fellows assembled in the Great Hall, spoke as follows: He said that it was probable enough that some of his predecessors had sought the Wardenship to enrich themselves, but that he, for his part, undertook the duties with far other intentions, wishing as he did to increase the wealth and prosperity of the College. At the same time he appealed earnestly and anxiously to the Fellows to cherish among themselves an harmonious friendship.'

[1] The Royal Society was founded in 1660 by Harvey's disciples and friends, including Scarborough, Highmore, Willis and Christopher Wren. Wren did not, however, know Harvey at Oxford, since he was not more than fourteen years of age when Harvey left the city. Wren was born at East Knoyle in Wiltshire in 1632.

During the year that Harvey was Warden of Merton the College was more like a royal Court than a seat of learning. From 1643 to 1646 the Queen lived in College when she was at Oxford, occupying a room in the Warden's Lodge still known as the 'Queen's Room', with a drawing-room adjoining. Anthony Wood says that during her occupation 'there were diverse marriages, christenings, and burials carefully registered in a private register by Mr. John Gurgany, one of the chaplains of Merton College; but about the time of the surrender of Oxford the said register, among other books, was stolen by the soldiers out of his window in his chamber joining to the church door'. A number of officers was also billeted at Merton, so that in August, 1645, when the annual meeting was held, it had to be convoked in the library as neither Hall nor the Warden's lodgings were available.

The year 1645–46, when Harvey was Warden, was one of the most memorable for its dramatic events in all the annals of Oxford. In May, 1645, the town was besieged by Fairfax. The King was at this time at Droitwich. On 14th June, the Royal forces were crushed at Naseby and on 27th November the College was called upon to lay in a stock of provisions against another siege. On 28th December, the King ordered a special form of prayer to be used in the chapel on Wednesdays and Fridays 'during these bad times'.

On the morning of 3rd April, 1646, the King, dressed as a servant with his hair and beard clipped close and ostensibly in attendance upon Ashburnham and Hudson, left Oxford. 'We cannot but believe,' wrote D'Arcy Power, 'that Harvey was one of the little band who closed the gates of the city with heavy hearts as his Majesty rode off to begin his wearisome captivity.' On 11th May Fairfax summoned the town to surrender. On 24th June it did surrender (on honourable terms), the garrison of three thousand men marching out over Shotover. The Duke of York fell into the hands of the Parliamentarians but Prince Rupert and Maurice with most of the members of the Court left Oxford just before Fairfax's troops entered.

The King, as we have seen, had already escaped. His intention was to seek both asylum and assistance in Scotland, but this fatal move led to his capture, his delivery by the Scots to the Parliament, and to his tragic end at Whitehall on 9th February, 1649.[1]

---

[1] The Scots handed over Charles to Cromwell for a monetary consideration at the beginning of 1647, when the King was imprisoned at Carisbrooke Castle, in the Isle of Wight. He was afterwards transferred to Windsor and then, for his trial, to London.

On the surrender of Oxford Harvey resigned his position of Warden of Merton; his place was taken by Brent, though the College archives make no mention of either occurrence. Anthony Wood has left an impressive account of the utter confusion into which the past three years had thrown the university—the colleges impoverished—lectures almost abandoned—students dispersed or demoralized. 'In a word, scarce the face of an University left, all things being out of order and disturbed.' An entry in the College register for 19th October, 1646, states that by Divine grace the Civil War had at last been stayed, and the Warden (Brent) with most of the Fellows had returned; but as there were no Bachelors, hardly any scholars and few Masters, it was decided to elect but one Bursar and one Dean. It is further mentioned that the Hall was still in a completely ruined state—*situ et ruinis squalida.*

At the end of his chapter on the Civil War and of Harvey's stay at Oxford, D'Arcy Power writes:

'Of the few students whom we know that the influence of Harvey's name attracted to Oxford that of Charles Scarborough, the first English editor of Euclid, is the most noted. Ejected from his fellowship at Caius College, Cambridge, on account of his Royalist tendencies, he immediately withdrew to Oxford, entered himself at Merton College, obtained the friendship of Harvey and rendered him considerable assistance in the preparation of his work on the development of animals. He was created a Doctor of Physic on June 23, 1646, by virtue of letters from the Chancellor of the University, and in these letters he is described as a Master of Arts of Cambridge of seven years' standing and upwards, who was spoiled of his library in the beginning of the Civil War, and afterwards for his conscience deprived of his fellowship. His letters testimonial are under the hand of Dr. William Harvey, who says that he is well learned in Physic, Philosophy, and Mathematics.' We may note that if this document really does date from 23rd June, 1646, it was issued on the very eve of the capitulation of Oxford.

Scarborough continued, after the fall of Oxford, with the Royal army, but finally heeded Harvey's appeal to join him in London and to take care of some of his patients. In addition to what D'Arcy Power states in the paragraph quoted above, we may add some notes on Harvey's life during the time preceding the King's execution at the beginning of 1649—that is to say, the three years before the physician's retirement.

What sort of years were those from 1647 to 1650? What was Harvey doing? In his chapter on 'Harvey's Last Years' D'Arcy

Power dates these 'last years' from the capitulation of Oxford in 1646, but I am inclined to think that is hardly justified. Power says:

'Harvey returned to London after the surrender of Oxford, and one of his first thoughts was to send to Charles Scarborough . . . the message—"Prithee leave off thy gunning and stay here. I will bring thee into practice." And well he kept his word, for on the 8th of October, 1649, Dr. Scarborough was elected by the Company of Barber Surgeons of London reader of the anatomical lectures. . . .'

But there elapsed between 11th May, 1646, and the time when Scarborough was certainly in London in 1649, quite a long period for which we have not much information about Harvey's movements. Those were troubled times in the capital; people who had been Charles's supporters were in danger if they did not keep very prudently in the background. So Harvey probably found it desirable to live a somewhat secluded life, though his renown as a physician and a scientist possibly secured him special consideration. I do not think there is good reason to believe that Harvey ceased entirely from practice in 1646. I should incline to place his final retirement as late as 1649, though D'Arcy Power argues a virtual retirement as early as 1645 from considerations given in the following passage:

'The surrender of Oxford in 1645 marks the period of Harvey's severance from the Court and of his practical retirement from public life. He was now 68; a martyr to gout, childless, and suffering under a series of heavy bereavements, he can have had but little heart to re-enter upon an active professional life in London. His twin brothers Matthew and Michael died in 1643. John, his second brother, died in 1645. His wife, who was alive in this year, must have died shortly afterwards, or she would probably have accompanied him to Oxford. Such a series of shocks would act prejudicially upon his affectionate nature, and would still further unfit him to pursue the harassing cares of his profession. His mind, always philosophical and reflective rather than empirical, was now allowed to follow its bent to the uttermost, and his time was employed in putting into shape his treatise upon Development.'

What we should like to know above all is the nature of Harvey's reactions to the imprisonment of the King, whose physician and friend he had been for so long. Was Harvey called in to aid the King during his captivity and the days which immediately preceded the execution? Where was Harvey on that fatal February day? How free was Harvey in London during the time of Cromwell's dictatorship? Unfortunately these are questions to which we can give no answer.

If, as is most probable, Harvey kept silent and remained in at least relative eclipse—for nothing could really damage his great reputation, which was becoming well known throughout the western world—we may feel almost certain that this silence and relative retirement were not due to fear of reprisals to which he might be exposed on account of his personal feelings for the King. It is striking, gratifying even, to note that Harvey did not fear to proclaim from time to time that he had been the King's physician. In the two editions (published at Cambridge in 1649) of the first *Exercitatio Anatomica de Circulationis Sanguinis ad Johannem Riolanum*, and in the *Exercitationes Duae* (issued in the same year at Rotterdam), Harvey printed upon the title-page below his name the phrase, *Serenissimae Majestatis Regiae Archiiatro*. One may, in passing, reflect what would have happened in France during the years from 1792 to 1794 if any scientist had dared openly and publicly to proclaim his position as physician to the King![1] The guillotine would not have had long to wait for them.

We may then, even if we know nothing of Harvey's attitude during these troubled times, be sure that he was not keeping in the background just because he feared for himself, or that he would be subjected to persecution on account of his long-standing attachment to the royal person. Maybe, however, within himself, he was beginning to measure the faults of the monarch and to judge of the terrible straits into which those faults had irremediably dragged the King's cause and the fortunes of the State. Perhaps, then, Harvey, whose great intelligence had possibly not been much exercised in weighing political matters, may have felt himself coming round to more democratic views and to a less indulgent attitude towards autocracy.

Indeed, let us note a curious change in the evolution of his scientific ideas, namely that the 'heart' must no longer be conceived as the source and origin of the well-being of the body, but that this must rather be sought in the organs that feed the heart and thus take precedence over it. It may not be fanciful to see in this change of view some echo of Harvey's new outlook upon public affairs. It is the nation that labours and produces, whereas the king is not the originator of prosperity but the co-ordinator and distributor of what has been created by others. Still, we may be sure that Harvey's

[1] Louis XVI was executed on 21st January, 1793 (2 Pluviose An I of the French Republic). Eighteen months later on 29th July, 1794 (10 Thermidor, An II of the French Republic), fell the head of him who had aimed at being the Cromwell of the French Revolution—Maximilien Robespierre.

great good sense kept him remote from any liking for demagogic despotism, and his temperament was such that—had he lived long enough—he would undoubtedly have approved the wise and wholesome compromise adopted after Cromwell's death.

In my view, D'Arcy Power's account of these years, and especially of 1649, is inadequate, for it gives the impression of unrelieved disappointment and decline whereas Harvey's enthusiasm and his wit were never keener than in this year of the publication at Cambridge and Rotterdam of the two *Exercitationes*. In two 'Letters' written in this year he replies in masterly fashion to Riolan's objections and confutes his adversaries with a vigour surprising in one who was no longer young.

D'Arcy Power and others after him seem entirely to have underestimated the importance of these Letters. D'Arcy Power writes, for instance, that 'these disquisitions differ very greatly from the original treatise. They are less clear and concise, and dwell more upon points of dispute which had arisen in connection with the controversy, which raged for many years around Harvey's discovery.' Regarding the second Letter he remarks: 'Amidst a mass of unprofitable speculation, the second Disquisition contains one or two gems of pathological observation, illustrating physiological conclusions.'

I cannot agree that these Disquisitions are less clear or less precise than the original Treatise, that they deal only with points of secondary importance, or that they contain a mass of unprofitable speculation. I hope to be able to show that my view is the right one. In analysing the Disquisitions (in Chapter VIII) I shall endeavour to demonstrate that the Letters of 1649 mark as important a date in the evolution of Harvey's thought as does the original Treatise of 1628, for in the intervening twenty-one years Harvey's conceptions concerning the circulation of the blood underwent some modification. My own opinion is, indeed, that the Letters to Riolan occupy a place of the first importance in Harvey's works.

It was, perhaps, as well to refer to these matters before we come to deal with what are too often and too hastily called the years of Harvey's decline. From 1650 onwards they were, indeed, years of relative retirement from the world, but they were, as we shall see, years of creative activity and of increasing renown.

Chapter VI

The Last Years and the Last Hours
(1649–1657)

Letter from Dr. Ent—His Christmas visit to Harvey in retirement—Ent entrusted with the MS. of *De Generatione Animalium*—Harvey's little eccentricities—His intellectual vigour intact to the end—His interest in literature and general scientific questions—The abiding link of esteem between him and the College of Physicians —An anonymous gift to the College in 1651 of a building to be used as a Hall and Library—Harvey's gift to the College of his patrimonial estate at Burmarsh in Kent—The College place a bust of Harvey in the hall of their building, 1652— Details of legacies mentioned in Harvey's Will—Harvey's portrait—The last hours of the great scientist and his serene deathbed in the little village of Roehampton, near London, on the evening of 3rd June, 1657

A T Christmas, 1650, Dr. Ent, desirous of once more seeing his old master who was then staying in the country with one of his brothers, paid him a visit which he reported in the form of a dedicatory epistle at the beginning of Harvey's new work, *De Generatione Animalium*. This was published under Ent's care by the presses of Ludovic Elzevir at Rotterdam in 1651, and runs:

> To the learned and illustrious, the President and Fellows of the College of Physicians of London.
> Harassed with anxious, and in the end not much availing cares, about Christmas last, I sought to rid my spirit of the cloud that oppressed it, by a visit to that great man, the chief honour and orna-ment of our College, Dr. William Harvey, then dwelling not far from the city. I found him, Democritus like, busy with the study of natural things, his countenance cheerful, his mind serene, embracing all within its sphere. I forthwith saluted him and asked if all were

well with him? 'How can it be,' said he, 'whilst the Commonwealth is full of distractions, and I myself am still in the open sea? And truly,' he continued, 'did I not find solace in my studies, and a balm for my spirit in the memory of my observations of former years, I should feel little desire for longer life. But so it has been, that this life of obscurity, this vacation from public business, which causes tedium and disgust to so many, has proved a sovereign remedy to me.'

I, answering, said, 'I can readily account for this: whilst most men are learned through others' wits, and under cover of a different diction and a new arrangement, vaunt themselves on things that belong to the ancients, thou ever interrogatest Nature herself concerning her mysteries. And this line of study as it is less likely to lead into error, so it is also more fertile in enjoyment, inasmuch as each particular point examined often leads to others which had not before been surmised. You yourself, I well remember, informed me once that you had never dissected any animal—and many and many a one you have examined—but that you discovered something unexpected, something of which you were formerly uninformed.'

'It is true,' said he; 'the examination of the bodies of animals has always been my delight, and I have thought that we might thence not only obtain an insight into the lighter mysteries of Nature, but there perceive a kind of image or reflex of the omnipotent Creator himself. And though much has been made out by the learned men of former times, I have still thought that much more remained behind, hidden by the dusky night of nature, uninterrogated: so that I have oftentimes wondered and even laughed at those who have fancied that everything had been so consummately and absolutely investigated by an Aristotle or a Galen or some other mighty name, that nothing could by any possibility be added to their knowledge. Nature, however, is the best and most faithful interpreter of her own secrets; and what she presents, either more briefly or more obscurely in one department, that she explains more fully and clearly in another. No one indeed has ever rightly ascertained the use or function of a part who has not examined its structure, situation, connections by means of vessels and other accidents in various animals, and carefully weighed and considered all he has seen. The ancients, our authorities in science, even as their knowledge of geography was limited by the boundaries of Greece, so neither did their knowledge of animals, vegetables, and other natural objects extend beyond the confines of their country. But to us the whole earth lies open and the zeal of our travellers has made us familiar not only with other countries and the manners and customs of their inhabitants, but also with the animals, vegetables and minerals that are met with in each. And truly there is no nation so barbarous which has not discovered something for the general good, whether led to it by accident or compelled by necessity, which had been overlooked by more civilized communities. But shall we imagine that nothing can accrue to the wide domains of science from such advantages or that all knowledge was exhausted by the first ages of the world? If we do, the blame very certainly attaches to our indolence, nowise to nature.

'To this there is another evil added. Many persons, wholly without experience, from the presumed verisimilitude of a previous opinion, are often led by and by to speak of it boldly, as a matter that is certainly known; whence it comes, that not only are they themselves deceived, but that they likewise lead other incautious persons into error.'

Discoursing in this manner and touching upon many topics besides with wonderful fluency and facility, as is his custom, I interposed by observing 'How free are you yourself from the fault you indicate all know who are acquainted with you; and this is the reason wherefore the learned world, who are aware of your unwearied industry in the study of philosophy, are eagerly looking for in farther experiments.'

'And would you be the man,' said Harvey smiling, 'who should recommend me to quit the peaceful haven where I now pass my life and launch again upon the faithless sea? You know full well what a storm my former lucubrations raised. Much better is it oftentimes to grow wise at home and in private, than by publishing what you have amassed with infinite labour, to stir up tempests that may rob you of peace and quiet for the rest of your days.'

'True,' said I; 'it is the usual reward of virtue to have received ill for having merited well. But the winds which raised those storms like the north-western blast, which drowns itself in its own rain, have only drawn mischief upon themselves.'

Upon this he showed me his 'Exercises on the Generation of Animals', a work composed with vast labour and singular care, and having it in my hands I exclaimed, 'Now have I what I so much desired, and unless you consent to make this work public, I must say that you will be wanting both to your own fame and to the public usefulness. Nor let any fear of farther trouble in the matter induce you to withhold it longer; I gladly charge myself with the whole business of correcting the press.'

Making many difficulties at first, urging among other things that his work must be held imperfect, as not containing his investigations on the generation of insects; I nevertheless prevailed at length, and he said to me, 'I intrust these papers to your care with full authority either speedily to commit them to the press, or to suppress them till some future time.'

Having returned him many thanks, I bade him adieu and took my leave, feeling like another Jason laden with the golden fleece.

On returning home I forthwith proceeded to examine my prize in all its parts, and could not but wonder with myself that such a treasure should have lain so long concealed; and that whilst others produce their trifles and emptiness with much ado, their messes twice, aye, an hundred times, heated up, our Harvey should set so little store by his admirable observations. And indeed so often as he has sent forth any of his discoveries to the world, he has not comported himself like those who, when they publish, would have us believe that an oak had spoken, and that they had merited the rarest honours—a draught of hen's milk at the least. Our Harvey rather seems as though discovery were natural, a matter of ordinary business; though he may nevertheless have expended infinite labour and study on his works. And we have evidence of his singular candour in this, that he never hostilely attacks any previous writer, but ever courteously sets down and comments upon the opinions of each; and indeed he is wont to say that it is argument of an indifferent cause when it is contended for with violence and distemper, and that truth scarce wants an advocate.

It would have been easy for our illustrious colleague to have woven the whole of this web from materials of his own; but to escape the charge of envy he has rather chosen to take Aristotle and Fabricius of Aquapendente as his guides, and to appear as contributing but his portion to the general fabric. Of him whose virtue, candour, and genius are so well known to you all I shall say no more, lest I should seem to praise to his face one whose singular worth has exalted him beyond the reach of all praise. Of myself I shall only say that I have done no more than perform the midwife's office in this business, ushering into the light this product of our colleague's genius as you see it, consummate and complete, but long delayed and fearing perchance some envious blast; in other words, I have overlooked the press; and as our author writes a hand which no one without practice can easily read (a thing that is common among our men of letters), I have taken some pains to prevent the printer committing any very grave blunders through this—a point which I observe not to have been sufficiently attended to in the small work of his which lately appeared. Here, then, my learned friends, you have the cause of my addressing you at this time, viz., that you may know that our Harvey presents an offering to the benefit of the republic of letters, to your honour, to his own eternal fame.

Farewell, and prosper

George Ent.

We have thought it worth while for a variety of reasons to reproduce *in extenso* this remarkable letter of Ent's. First of all, we learn here better than in any other documents what were Harvey's occupations in his country retreat. His curiosity was ever aroused by the problems of natural history to which his mind was constantly directed. And then, again, the letter shows how lively, distinguished and wise Harvey's conversation had remained. His shrewd and witty remarks are well matched by Ent's replies. This conversation, indeed, brings out with admirable clarity the simplicity, the disinterestedness and the candour of the great man who was so contemptuous of worldly vanity.

Following this epistle of Ent's we may, perhaps, add a few touches to the picture and recount here some of Harvey's little eccentricities—innocent manias such as those that mark nearly every man when he reaches a certain age and are often very noticeable in those whose intellectual labours so continuously occupy their minds that the bodily automatism has free play to manifest itself as it will. Aubrey has left us some anecdotes, for what they are worth, as have also some other persons in Harvey's immediate circle.

Let us remember, first of all, that with the exception of rare and fleeting appearances in London (when he lodged with his brother Eliab at Cockaine House, supposedly in Broad Street) Harvey spent most of his time from 1650 onwards at one or other of the country estates of his other brothers. These were situated at Roehampton to the south-west of London, at Rolls Park near Chigwell in Essex, and at Winslow's Hall, a property quite near to the little church of Hempstead where, as we shall see, stands Harvey's tomb together with those of several other members of his family. Often, too, Harvey stayed with his brother Daniel in the suburban village of Lambeth, or at Combe near Croydon in Surrey. A map showing Harvey's principal places of residence (except those within the present London area) is given in Fig. 7.

Aubrey relates that 'he was much and often troubled with the gout, and his way of cure was thus; He would sit with his legs bare, though it were frost, on the leads of Cockaine House, put them into a pail of water till he was almost dead with cold, then betake himself to his stove, and so 'twas gone', a method of treatment, says Heberden, 'which I neither recommend nor propose to others for imitation, although Harvey lived to his eightieth year, and died not so much from disease but from old age'.

An interesting note attributed to Dr. Heberden from the handwriting and now preserved at the Royal College of Physicians confirms this observation of Aubrey's. It reads as follows:

'1761, May 26th.—Mrs. Harvey (great-niece to Dr. Harvey) told me that the Doctor lived at his brother's at Roehampton the latter part of his life. That he used to walk out in a morning, combing his hair in the fields.

'That he was humoursome and would sit down exactly at the time he had appointed for dinner whether the company was come or not. That his salt-cellar was always filled with sugar which he used to eat instead of salt.

'That if the gout was very painful to him in the night he would rise and put his feet into cold water.'

Aubrey again tells us that 'he was always very contemplative and was wont to frequent the leads of Cockaine House, which his brother Eliab had bought, having there his several stations in regard to the sun and the wind for the indulgence of his fancy; whilst at the house at Combe in Surrey, he had caves made in the ground in which he delighted in the summer-time to meditate. . . .'

Harvey also loved the darkness and told Aubrey that he could 'then best contemplate. . . . His thoughts working would many times keep him from sleeping, in which case his way was to rise from his bed and walk about his chamber in his shirt till he was pretty cool and then return to his bed and sleep very comfortably.' He was always ready to tell others of what he knew and to instruct any that were 'modest and respectful to him'. When Aubrey was setting out for Italy 'he dictated to me what to see, what company to keep, what books to read, and how to manage my studies—in short, he bid me go to the fountain head and read Aristotle, Cicero and Avicenna, and did call the Neoteriques[1] by a foul name'.

These little fads that Harvey's friends have recorded do not, of course, indicate any feebleness of mind, but rather show how active his intellect was since it allowed him to lead his 'vegetative' life without his having to think about it. Such is the case with not a few eminent men about whom it is reported that they cherished such and such a 'mania'.

Harvey, realizing his need for repose and relaxation, would not engage in the writing of any further full-length medical treatise. Nevertheless, as the great physician himself expressed it in letters to several different correspondents, he employed his leisure in enriching his mind with knowledge which he had been unable to acquire in former days when his whole attention was devoted to the one problem of the circulation of the blood. Thus we find him writing that he is applying himself to the 'art of Apollo', by which he no doubt meant reading the poets but also the composition of verse. At other times, if he felt like it, he would seek satisfaction for his spirit

---

[1] 'Neoteriques' was Harvey's pet name for young, contemporary authors.

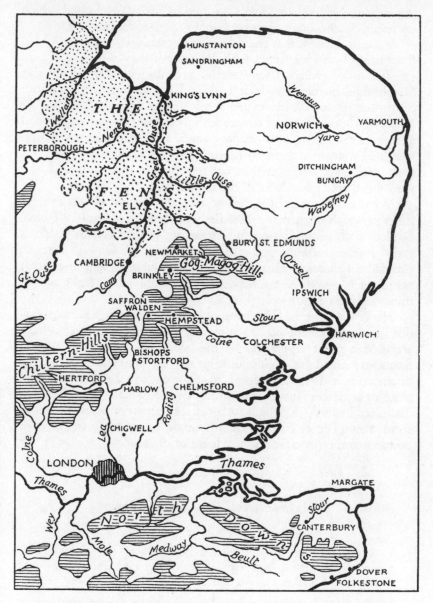

FIG. 7. Map of East Anglia and the county of Kent, showing places with which Harvey's name is associated and other landmarks. Harvey's principal places of residence were, successively: Folkestone, Canterbury, Cambridge, London, Chigwell, Rolls Park (a little to the north of Chigwell), and Hempstead.

in mathematics and in reading Oughted's *Clavis Mathematica*[1] which his friend Scarborough most probably procured for him.

It seems, indeed, that the *Clavis Mathematica* so much delighted Scarborough and his friend Seth Ward that they were the first to use the book (which later became a classic) in their lectures at Cambridge. In their youth, it is related by Anthony Wood, both Scarborough and Ward made a pilgrimage to visit Oughted at Albury in Surrey in order to seek enlightenment concerning several points in the *Clavis Mathematica* which seemed to them obscure. Oughted welcomed them with much good grace, was moved to see such intelligent young men so interested in mathematics, and in a very short time gave them all the explanations they desired.

We may remember that the late 16th and the 17th centuries were times in which mathematical studies were in high honour. We have Galileo, with his studies on the properties of the cycloid, Galileo's early Italian masters, and then Mersenne, Roberval, Fermat, Gassendi, Descartes, Huyghens, Pascal, Leibnitz, and the great genius of Newton. A magnificent coruscation whose light was to shine down the centuries!

Harvey was, then, for a time at least interested in mathematics, but in his retirement he had also other hobbies. He had, indeed, acquired a great reputation in the world of letters and was as frequently asked for his opinion as any eminent critic. Here, for instance, is a letter addressed to Harvey by the polemist and philologist, James Howell, the author of the *Epistolae Ho-Elianae* or 'Familiar Letters', in which he professed to have received letters from a number of correspondents in order to set forth his own opinions and observations in the form of replies:[2]

XXXVII

To Doctor Harvey, *at* St. Laurence Poultney.

Sir,
    I remember well, you pleas'd not only to pass a favourable Censure, but give a high Character, of the First Part of *Dodona's Grove*; which makes this Second to come and wait on you, which,

[1] William Oughted, theologian and eminent mathematician, was born at Eton in 1576 and died at Albury in 1660.

[2] *Epistolae Ho-Elianae*, that is, 'Ho(well)elianae'. Howell (1594-1666) was a historian of repute, an excellent linguist and a witty pamphleteer, and was, also during the time of the Civil War, more or less the originator of the journalistic 'reporting' style of writing.

The inscription on the tomb reads:

THE REMAINS OF WILLIAM HARVEY
DISCOVERER OF THE CIRCULATION OF THE BLOOD
WERE REVERENTIALLY PLACED IN THIS SARCOPHAGUS BY
THE ROYAL COLLEGE OF PHYSICIANS OF LONDON
IN THE YEAR 1883

PLATE XII. The Harvey chapel at Hempstead parish church, Essex, showing the tomb and the wall bust of William Harvey

WILLIAM HARVEY

PLATE XIV. The 'Glasgow'
portrait of William Harvey.
In the background is a view
of Rome

I dare say, for variety of Fancy, is nothing inferior to the First: it continueth an historical account of the occurrences of the Times, in an allegorical way, under the shadow of Trees; and I believe it omits not any material passage which happed'd as far as it goes. If you please to spend some of the parings of your time, and fetch a Walk in this *Grove*, you may haply find therein some recreation. And if it be true what the Ancients write of some Trees, that they are Fatidical, these come to foretel, at leastwise to wish you, as the Season invites me, a good New-Year; and according to the Italian Complement, *buon principio, miglior mezzo, ed ottimo fine.* With these Wishes of Happiness, in all the three degrees of Comparison, I rest,

Your devoted Servant,

J. H.

Lond. 2. Jan.

'As a rule,' writes D'Arcy Power, 'it is almost impossible to fix the dates of the "Epistolae Ho-Elianae", but the first part of "Dodona's Grove" was issued in 1640, and the second part in 1650, so that the letter was probably written in 1651. Even if the letters were never really sent to those to whom they are addressed, Howell selected his apparent correspondents with such care that he would not have addressed Harvey in this manner unless he had been credited with some skill as a critic of general literature.'

We have seen that Harvey, in letters to various private correspondents of this period of his retirement, declared that he was no longer of a mind to address himself to medical problems which would demand, if they were to be conscientiously treated, extensive research and prolonged study. In this connection, we have a letter which Harvey addressed (on 1st February, 1654-55) to an eminent physician of Hesse-Darmstadt, who had asked his advice:

'I am much pleased to find that in spite of the long time that has passed, and the distance that separates us, you have not yet lost me from your memory, and I could wish that it lay in my power to answer all your inquiries. But indeed my age does not permit me to have this pleasure, for I am not only far stricken in years, but am afflicted with more and more indifferent health.'

Again, in a letter dated five months later and written to this same Dr. Horst, Harvey says:

'Advanced age, which unfits us for the investigation of novel subtleties, and the mind which inclines to repose after the fatigues of lengthened labours, prevent me from mixing myself up with the investigation of the new and difficult questions; so far am I from courting the office of umpire in this dispute[1] that I send you the substance of what I had formerly written about it.'

Nevertheless, if Harvey amused himself in his old age by walks, as we might say, in the garden of scientific curiosities and of literary fruits, he kept in close touch with the College of Physicians and on terms of friendship with its Fellows, since the welfare of the College had always been one of the great passions of his life. During his latter years, although he would not accept any of the positions of honour that the College was always ready to offer him, Harvey frequently displayed by acts instinct with nobility and delicate attention his affection for the great company of physicians. Thus in 1651, when Harvey was seventy-two years of age, the President was able to lay before his colleagues an anonymous proposal by which 'someone' offered to assume the expense of building an annex to serve as a meeting hall and library, on the condition that the anonymous donor was to be permitted to draw up the plans and to supervise the work—with the aid of a few persons chosen by him as competent for the task.

In the following year the new edifice was opened with some considerable ceremony, and the College decided (for the anonymity of the benefactor was not long preserved) that Harvey's bust should be placed in the vestibule of the College. When the doors of the new building were formally opened Harvey made over to the President and Fellows the title-deeds and his whole interest in the structure and its contents. Unfortunately the building (and the bust) disappeared in the Great Fire of 1666, which in five days devoured ninety churches and thirteen thousand two hundred houses.

In 1655 Harvey resigned as Lumleian lecturer and made over to the College in perpetuity his patrimonial estate at Burmarsh in Kent (then valued at £56 a year) as well as a number of objects from his library and study. In this same year, or perhaps a little earlier, was painted the celebrated portrait of Harvey that is now the principal adornment of the Library in the present building in Pall Mall East (*see* Plate IX), which contains also a number of other relics and souvenirs of the great man. To round off this sketch of Harvey's later years we cannot do better than quote what Sir Geoffrey Keynes has written (in his excellent work, *The Personality of William Harvey*) concerning this picture:

'This portrait is in most respects a good painting, though it has rather the appearance of a State portrait, made for the College and

---

[1] The questions related to digestion.

invested with all the dignity of the subject's pre-eminent position in his profession. The arms of the Harvey family are discernible on the pillar at the back. The pose is conventional except for the peculiar appearance of the right hand, and this, I think, is plainly due to injury to the canvas with clumsy repainting. I discovered in the Journal of the Royal College of Physicians that the picture was sent for repair in 1711,[1] and this uncomfortable hand is likely to be the result. Its position suggests that the hand may have held a scroll of paper before the repair was done. The left hand is beautifully shaped, with long, delicate fingers, but this may be only the conventional mode of the time. The face seems to have been somewhat smoothed out by the painter who was clearly aware that he was making a ceremonial picture. Thus the evidences of age are less apparent than they should be, and possibly the expression is rather more serene than we should expect. Note the lift of the eyebrow, which is so characteristic of the . . . authentic images of Harvey. It helps to give him a slightly quizzical expression that accords well with our knowledge of his character.'

I can only urge, once again, all those curious about Harvey's appearance and personality to consult this most interesting work. With regard to the coat-of-arms on the portrait (and to one that Keynes considers as genuine which appears on other portraits) we have already remarked that the quartered coat was probably assumed after Harvey's death and may have been added to this portrait after it had been executed.

Now that we have given the main facts of Harvey's life from 1650 to 1657, we must come to the last days of this truly great man and attempt to convey their moving character. Harvey, as we have seen, suffered for many years from frequent attacks of gout which he treated in the curious fashion related by Aubrey, and he had, no doubt, a marked tendency to arteriosclerosis. The prominence of his temporal artery, so evident in his later portraits and in the bust above his tomb, indicates well enough that he was destined one day to be the victim of a cerebral 'attack'. He himself can have had no illusions on the subject.

In this connection there is a piece of gossip retailed by that busy-body Aubrey (who was always ready with anecdotes in and out of season) which, he averred, had been related to him by Scarborough. This is that Harvey kept by him as a last resort a preparation of opium 'and I know not what else' in his study, so that if occasion

[1] This appears to be an error, for the occasion is recorded in the College account books where the date is given as 1706.

arose he might therewith calm his sufferings, which drug Scarborough promised to administer to him. There is in that nothing extraordinary, for no sick man would hesitate to demand, and no physician hesitate to administer, an opiate to alleviate the sufferings caused by a long and incurable malady. However, Aubrey also remarks of Scarborough, 'I think it is true but I cannot believe that he administered it to him. The Palsy furnished him an easy Passport.'

With reference to this opiate of Harvey's it is interesting to recall that another illustrious sufferer from gout was, some years later on, to give the world what came to be known as 'Sydenham's laudenum'. It seems that Sydenham (1624-89) got the formula at Montpellier sometime during the years 1659 and 1660 while he was completing at that University his medical studies which were interrupted by the Civil War. We have seen (p. 145) that Sydenham left Oxford and enlisted in the Parliamentary army, with which he entered Oxford in 1646. During the second phase of the Civil War, in 1650 (when Charles II landed in Scotland), Sydenham was a captain in the Commonwealth forces. It was only in 1656 that, but 'half a doctor', he settled at Westminster and had to complete his studies as best he could. He was not qualified to be elected a Fellow of the College of Physicians, but nevertheless he was a skilled and conscientious general practitioner whose experience and gifts as a physician are admirably expressed in his famous *Tractatus de Podagra et Hydrope*. He does not seem to have accepted Harvey's doctrines, but is notable chiefly as a great clinician and as one of Harvey's more illustrious contemporaries.

It was in the early days of June, 1657, that the stout-hearted old man who for some weeks had obviously been failing became confined to his room in the house of his brother Eliab at Roehampton, then a charming retreat in the Surrey countryside. His grand-niece looked after him. His friends often visited him and he spent most of his waking hours seated in a large armchair near an open window looking out upon the pleasing prospect of late spring and early summer in southern England. He could still enjoy the colours and scents of the flowers, although his legs would no longer carry him to vantage-points where he could observe the teeming life half-hidden in the plants and grasses.

On the evening of 3rd June he had just been settled down at his look-out post when he complained that he could no longer see clearly. At the same time his words became slurred and jumbled so that very soon he could utter only confused and indistinct sounds. He realized, so Aubrey relates, that he could have no further hope of recovery. He made signs that his young relations should be sent for. Among them he distributed the minute-watch he had used in making his experiments, his signet-ring and other mementoes. As the paralysis of his tongue would not allow him to speak, he made signs to Pembrose, the Blackfriars apothecary, to bleed him in the tongue, which operation the man seems to have performed unskilfully.

Before long, Harvey was seen to be losing consciousness. He was already passing on, and in his tangled dream maybe he could see some incidents of his long and glorious career. However, little by little the veil woven by the cerebral haemorrhage dropped and obscured all.

And thus died, under the sign of the Sun and the Blood, William Harvey, the author of the most significant discovery ever made in physiology.

Chapter VII

The Tomb, the Will, the Portraits and the Relics

Harvey's funeral—The leaden shell taken to the family burial chapel at Hempstead —The restorations undertaken at the instance of the Royal College of Physicians —Dedication of the new tomb on 18th October, 1883—The bust against the wall and the inscriptions relating thereto—Other details concerning the Harvey Chapel—Harvey's will—Imaginative writers who have sought to enliven their accounts by inventing imaginary legacies—Authentic portraits executed during Harvey's lifetime—The portraits examined by Sir Geoffrey Keynes—The youthful portrait—Portraits at the Royal College of Physicians and in the Hunter Collection—The Ditchingham portrait—The Padua Diploma—Some books— The lecture notes and some letters—The disappearance of Harvey's residences— Some memorable commemorations

WE have seen that Harvey died on the evening of the 3rd of June, 1657, in the house of his brother Eliab at Roehampton. The body was enveloped in a shroud and then 'lapt in lead'; that is to say, it was placed in a leaden case having roughly the shape of the body. The body was then taken to London and kept in Eliab's house in the City until 26th June, when the funeral procession set out for Hempstead in Essex, some fifty miles to the north-east of London, there to be buried in the Harvey family tomb. D'Arcy Power relates the details of the funeral, basing his account on Aubrey, as follows:

'The body was brought to London, where it seems to have been placed in Cockaine House, which also belonged to Eliab Harvey, and in that room of the house which became afterwards the office of Elias Ashmole, the antiquary to whom Oxford owes the Ashmolean Museum. Here it rested many days because, though

Harvey died on the 3rd of June, it was not until the 25th of June that the Fellows of the College of Physicians received a notice requesting them, clothed in their gowns, to attend the funeral on the following day. In the meantime, Eliab, as his brother's executor, had decided that Harvey should be buried at Hempstead in Essex, and accordingly, on the 26th of June, 1657, the funeral procession started from London. It was followed far beyond the City walls by a large number of the Fellows of the College of Physicians, many of whom must afterwards have hurried back to Westminster Hall, where, on the same day, with the greatest ceremony and with all the pomp of circumstance, Cromwell was a second time inaugurated after the humble petition and advice had given him the power of nominating his successors and of forming a second House of Parliament, whilst it assigned to him a perpetual revenue.

'There is no record of the time when the funeral party reached Hempstead, nor where it stopped on the way. The village is situated about fifty miles from London and seven miles east of Saffron Walden, so that one, if not two, nights must have been spent upon the journey. Here, about 1655, Eliab Harvey had built "the Harvey Chapel", a plain, rectangular building of brick with a high-pitched tile roof, on the north side of the church, adjoining and communicating with the chancel and lighted by three large windows. He had also built the outer vault beneath it as a place of sepulture for his family, and when this became full in 1766, one of his descendants, also an Eliab Harvey, but of Claybury, built the inner vault. Twice before had Eliab made a similar journey. Once in 1655, after the death of his daughter Sarah, a girl of twelve, and again in 1656, at the funeral of Elizabeth, another daughter aged nine. Harvey was laid in the outer chapel, between the bodies of his two nieces, and like them he was "lapt in lead", coffinless, and upon his breast was placed in great letters—

DOCTOR
WILLIAM + HARVEY +
DECEASED + THE + 3 +
OF + JUNE + 1657 +
AGED + 79 + YEARS.

' "I was at the funeral," says Aubrey, "and helped to carry him into the vault." The simple wrapping of the body in lead seems to have been a custom peculiar to the Harvey family. The leaden case used for William Harvey was roughly shaped to the form of the body, the head part having the rude outline of a face with mouth, nose, and eyes; the neck wide and the shoulders expanded. The breastplate was broad and the inscription upon it was in raised letters. The body of the case was long and tapering towards the feet, where the lead was turned up at a right angle. The measurements of the case show that it afforded no data as to Harvey's size, for though he was a man "of the lowest stature", its extreme length from the crown of the head to the toes was no less than six feet and a quarter.

'When the late Sir Benjamin Ward Richardson first entered the vault in 1847, the remains of Harvey had not been visited within the memory of man, though the villagers knew by tradition that "Dr. Harvey was a very great man, who had made, they were told, some great discovery, though they did not know what it was." At that time the vault was practically open to the public, for the window in it at the eastern end was uncased and badly barred. The leaden shell containing Harvey's remains lay upon the floor just beneath the window and with the feet directed towards it. It was therefore exposed to the drift of rain when it beat into the vault with an east wind, and the sarcophagus was so unprotected that boys could throw stones upon it, and did so. The lead in the upper third of its length from the feet was almost torn through on its upper surface, though the rent was only a small one. The leaden case, too, was beginning to bend in over the middle of the body like a large scoop or spoon, in which water could accumulate.

'Some repairs were made in the vault after it had been visited and its condition had been reported upon by Dr. Stewart and (Sir) Richard Quain in 1868, but the leaden case still remained upon the floor and the opening had become so large that a frog jumped out of it on one occasion as soon as it was touched. Ten years later Sir Benjamin Richardson made a further examination of the case and reported that the centre of the shell, extending from the middle of the trunk to the feet, had so far collapsed that the upper surface all but touched the lower one, whilst the crack in the lead was now so large that it measured fully six inches in length. But owing to the greater collapse of the lead the fissure was not so wide as it was in 1868; indeed, the edges had now closed, leaving only a space of half an inch at the widest part.

' "The question which interests us most," says Richardson, "has yet to be considered. Are any remains of Harvey left in the sarcophagus? Expecting to find the opening in the lead in the same condition at my latest visit, as it was at the latest but one, I took with me a small mirror, a magnesium light, and every appliance for making what may be called a sarcophoscopic investigation. To my dismay, I discovered that the opening is now almost closed by the collapse of the lead, so that the reflector could not be used, while the shell is positively filled at the opening with thick, dirty fluid, like mud—a fluid thick as melted pitch and having a peculiar organic odour. This extends into the case above and below the crack or fissure. There can be little remaining of the body, not much probably even of the skeleton."

'Sir Benjamin concluded his report with the suggestion that "these honoured remains should be conveyed to their one fit and final resting-place—Westminster Abbey. There, laid two feet deep in the floor in some quiet corner and covered merely with a thick glass plate, the leaden sarcophagus, still visible to those who take an interest in the history of science, would be protected for ages, instead of being destined, as it now certainly is, to fall into a mere crumbling, unrecognizable mass, in the course, at the furthest, of another hundred years." The failing health and the subsequent death of Dr. Stanley, the Dean of Westminster, prevented the execution of this project, which would probably have been carried into effect had he lived, for it is thought that he was willing to allow the remains of Harvey to be placed near those of Hunter or Livingstone.

'On the 28th of January, 1882, the whole tower of Hempstead Church fell towards the south-west into the churchyard. No injury was done to the Harvey Chapel, but the accident led to a further examination of Harvey's shell. It was found that the lead was perishing rapidly, and that the shell itself was full of water. A formal report was made to the College of Physicians, who appointed a committee of its Fellows to advise upon the best method of procedure. The labours of the Committee resulted in a decision to leave the remains at Hempstead, but to remove them to the chapel above the vault. The necessary consent having been obtained, and a marble sarcophagus to receive the leaden case having been selected, an architect was invited to examine the vault and the floor of the chapel. Under his directions pillars were built in the vault to sustain the additional weight upon the floor of the chapel, and on St. Luke's Day, 1883, the leaden case containing Harvey's remains was carried reverently from the vault by eight Fellows of the College. It was immediately deposited in the sarcophagus in the presence of the President, the Office Bearers, and many Fellows of the Royal College of Physicians' (*see* Plate XII). 'A leaden case was also deposited within the sarcophagus containing the quarto edition of Harvey's works in Latin, edited in 1766 by Drs. Akenside and

Lawrence, with a memorial bottle hermetically sealed and containing a scroll with the following memorial:

' "The body of William Harvey lapt in lead, simply soldered, was laid without shell or enclosure of any kind in the Harvey vault of this Church of Hempstead, Essex, in June, 1657.

' "In the course of time the lead enclosing the remains was, from exposure and natural decay, so seriously damaged as to endanger its preservation, rendering some repair of it the duty of those interested in the memory of the illustrious discoverer of the circulation of the Blood.

' "The Royal College of Physicians, of which corporate body Harvey was a munificent Benefactor, and which by his favour is the possessor in perpetuity of his patrimonial estate at Burmarsh, Kent, did in the years 1882–83, by permission of the Representatives of the Harvey family, undertake that duty.

' "In accordance with this determination the leaden mortuary chest containing the remains of Harvey was repaired, and was, as far as possible, restored to its original state, and on this 18th day of October, 1883, in the presence of four representatives of the Harvey family and of the President, all the office bearers and many other Fellows of the College of Physicians (whose names are hereunto appended), was reverently translated from the Harvey vault to this Sarcophagus, raised by the College for its reception and preservation."

'High in the wall of the Church at Hempstead is a marble monument containing a bust of William Harvey. The ornamentation of the tablet is bold and effective, and below the bust is a long Latin inscription testifying to Harvey's good works. The bust was carefully examined by Mr. Thomas Woolner, R.A., who came to the conclusion that it was made from a death mask. He says that "the features presented by the bust are clearly those of a dead face. The sculptor exhibits no knowledge of sculpture except when he was copying what was directly before him. With the cast of the face for his copy he has shown true artistic delineation, but all that he has been obliged to add to make up the bust as it stands is of the worst possible quality. The ears are placed entirely out of position, the large, redundant head of hair is altogether out of character, imaginary and badly executed, and the drapery of the shoulders is simply despicable." We have nevertheless to thank the rude sculptor for the care he has devoted to the face, and we are enriched by the knowledge supplied to us by a great contemporary authority in sculpture, that the true lineaments of William Harvey, as they were seen at the time of his death, are still in our possession—lineaments which indicate a face at once refined, reflective, and commanding.'

Thus D'Arcy Power. Sir Geoffrey Keynes, while agreeing that the bust shows a face that is a perfect likeness of Harvey, expresses in his *The Personality of William Harvey* a rather different opinion as to the mode of execution of this work. After having myself carefully examined the memorial and having long meditated before it, I am inclined to agree with Sir G. Keynes, who says:

'The monument is on the wall above the vault, and is known to be the work of Edward Marshall, one of the master-masons of the time. The bust of Harvey, 27 inches in height, is so well fashioned and is so life-like that I am unable to subscribe to the idea that it was made from a death-mask. From a life-mask perhaps; or it may else have been made during Harvey's life, at the same time as the statue placed in the College of Physicians in 1652. The face with its wrinkles and creases (and again note the distended temporal vein) is not dead. Here you have the authentic Harvey looking at life as it really is, honest, forthright, in the best sense of the word *scientific*.'

Let us now consider that most interesting document, Harvey's will. This is not dated but it seems to have been made sometime between July, 1651, and February, 1653. After the signature 'Wil. Harvey' are the words, 'Signed, sealed and published as the last will and testament of me William Harvey in the presence of us Edward Dering. Henneage Finch. Richard Flud. Francis Finche.'

A codicil, also undated, was possibly drawn up a little before Sunday, 28th December, 1656, the day that Harvey re-read the document and formally declared and published, in the presence of Heneage Finch (his nephew by marriage and afterwards Lord Chancellor) and his faithful servant, John Raby, that it contained his last will and testament.

From this will we need to extract but those passages which present an interest for us today. We shall, then, pass over the long list of bequests to members of the family. The will begins with an invocation of the name of God (as did, we may remember, the Padua Diploma of sixty years before), thus:

I, William Harvey, of London, Doctor of Physic, do by these presents make and ordain this my last Will and testament in the manner and form following, revoking hereby all former and other wills and testaments whatsoever.

Imprimis, I do most humbly render my soul to Him that gave it and to my blessed Lord and Saviour Christ Jesus, and my body to the earth to be buried at the discretion of my executor herein after named.

Then follow instructions for the disposing of his estate of all kinds ('goods, household stuff, ready monies, debts, duties, arrear-ages of rents or any other ways whatsoever and whereof I shall not etc. . . .') to different members of his family and other legatees, it being specified that everything not otherwise bequeathed should go to 'my loving brother, Mr. Eliab Harvey, merchant of London, whom I name executor of this my last will and testament'.

Among the detailed bequests we may note those made to the College of Physicians:

And first I appoint so much money to be raised and laid out upon that building which I have already begun to erect within the College of Physicians in London as will serve to finish the same according to the design already made. . . .

Touching my books and household stuff, pictures and apparell of which I have not already disposed I give to the College of Physicians all my books and papers and my best Persia long carpet and my blue satin embroidered cushion, one pair of brass Andirons with fire shovel and tongs of brass for the ornament of the meeting room I have erected for that purpose.

The will ends thus:

Item, I give my velvet gown to my loving friend Mr. Doctor Scarborough desiring him and my loving friend Mr. Doctor Ent to look over those scattered remnant of my poor Library and what books, papers or rare collections they shall think fit to present to the College and the rest to be sold and with the money buy better. And for their pains I give to Mr. Doctor Ent all the presses and shelves he please to make use of and five pounds to buy him a ring to keep or wear in remembrance of me.

And to Doctor Scarborough all my little silver instruments of surgery.

Then, after a few final bequests to members of his family, the will terminates thus:

Thus I have finished my last Will in three pages, two of them written with my own hand and my name subscribed to every one with my hand and seal to the last.

The entry of the issue of probate upon this will runs thus in the books at Somerset House:

> May 1659. The second day was proved the will and Codicil annext of Dr. William Harvey, late of the parish of St. Peter's Poore, in London, but at Roehampton in the County of Surrey, deceased, by the oath of Eliab Harvey, the brother and sole executor, to whom administration was committed, he being first sworn truly to administer.

Before we leave Harvey's will we may, perhaps, note a curious reservation therein made. It is of little apparent importance though still of interest. The passage reads:

> Item, I give unto my niece Mary West and her daughter Amy West half the linen I shall leave at London in my chests and chambers together with all my plate excepting my coffee-pot.

Since nowhere else in the will is there made any mention of the coffee-pot this must have gone to Eliab, the residuary legatee:

> . . . whatsoever and whereof I shall not by this present will or by some Codicil to be hereunto annexed make a particular gift and disposition I do after my debts, funerals, and legacies paid and discharged, give and bequeath the same unto my loving brother Mr. Eliab Harvey, merchant of London, whom I make executor of this my last will and testament.

Thus Eliab got the coffee-pot, perhaps as a souvenir of the pleasure that both brothers had had from drinking the Arabian brew. We may also mention here an amusing anecdote quoted by a writer in search of picturesque touches to enliven his *History of the Beginnings of Coffee in Europe*. The author alleges that he found it in a German work entitled *Sage und Siegenzug des Kaffees*, written by one H. E. Jacob and published by Rowohlt at Berlin in 1934. In this volume are many references to British coffee-drinkers (John Ellis, Garnett, Macaulay, Moseley, Robinson, Ward, etc.). An article that appeared in 1953 in a little French review called *Grandgousier* comments thus upon the anecdote:

'The first consignment of coffee-beans seems to have reached London in 1616, but we know little about the beginnings of coffee-drinking in England. By the middle of the seventeenth century, coffee was still a rare and precious commodity reserved for a small number of the elect, as is shown by this anecdote: when the illustrious Harvey died in 1657, he left, by his will, to his London colleagues, fifty-six pounds of coffee on the condition that until the stock was exhausted they should meet together and drink coffee each month on that day of the month which was that of his death. Would this scientist whose discovery of the circulation of the blood had made him famous in all Europe, have made such an extraordinary bequest if his small stock of coffee had not constituted a real treasure that he wished to offer to colleagues who were less well situated than himself?'

This story, however entertaining, seemed to me so improbable in such a solemn document as Harvey's will that I sent a copy of the article to my friend Sir Geoffrey Keynes, who assures me that Harvey's will contains no such stipulation. So we may leave the coffee-pot, and the evidence it affords of the Harvey family's taste for this new-fangled beverage, and now consider some of the relics and souvenirs of the great scientist.

We may begin with the portraits, or at least with those which afford an authentic presentation of his appearance. We have already noted (pages 162–3) the account Keynes gives of the portrait at the College of Physicians reproduced in the *Frontispiece*. Harvey's age when it was painted is sometimes given as seventy-seven, but it is more likely that he was nearer seventy. The portrait has undoubtedly deteriorated with time and the varnish has darkened so as to obscure the scalloped edges of the collar and some of the hair and beard. This does not appear to have been noticed by Sir Geoffrey Keynes, though these details seem to have been clearly visible in 1878 when an engraving was made from it for *Nature* by C. H. Jeens. As may be seen in the reproduction in Plate XIII, this engraving suggests that the portrait originally showed a younger man, and this is almost certainly the case even if we allow the engraver a certain freedom of rendering.

Keynes's patience and perspicacity in his search for anything which might add to our knowledge of Harvey's appearance led him to discover in the derelict, half-ruined and ransacked house of Rolls Park near Chigwell (once the property of Eliab Harvey and well known to William himself as a place of rest and repose) several Harvey family portraits, including one of the scientist. In describing this picture, which shows Harvey twenty-five or thirty years younger than in the 'official' portrait, Sir G. Keynes expresses himself in the following words:

'This picture has just been rescued from a derelict house, Rolls

Park, near Chigwell in Essex about fifteen miles east of London. Rolls Park was an estate bought by William Harvey's brother Eliab, early in the seventeenth century, and it has remained in the possession of Eliab Harvey's descendants to the present day. In the second half of the eighteenth century the house belonged to Admiral Sir Eliab Harvey, who afterwards commanded the *Téméraire* at the battle of Trafalgar. About 1760 he carried out some elaborate decorations in the house, including the placing of a number of family portraits in plasterwork frames in one of the larger rooms. The group of these portraits consisted of the panel showing old Thomas Harvey . . . surrounded by his seven sons in uniform ovals. . . . The house was quite empty except for these pictures and is rapidly decaying. Two of the oval portraits had already been stolen by intruders. Evidence derived from the five remaining portraits of Thomas Harvey's seven sons shows that they were certainly painted between 1620 and 1630. They can none of them have been painted after 1630, as the sons all wear falling ruffs, a fashion which passed out about that date. The pictures had not been disturbed for nearly 200 years, and are in a sad state of dirt and neglect; but it can now be seen that they all bear the subject's names, though it was possible to recognize William's features without this help. I may mention that the portraits are now safely housed at the National Portrait Gallery.[1] There can be no doubt . . . that you are looking at the image of William Harvey as he was about 1622, when he would be aged forty-five. His hair and eyes are dark. He has a heavy moustache and a small peaked beard. You will notice the slight lift in the eyebrow, which became more pronounced in later life as the outer part of the eyebrows thinned. He is wearing a doublet without a doctor's gown. There are no fanciful attributes and no dates, merely the name, Doctor William Harvey inscribed on the background.'[2]

Sir Geoffrey then makes the just observation that it is rather rare to possess a youthful portrait of a man destined to become famous. It is usually towards the end of an eminent man's life—and even after his death, when his merits are common knowledge—that there is a rush to perpetuate his features as they appeared in old age. Generally speaking (as we may observe in the case of Harvey) no

---

[1] We may note that before thefts occurred at the mansion, the seven sons of Thomas Harvey were portrayed at Rolls Park. As one of them (the third, Thomas) died in 1622, the portraits were almost certainly executed before that date. A correction should be made to this text (written in 1949), for the portraits from Rolls Park have since been consigned to the care of the Royal College of Physicians in Pall Mall East.

compunction is felt in fabricating posthumous likenesses, replicas, copies of copies, completely bogus portraits, or even in utilizing pictures of quite different people to whose portraits the famous name is shamelessly affixed.

After his careful examination of all the supposed portraits of Harvey, Keynes came to the conclusion that, in addition to the painting in the library of the Royal College of Physicians, the only authentic and well-vouched-for portrayals of the great physician are those from Rolls Park and from the Hunter collection, the latter of which (reproduced in Plate XIV) is now at Glasgow. This is what Sir Geoffrey writes about this last:

'Oddly enough it has hitherto escaped the notice of Harvey's biographers, though its pedigree is very fully known. It was acquired very early in the eighteenth century by the famous Dr. Mead, who knew all the celebrated men of his time, including some that must have known Harvey.[1] At the sale of Mead's collection in 1754 it was bought for Hunter, and in his collection it has remained ever since.[2] It is a much less formal, more intimate picture of Harvey than the ceremonial portrait at the Royal College of Physicians. He does not look a very happy or satisfied man, as we have reason to know that he was not. The characteristic eyebrow is there, and the complexion in the picture itself entirely agrees with Aubrey's description as olivaster, the colour of wainscot. The patches on the cheek are due to high colour, agreeing with Aubrey's description of his hot-headedness, and our knowledge that his blood-pressure was certainly raised in his last years. Notice also the faithful rendering of the distended temporal vein. But you may ask, why does he finger the leaves of a book with a Vesalian engraving of a skull, and why a background representing a view of Rome? The book is the *Works* of Spigelius, 1645.[3] It happens to contain a reprinting of Harvey's *De*

[1] Richard Mead (1673–1754), one of George II's Physicians in Ordinary. Mead was an antiquarian, art collector and also the author of what was for his day a daring book entitled *Medicina sacra* in which he attributed to natural causes the cases of so-called 'demoniac possession'.

[2] John Hunter (1728–93), the celebrated British physiologist and sargeon, may be considered as the founder in Britain of experimental pathology. He made a valuable anatomical collection, now at the Royal College of Surgeons.

[3] Adrian Spigelius (1578–1625) was born in Brussels in the same year that Harvey was born in Folkestone. Spigelius died aged only forty-seven years at Padua, to which he had moved from Moravia in 1616 when the Venetian Senate summoned him to teach anatomy in the Italian university. A worthy successor of his fellow-countryman, André Vésale (Vesalius), Spigelius also wrote a *De Humani Corporis Fabrica* in ten sections (decem libri) which was published at Venice two years after the author's premature death, that is to say in 1627. This first edition of

Motu Cordis, but in fact it serves also to remind us that Harvey was a general anatomist, not merely the demonstrator of the circulation of the blood. The background shows the Church of Santa Maria di Loreto and Trajan's Column; for Harvey had visited Rome in 1636, and the library he had built for the College of Physicians was inspired by an admiration for Roman architecture. If further evidence of authenticity be demanded, there is in the Royal College of Physicians the companion picture of Harvey's close friend, Sir Charles Scarborough, again with a Vesalian illustration in his book and another view of Rome in the background, this time showing St. Peter's and the Horse-Tamers on the Quirinal.'

Another very fine portrait of Harvey, known as the 'Ditchingham' from the place in Norfolk where it is still preserved, represents him three-quarter length, standing. His right hand rests upon a walking-stick, while he holds a gold-fringed handkerchief in his left hand. Since this picture does not show certain facial characteristics of Harvey, such as the raised eyebrow, Keynes inclines to the view that it was painted after Harvey's death by some artist who was ignorant of such details of Harvey's features. However, despite Sir Geoffrey's competence in all matters dealing with the Harvey iconography, it is not easy to imagine that so striking a painting could have been executed other than from a living model. The painter may have idealized away some of the peculiarities, or have not regarded them as permanent features. But if the portrait was made after Harvey's death, then surely the painter must have had at his disposal some approved drawings or sketches made during Harvey's lifetime, and the characteristic feature would almost certainly have been repeated.

Lady Moran, who has helped to clear up so many obscure points in connection with Harvey and his family, and who collaborated with Sir Wilmott Herringham[1] in these researches, discovered a magnificent portrait in 1928, during the sale of the contents of Surrenden Dering, in Kent, a house she had reason to think

Spigelius could not, then, have included any allusion to Harvey's *Exercitatio*, which did not appear until 1628. Thus the works to which Sir Geoffrey Keynes makes allusion must be the second edition of Spigelius, which appeared in 1645. The book, in two volumes, is a magnificent folio published by Van der Linden and printed by Blacu at Amsterdam. This edition contains quotations from Casserius, Asellius and Wallaeus as well as from the *Exercitatio* of Harvey.

[1] Sir Wilmott Herringham was, during the 1914–18 war, head of the British medical services in France, and, in 1929, he delivered the Harveian oration at the Royal College of Physicians.

might contain souvenirs of Harvey. She purchased the picture, which had been tucked away in a dusty corner and ignored by everyone, for a small sum and submitted it to experts, who concluded that it was undoubtedly a portrait of Harvey and was to be attributed to either William Dobson or Van Dyck. This 'Surrenden Dering' portrait, though of the head and shoulders only, is very like the one at Ditchingham.

To return to the Ditchingham portrait, this bears in the right-hand top corner the coat-of-arms illustrated in Fig. 1, centre. We have already noted how complicated is the problem of the Harvey arms, and the uncertainty of the date at which any official grant may have been made. However, we know of no record of any grant before that of 1660 in favour of Daniel Harvey, William Harvey's grand-nephew, and it therefore seems probable that the Harveys were not 'officially' entitled to bear arms before that date, although some would hold that Thomas Harvey, the father, was granted arms at the time that William Harvey was physician to James I.

I am inclined to agree with Sir G. Keynes that the coat-of-arms on the Ditchingham portrait, as well as that on the picture at the Royal College of Physicians, were additions made when the pictures were restored at some later date. We know that the latter portrait was restored in 1706, since mention is made of the fact in the records of the Royal College of Physicians.

All things considered, I think that in the five portraits mentioned above—that is to say, those of Rolls Park, of the Royal College of Physicians, of the Hunter collection, of the Ditchingham collection and of Surrenden Dering—we have enough material and evidence to provide us with a really authentic likeness of Harvey as he appeared in life.

To complete the list of Harveian souvenirs, we may note that in addition to the portrait of about 1650 the Royal College of Physicians is now in possession of the six family pictures found in the derelict mansion of Rolls Park (which has been pulled down). The large portrait of 1650 is hung over the fireplace in the main apartment of the library and is, perhaps, the first object to catch the visitor's eye as he enters the room. The other family pictures were, until recently, hung against the north wall of the dining-room on the ground-floor, but they have recently been placed in the vestibule and may be seen immediately to the right as one enters the building.

At the Royal College of Physicians is also the Padua Diploma (which, as we have seen, was presented to the College on 7th July, 1754, by the Rev. Osmund Beauvoir, headmaster of the King's

School, Canterbury) as well as a reproduction of the Padua *stemma* given, in 1893, by representatives of the University of Padua to Gonville and Caius College, Cambridge (*see* Fig. 3). Among the treasures in the library of the Royal College of Physicians is a copy of the *Falopii Opera*, which belonged to Harvey and bears annotations in his handwriting. Then, as we have said, the College also possesses the instruments for dissection which are believed to be Harvey's, as well as the wand he used at his lectures, and six engravings of anatomical preparations reputed to have been dissected by Harvey.

In the British Museum is the notebook of Harvey's MS. jottings used for his first 'visceral' Lumleian Lecture in 1616, an object that turned up after having been considered lost for many years.[1] Harvey's notes for his 'muscular' lecture in 1627 are also preserved in the British Museum Library.

In his *Bibliography of the Writings of William Harvey* (2nd Edition, 1953) Sir Geoffrey Keynes mentions also:

1. Some letters published in 1912 in the *Transactions* of the College of Physicians of Philadelphia, U.S.A., and reproduced by D'Arcy Power in the *Proceedings of the Historical Section of the Royal Society of Medicine*, 1916.

2. Eleven letters from William Harvey to Lord Feilding, dated from 9th June to 16th November, 1636. These were published in 1912, in a limited edition, by Sir Thomas Barlow for the Royal College of Physicians.

In his preliminary note to the *Miscellanea* relating to William Harvey (p. 68 of his *Bibliography*), Sir Geoffrey Keynes, after having remarked how little there remains of Harvey's own notes and personal papers (probably because of the destruction of the College of Physicians during the Great Fire of 1666), laments that only fourteen of the letters 'have survived in the original MSS. Twelve of these are in the library of the Royal College of Physicians, the other two are in the Bodleian Library and in the Library of Sidney Sussex College' at Cambridge.

Of the houses occupied by Harvey at Folkestone, in London or in the country with his brothers, little remains except the 'patrimonial estate' at Burmarsh in Kent, given by Harvey to the College of Physicians in 1652. Of Winslow's Hall, near Hempstead in Essex, there is nothing but a moat choked with vegetation half-hidden in a thicket. It was at Winslow's Hall that Harvey, in his later years, often resided with his brother Eliab, and I am inclined to think that

[1] *Praelectiones Anatomica*, 1616. (British Museum, Sloane MS. 230A.)

the Letters to Riolan (in 1649), though dated as from Cambridge, were really composed at Winslow's Hall.

Of William Harvey's family there remained in 1883 a few distant relations, since they are mentioned as having been present in 1883 when the scientist's remains were placed in the new sarcophagus. But now it seems that the Harvey family has become extinct.

We may note here some of the celebrations which have, from time to time, helped to perpetuate Harvey's memory. There was the ceremony of the handing over of the Padua Diploma by Beauvoir, the presentation of the *stemma*, the dedication of the new sarcophagus and the ceremonies that marked the tercentenary of the publication of the *Exercitatio*, both in London and in the British universities. On this occasion splendid photographic reproductions were made of both the *Exercitatio* and the Diploma, while a film was shown of Harvey's life. However, this film unfortunately did not convey Harvey's real teaching regarding the beginning of the circulation in the *vena cava*: it attributed to him, in error, the commencement of the circulation in the heart.[1] However, as we have seen above, the authors of the 1928 film did not forget to include Caesalpinus among the number of Harvey's predecessors. This is a point we shall appreciate if we remember the texts relating to Caesalpinus cited in Chapter IV. Though his predecessors produced nothing to compare with Harvey's great achievement, there can be no doubt that it was in response to their timid suggestions that he started his own investigations.

[1] There are also other details, which, in my opinion, need correction in this film in view of our present knowledge. For my own satisfaction I have sketched out a scenario based on the documentation at my disposal and on my long acquaintance with Harvey's life and work. I must confess that what I have set down is something very different from that prepared for the film in 1928.

Gardez-vous de faire dire à
un homme ce qu'il n'a pas
voulu dire.

Chapter VIII

Harvey's Work and the Texts

The immortal little book that laid the foundation of all our knowledge of physiology—The Dedication—The *Proemium* discussing the obscurities and contradictions of Galen's teaching—Analyses of the seventeen chapters of the *Exercitatio*—The happy error of interpretation relating to the single heart of fishes —Comparison of the text of the *Exercitatio* of 1628 with that of the *Exercitationes* of 1649—A refutation of the erroneous attribution to Harvey of the commencement of his cycle with the heart-motor—The circulation according to Harvey— The *Exercitatio Anatomica de Generatione Animalium*—Its publication in 1651 at the instance of Dr. Ent—The main divisions of the book and their subdivisions into 'exercises' or propositions—Analysis of the essential ideas expressed in the book— Harvey and the doctrine of evolution

WHEN Harvey's work is mentioned most people think only of his masterly description of the circulation of the blood and of the mechanism of the heart. We should therefore emphasize that he conducted other researches of great importance in different fields of comparative zoology and that these are preserved in his *De Generatione Animalium*, which has come down to us intact. There was also his treatise on insects which unfortunately disappeared during the troublesome times of the Civil War. It is clear that Harvey was a many-sided genius and far from being bound within the narrow limits of a specialization. The precious gleanings that he made during his observations in various branches of natural science served to provide him with valuable material for throwing light upon his main interest in life—medicine. No one better than

Harvey, indeed, realized the truth of the opening lines of Hippocrates's Aphorisms: 'Life is short, art is long, opportunity fleeting and enquiry difficult.'

We shall have something to say concerning the *De Generatione Animalium* at the end of this chapter, but to put first things first we shall begin with the masterpiece, the *Exercitatio* of 1628, wherein he expounded the elements of his new doctrine. A general description of this small volume will be followed by a list of the chapter headings in which Harvey summarized his ideas. After discussing these we shall consider the two *Exercitationes* of 1649, in which Harvey further explained and added to his main work, and in which he expressed his final opinions upon the circulation of the blood.

The first edition of the *Exercitatio Anatomica de Motu Cordis et Sanguinis in Animalibus*, published at Frankfurt in 1628 by William Fitzer, was a thin book of seventy-two pages printed in small type. The title-page is reproduced in Plate XV a little smaller than the original.

The *Exercitatio* begins with a Dedication to the King and another to the President and Fellows of the College of Physicians, Harvey's colleagues. In an Introduction, or *Proemium* (which I, contrary to the judgement of many, think to be of capital importance), Harvey gives a list of the obscurities, the confusions, the contradictions that permeated the traditions of the time. It was these that had induced him to reflect long and deeply upon the problems of the circulation, and had spurred him finally to seek the truth in a long series of patient observations.

At this point I should like to recall briefly the teaching derived from Galen that was still dominant at the beginning of the 17th century. The teaching of Galen (or Galenos, the great Greek physician from Pergamum in Asia Minor who, however, practised at Rome), though it marked a considerable advance upon the vague theories held up to his time, had not been modified in any way for fourteen hundred years. It was believed that no one could be wiser and better informed than the divine master of Pergamum, or would dare to differ from him. If we do not, first of all, examine this teaching and its errors, we cannot form any true concept of the complete revolution effected by Harvey when he swept away, in one small treatise, the accumulated rubbish of many centuries.

We may start off by admitting that Galen had adopted a singularly just view in ascribing the origin and movement of the blood to the restorative action of the food absorbed by the stomach and the intestines. Starting with this postulate, Galen considered

that obviously the first path of the blood was through the gastric and
intestinal vessels of the portal vein (Fig. 8) which conducts the aliments from the digestive organs to the liver. Here, he considered
that an elaboration or 'primary decoction' was effected which
rendered the blood venous. So far, so good, except that it is only
partly true that the venous blood is elaborated in the liver.

However, after that Galen's teaching became completely false,
mainly owing to an inexact interpretation of the function of the
hepatic vein which leaves the liver on its posterior edge. We can
see in Fig. 9 how this joins up with the great *vena cava* which,
having come from the farthest parts of the body, now receives from
the hepatic vein blood fortified with elements from the organs of
digestion and conducts it to the right heart. But Galen considered
the hepatic vein to be the origin or 'root' of the *vena cava*, which
he regarded as forming two branches, one descending and taking
venous blood from the liver to all the lower portions of the body,
and the other ascending and taking venous blood from the liver to
the upper parts of the body. This is clearly shown in Fig. 8.

Further, since it was obvious that the stomach and the intestines
(which had sent alimentary matter in its raw state through the portal
vein to the liver) must themselves require a proper provision of
venous blood elaborated in the liver, it was held that the portal
vein could at certain times carry a stream in the opposite direction,
and pass elaborated blood back to the stomach and intestines. Thus,
for Galen and his disciples the liver was a sort of 'first heart' or
'ante-heart', making and distributing venous blood, whereas the
'second heart'—*i.e.* the real heart—was regarded by Galen in the
following curious way.

He considered that when the so-called 'ascending *vena cava*'
reached the thorax it produced an actively expanding and pulsatile
dilatation—*i.e.* the right heart—so as to secure an abundant supply of
venous blood to the *vena arteriosa*[1] leading to the lungs, whose
considerable size, thought Galen, indicated that they must need a
rich provision of blood. After exhibiting this lateral expansion (the
right heart) the ascending *vena cava* continued with its distribution
of venous blood to the other organs of the upper part of the body,
just as the descending *vena cava* was believed to distribute blood to
the lower part of the body. The right cardiac cavity, according to
Galen, received the venous blood when it was contracted or in
systole (!), but did not require it merely to nourish the lungs. Part of
the blood was transferred through the inter-ventricular wall or

[1] Now called the pulmonary artery.

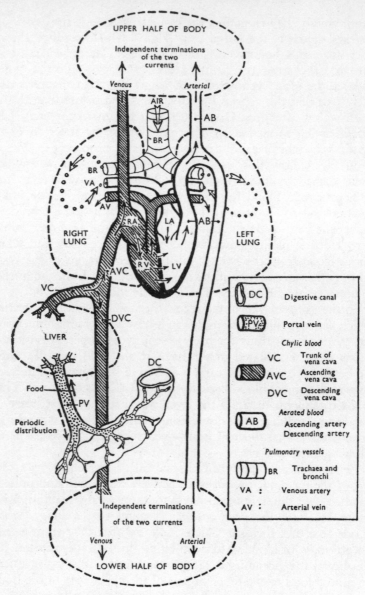

Fig. 8. The traditional system of the movements of the blood as taught by Galen in the 2nd century A.D. Galen's fundamental error was the assumption that the left and right ventricles are connected by perforations through their dividing wall. RA, LA: right and left auricles, respectively. RV, LV: right and left ventricles.

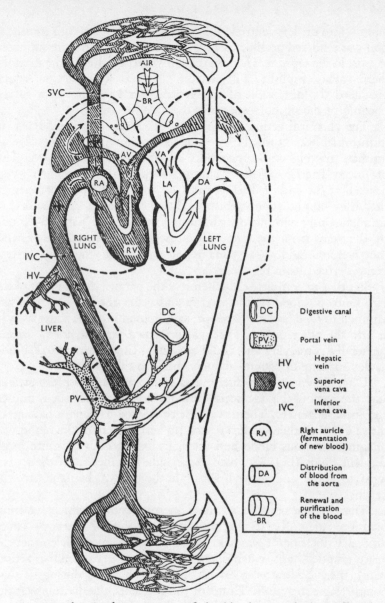

FIG. 9. The circulatory system of the blood as taught by William Harvey in the 17th century. Compare with Fig. 8 opposite. Harvey conceived the circulation to start at the point marked by a cross in the inferior *vena cava*. LA: left auricle. RV, LV: right and left ventricles, respectively.

septum into the left ventricle (likewise in systole!), and this transudation was rendered possible by tiny perforations which were supposed to exist in the septum. Then, in the left ventricle, during the diastole, there was accomplished a mysterious chemical 'fermentation' which produced the distension of the ventricle and resulted in a forced opening of the sigmoid apertures towards the aorta.

The chemical action was held to occur under the influence of 'primordial heat' (thought to reside in the heart), and to involve an intimate mixing and concoction of air and venous blood. This produced 'arterialized' blood charged with 'vital spirit' which 'overflowed' at the end of diastole into the aorta and all the arteries, so that they might supply this 'vitalized' blood to all the organs simultaneously with the distribution of venous—or 'natural'—blood by the veins from the liver. (The arteries were so named because they were thought to carry mainly air and 'spirit', the word 'artery' being derived from the Greek *aer*, air.)

In order to complete the scheme of the parallel distribution of the two kinds of blood by the arteries and veins, the left ventricle was assumed to send 'spiritualized' or 'vital' blood into the lungs as well as into the other organs, so it was imagined that the *arteria venosa*[1] (generally conveying air) could at certain times carry 'vital' blood in the opposite direction—namely, back to the lungs.

. Once they had been distributed to the organs, both the arterial and the venous bloods were thought to evaporate their unused surpluses separately. There was not conceived to be any passage of the one to the other—that is to say, no 'circulation' of the blood was imagined. Venous blood and arterial blood were two quite independent fluids (Fig. 8) which arose, side by side, from their own separate roots and flowed through their own branches to the organs.

There is one point in all these ancient theories which we must mention again, for it was the starting-point of Harvey's revolutionary doctrine. It was held by all the followers of Galen that the heart 'emptied itself' when dilated or in diastole (termed the 'active' state); then it admitted a few drops of fresh blood during its supposed relapse in systole. Thus, for the Ancients, the diastole was the active 'aspiration' of the cardiac walls, and the systole the passive relapsing of the walls. And this idea was, moreover, extended to cover also the walls of the arteries. Furthermore, because of the 'fermentation' that the blood was thought to undergo in the heart's cavities (the centre and origin of all 'vital heat') their 'active' diastole

[1] Now called the pulmonary vein.

was augmented by the passive effect of this 'ebullition' pressing against the walls of the heart, thus the exit valves, or sigmoid valves, both of the *vena arteriosa* (our pulmonary artery) and of the great artery (the aorta), were forced open.

All of that we have said above about the separate distribution and peculiar origins of the two sorts of blood, the one in the liver and the other in the left heart, and of the paradox of the heart's emptying itself while expanding and filling while contracting, formed part of the classical doctrine taught in Harvey's time and, indeed, for long after his death. It is true that a few timid attacks had been made, almost furtively, on this system (notably by Servetus, Colombo and Caesalpinus, as we have seen), but they did not succeed in shaking the edifice of error.

D'Arcy Power has mentioned the curious positions occupied by two distinguished scientists, Harvey and Alexander Reid (the latter the junior by eight years, though in 1624 they were colleagues and Fellows of the Society of Physicians). They were both teaching between 1628 and 1634, Harvey in his Lumleian Lectures at the College of Physicians on Tuesdays, Wednesdays and Thursdays of each week, and Reid on Tuesdays only at the nearby headquarters of the Barber-Surgeons. Although Reid must have been acquainted with the arguments Harvey had been giving orally for at least fifteen years, he continued to teach an unmitigated Galenic doctrine. Power also shows how long Reid's interpretation of Galen's theories endured, for in 1637 the Scottish physician compiled a manual expounding the traditional ideas about the blood-stream. This book was reprinted in 1638, while editions were put out after his death in 1642, 1650, 1655 and 1658 without the slightest modification in the text. The old errors died hard.

An example of the opposition which the new doctrine had to face in France is afforded by the attitude adopted by Descartes. We shall see in the following chapter that Descartes did accept Harvey's general notion of a closed circulation of the blood, but he was resolutely opposed to the new theory of the action of the heart. He adhered obstinately to the ancient doctrine that the ventricles are expanded by the sudden 'vaporization' of small quantities of blood by the heat of the heart, the valves blowing open like 'safety valves'. The type of action pictured by Descartes's mechanistic mind resembled that of Denis Papin's celebrated 'saucepan' or *marmite*—or, indeed, that of an internal combustion engine. Descartes, in fact, here fell into the worst errors of Scholasticism, and invoked against Harvey's solid experimental results both 'common-sense' and the general opinion of established physicians—criteria that Descartes himself knew better than anyone must be regarded with suspicion.

In setting forth his own arguments (in some ten pages inserted in the middle of the *Discourse on Method*) Descartes would seem to have desired to display 'reasoning well conducted from simple and elementary evidence as leading to truth in science', and was so oblivious of his fallacies that he went so far as to stake his whole philosophy on the truth of his conclusions. In a letter he wrote to Father Mersenne (dated 9th of February, 1639) he wrote, 'I am quite ready to accept that if anyone should think that what I have written about this' (that is, the movements and mechanism of the heart) 'should prove false, all the rest of my philosophy is of nothing worth.' Nevertheless, Descartes's attempt to apply his Method to the subject of the heart led him into statements that are completely false.

Now we come to a consideration of the great work of demolition effected by Harvey and of the creation he substituted for the old edifice of error. Perhaps I may be allowed to repeat that in order to be quite impartial we must admit that Harvey was, at the beginning, influenced and guided by those of his precursors in the 16th century whose teachings had come to his ears. But when we compare their uncertain and half-hearted speculations with the masterly array of observed fact and experimental proof displayed in the *De Motu Cordis*, we are forced to accord to Harvey, unreservedly, the title of 'Discoverer of the Circulation of the Blood'. He alone was able to demonstrate, to prove and to display the whole process of the circulation in all its magnificent harmony.

After the criticism of the Galenic doctrines in the *Proemium* we have the seventeen chapters composing the book. Their titles are as follows:

Chapter   I.   Reasons the author had for dealing with this subject.
Chapter   II. What vivisection shows of the movements of the heart.
Chapter   III. What vivisection shows of the movements of the arteries.
Chapter   IV. What vivisection shows of the movements of the heart and the auricles.
Chapter   V. Mode of action and functions of the heart's movements.
Chapter   VI. The paths by which the blood is carried from the *vena cava* to the arteries, or again, from the right ventricle to the left ventricle of the heart.
Chapter   VII. The blood travels from the right ventricle of the heart, through the lungs, into the *arteria venosa* and the left ventricle.

Chapter VIII. Of the quantity of blood that passes through the heart to the veins and arteries and of the circulatory movement of the blood.

Chapter IX. The circular movement of the blood is proved from this first hypothesis verified.

Chapter X. The conclusion that a circulation of the blood is necessary is deduced from the abundance of it that traverses the heart, and is freed from objections and proved by experiment.

Chapter XI. A second hypothesis confirmed.

Chapter XII. From this second hypothesis, so confirmed, it appears that the blood follows a circular course.

Chapter XIII. A third hypothesis confirmed which, in its turn, proves the existence of the circulation of the blood.

Chapter XIV. Conclusion of the demonstration of the circulation of the blood.

Chapter XV. The circulation of the blood is indicated also by a number of other very probable considerations.

Chapter XVI. The circulation of the blood proved by its results.

Chapter XVII. The circulation of the blood established by means of observations which may be made on the heart, and by those which are quite obvious in dissections.

After this list of the chapter-headings of the *Exercitatio* of 1628, we shall endeavour, by making a few comments on the work, to exhibit the masterly train of thought which led to Harvey's irrefutable conclusions on the methods of the heart's action and of the circulation of the blood. The finer details were, however, to exercise his mind for many years after 1628. Indeed, the explanations then given are not quite the same as those in the Letters of 1649, as we shall see.

In Chapter I of the *Exercitatio*, on the 'reasons the author had for dealing with this subject', Harvey gives some account of the difficulties and discouragements he met with in determining the phases of the heart's rhythm, despite a great number of experiments on and observations of different kinds of animals, and of the light finally thrown upon the whole matter by an interpretation of the phenomena which he thought to be irrefutable. He felt under an obligation to communicate his views to all and sundry, since his adversaries had not hesitated to spread abroad misinterpretations of his ideas so as to cast ridicule upon him. He felt certain that the future would confirm his affirmations and accept his proofs, even if in certain details they might have to undergo that modification and correction from which no scientific work can be wholly immune.

In Chapter II Harvey begins an account of the observations and experiments he conducted not only on the human heart and on those of the more highly organized animals, but also on the hearts of cold-blooded creatures whose heart-beats are naturally very slow (*see* Fig. 10). In this way he solved the mystery of the heart's rhythm in many species of animals. Thus, he was able to perceive that (contrary to what had always been maintained) the heart is 'active' only in systole, that is to say when it becomes thickened and hardened like a contracted muscle, and when with its raised apex it touches the thoracic wall. He recalled the feeling of hardening, apparent if a finger is placed, during systole, on the heart of eels and other cold-blooded animals, while at the same time the heart becomes pale as though emptied of blood. Hence his conclusion that it is by the compression of the cardiac cavities caused by the heart's contraction that the blood is expelled, and that none enters the heart except during the dilatation or systole.

In Chapter III we have the statement that in Man as in all other animals the arteries, including those connected to the lungs, are distended in diastole at the times when the heart is contracted in systole, and that it is then that blood may be forcibly expelled from a punctured artery, while if the artery has suffered no damage we can, with the finger, feel the arterial pulse. This is further shown by the feebleness of the pulse in the extremities of the body when an aneurysmal 'pocket' nearer to the heart absorbs the blood impelled by the contraction of the heart. Harvey denies again that the arteries draw up the blood by the expansion of their tunics 'like a pair of bellows', holding that they become dilated solely because of the pressure of blood which comes from within, like 'bladders filling out with air or liquid poured into them'.

In Chapter IV Harvey deals with the auricles, whose proper movements are distinguished from those of the ventricles though their combined effect is two movements of the heart as a whole. First, the systole of the two ventricles: second, the diastole of the auricles and the simultaneous systole that empties the ventricles. The movement begins with the auricles and, in a dying heart, it is they which still flutter when the ventricles have already ceased their movement. Indeed, in such dying hearts (and normally in the hearts of fishes and other cold-blooded animals) we can observe a clearly defined pause between the alternating action of the auricles and ventricles. Furthermore, Harvey says, in hearts whose movements of contraction and dilatation have quite stopped, there can still be observed in the right auricle a kind of palpitatory movement of

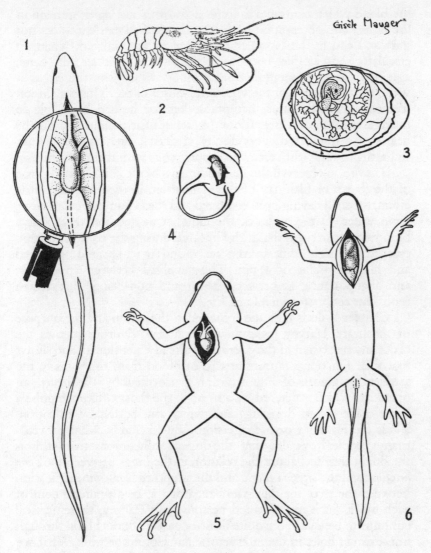

Gisèle Mauger

FIG. 10. Harvey found the slow heart action of the lower animals easy to observe and analyse, and examined, with the help of a magnifying-glass, the heart-beats of (1) the eel, (2) the shrimp, (3) the egg, (4) the snail, (5) the frog, and (6) the newt.

the blood which continues as long as warmth and 'spirit' remain in the heart. This observation leads him to ask if all existence does not start and end in the blood itself, and if in the embryo, when no circulatory organ has been formed, there is not already some agitation, some palpitation in the blood which constitutes, as it were, the foundation of the vital mechanism of life. This conclusion seemed to him the more acceptable because he had been able to make a number of observations (under similar conditions) on the hearts of a number of very lowly creatures, such as crustaceans, slugs, snails, squill-fish, etc. The chapter ends with these words:

'I have also observed the first rudiments of the chick in the course of the fourth or fifth day of the incubation, in the guise of a little cloud, the shell having been removed and the egg immersed in clear, tepid water. In the midst of the cloudlet in question there was a bloody point so small that it disappeared during the contraction and escaped the sight, but in the relaxation it reappeared again red and like the point of a pin. Thus evolved between appearance and disappearance, as between being and non-being, that which represents the first principle of life.'

Chapter V deals with the movement, the action and the purpose of the heart. Harvey recapitulates in a few vigorous phrases the order and succession of the operations already mentioned, and shows that their function is a transference of blood from the veins to the arteries by a sort of ingurgitation performed by the heart, an operation which is marked by a noise in the thorax (like the noise a horse makes when drinking) and which can be felt by palpation. These are Harvey's own expressions. But, he adds, what prevents many people from drawing the logical conclusions from this is the doubt they feel about the relation in the lungs between the *vena arteriosa* and the *arteria venosa*, and the supposed non-communication between the two, for they were regarded as being independent of each other. Such misinformed persons, says Harvey, therefore still continue to believe in the quite illusory passage of the blood through non-existent holes in the interventricular septum or wall. What we must therefore do, says he, is to demonstrate to them the real passage by which the blood is transmitted from the *vena cava* to the aorta— in a word, show the reality of the passage of blood through the lungs.

Such a demonstration is the subject-matter of Chapters VI and VII. The former explains the manner in which the blood passes from the *vena cava* into the arteries, and from the right to the left ventricle of the heart. The latter describes the way in which the blood passes

EXERCITATIO
ANATOMICA DE
MOTV CORDIS ET SAN-
GVINIS IN ANIMALI-
BVS,

GVILIELMI HARVEI ANGLI,
Medici Regii, & Professoris Anatomiæ in Col-

legio Medicorum Londinensi.

FRANCOFVRTI,
Sumptibus GVILIELMI FITZERI.

ANNO M. DC. XXVIII.

PLATE XV. The title-page of the first edition (1628) of Harvey's great work on the circulation of the blood (often referred to as the '*Exercitatio*' or '*De Motu Cordis*')

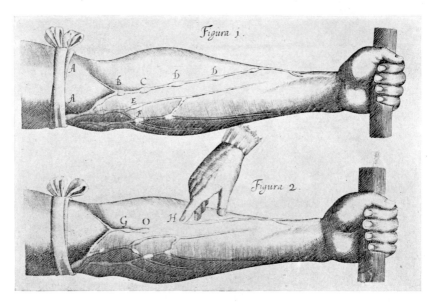

PLATE XVI. Two figures from the *Exercitatio* of 1628 illustrating the valves of the veins (artist unknown). The forearm is shown arranged for bloodletting. The upper arm is bound with a tourniquet to check the flow of blood to the heart and so distend the veins. The hand grasps a barber's pole

through the substance of the lungs from the right ventricle of the heart into the pulmonary veins.

What had hitherto prevented anatomists from discovering these facts, says Harvey, was their obstinacy in basing their theories solely upon Man and, indeed, upon human corpses. If these anatomists had had a care to vivisect animals as well as to dissect human bodies, all their hesitations would have vanished, as witness what we may learn from fish which, having no lungs, have but one auricle and one ventricle. These, he thought, correspond to the left heart of the human body, for he took the large vessels which emerge from a fish's heart to be the equivalent of the aorta (see Fig. 11).

I have shown on several occasions that this interpretation was erroneous.[1] Harvey considered that the single ventricle of fish is an arterial ventricle whereas it is a venous ventricle. The venous vessels which emerge from it lead towards the organs we call gills (whose significance and analogy with the lungs were unknown in Harvey's time). The gills were, in fact, looked upon as mysterious structures nourished like all other organs by the aorta, so that the vessels connecting the heart to them were identified by Harvey with the aorta. He was, of course, mistaken, but his error may, without hesitation, be called a felicitous one. It was this error of interpretation which led him to the idea of a direct and uninterrupted communication through the hearts of fishes from their *vena cava* (alias 'venous sinus') to the so-called 'artery-aorta' that leads out of the heart. And this erroneous conception was the origin and foundation of all Harvey's argument. True conclusions drawn from false premises!

Harvey contended that this supposed direct communication from *vena cava* to aorta through the heart of a fish was a constant and regular phenomenon to be observed throughout the animal kingdom, in the more primitive creatures throughout their lives, and in the more evolved creatures observable only in the foetus. He argued that in the more evolved animals, where there is at the moment of birth a complete closing up of the wall or septum dividing the two sides of the heart, the blood-stream whose passage is thus suddenly obstructed must find another which is open, and the only possible one is through the lungs. Harvey conceived of this 'long passage' as a mere equivalent of the short passage he thought that he had observed through the ventricles of fish and other creatures with gills, for he did not know that these latter organs are really lungs receiving venous blood (see Fig. 12).

[1] For example, in my '*Du coeur des Poissons . . . au coeur de l'Homme*', published in *La Presse Médicale* by Masson et Cie., Paris, January, 1953.

We must bear in mind that the significance and function of the lungs (whose duty Lavoisier was later to show is to supply oxygen to the body) were, for Harvey and all the men of his age, quite obscure and mysterious. He confesses, indeed, that in order to explain the functions of the lungs he was reduced to hypotheses, the most plausible of which we shall note below.

Throughout Chapter VI we get an excellent description of the foetal conditions in the more evolved animal species. First there is the oval aperture allowing of a direct passage of blood from the *vena cava* into the left auricle, the left ventricle and the aorta. Then,

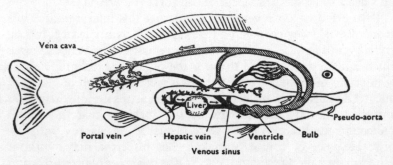

FIG. 11. Harvey's conception of the circulation of the blood in fishes. The function of the gills was at that time unknown and they were held to be mysterious organs situated in the path of the aorta. The vessel of the heart from which the aorta proceeded was assumed to be an arterial ventricle (corresponding with our left ventricle), a mistake which had happy consequences. See the text.

again, the arterial canal, a direct prolongation of the foetal *vena arteriosa* (our pulmonary artery) to the aorta at the point where it prepares to become descending. Why, at birth (in the more evolved and warm-blooded animals), does nature shut the short passage from the *vena cava* to the aorta and suddenly send all the blood by a long, roundabout route through the lungs? Perhaps, thought Harvey, because in the more highly organized animals (which by reason of their higher organization need warmer blood) the body-heat would tend to consume and suffocate them unless a continually repeated inhalation of fresh air from without did not temper the excessive heat of the blood that was being regenerated. Thus did Harvey look upon the function of pulmonary respiration.

But, apart from this 'explanatory hypothesis', Harvey's immediate aim was to demonstrate (in Chapter VII) that (*a*) the 'long' passage of blood through the lungs *could* take place, and (*b*) that it *does* take place. That it could take place is not difficult to conceive if we think of water seeping through compact soil, or sweat exuding from the skin, of urine issuing from the kidneys and (here a reference to Padua and to the water-drinkers of La Madonna) of the alimentary juices traversing the liver. These things are evident, but how much more easily, then, could the blood pass through the spongy mass of the lungs, which are alternately dilated and compressed and thus favourably disposed to transmit a current of blood?

That such a process actually took place might be deduced from the writings of Galen himself, who mentioned that during the

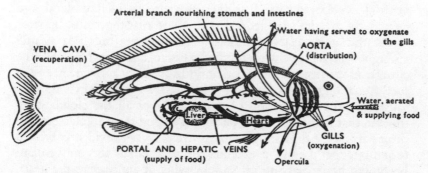

FIG. 12. The modern conception of the circulation of the blood in fishes. It is clear that what leaves the heart is venous—not arterial—blood, and that the term 'aorta' is properly applicable only to the vessel leaving the gills. The single heart of fishes is therefore a venous or right heart and a fish has no need of a left heart. See the text.

expiratory contraction of the thorax there were expelled the vapours that were contained in the intrapulmonary veins, and that during the expansion of inhalation these same veins (whose narrow passages were now somewhat distended) admitted a certain quantity of blood which was retained thanks to the closing of the entrance valve to the veins, called the sigmoid valve. And Harvey recalls the action of those valves which were well described by Galen, valves which, when blood was admitted from one direction, forced it onwards and never allowed it to flow back. It results from all this (both by reasoning and by experiment) that blood arrives continuously and uninterruptedly into the right ventricle of the heart, and that blood flows also constantly from the left ventricle. In these circumstances, it is quite impossible that there should not be a continuous flow from the *vena cava* through the lungs and the heart to the aorta. Here, Harvey once again put forward the argument that assuredly the right auricle, the right ventricle and the *vena arteriosa* would not be of such considerable size were their function merely to feed the lungs (as had always been taught). Their development could be explained solely by the continual impulse which they communicated to the blood on its way to the left ventricle and through the lungs.

In Chapter VIII Harvey demonstrates that the quantity of blood that the heart communicates to the arteries at each systole necessitates the existence of a circulatory movement of the blood-stream. The argument is briefly as follows. If we take into account the un-interrupted projection of blood that occurs at each systole, we shall see that if this blood did not return through the veins to the right ventricle we should have, first, the veins soon drained of blood, and second, the arteries so distended with blood that they must burst.

At this point Harvey makes a comparison (but it is a little ambiguous, it is true, owing to his mixture of analogies) between the circular movement of the blood and the apparent movement of the sun. According to its position with regard to the earth the sun causes (by the evaporation of water) first of all the clouds, then the rain that falls from them, and finally a return of the waters into the earth and the beginning of a new cycle. Harvey evidently wished to indicate that the blood executes a similar circulatory movement, becoming heated, giving off vapour when it approaches the heart, which is as a sun, and then growing colder as it retreats from the heart. But if we interpret this analogy as showing that Harvey adhered to the classical and religious dogma then in force—that is to say, that the sun described a circular movement round the earth—we must also admit that in Harvey's opinion the heart (the sun of our microcosm) also revolves—which is absurd.

So for Harvey's comparison to have any validity we must assume that he held the new Copernican doctrine, and regarded the heart, which is the fixed nucleus of our bodily microcosm, as a type of the sun, which is the fixed centre of the macrocosm—*i.e.* our universe. It is around the sun that the earth, with its seas and clouds, revolves, being carried farther from or nearer to the sun according to the seasons. Such surely is the sense in which we must under-stand two phrases standing near to each other in the text of the *Exercitatio*, namely that 'the blood, then, returns to its point of departure, that is to say the heart, as to its source in the centre of the body, there once more to assume its perfect condition', and again, 'the sun is worthy of being called the heart of the world', which presupposes, of necessity, that it is at the centre and fixed while it is its vassals or planets which draw near to it or away from it.

Thus Harvey, perhaps without meaning to say it, expresses the doctrine of Galileo who had already, in his Padua days, proclaimed himself a follower of the Polish canon, Copernicus, whose teaching was, thirty years later, to be condemned as heretical and subversive, but of which Harvey must have been fully aware.

But this comparison between heart and sun is only a digression from the main thesis of this chapter, namely that the circulation of the blood is proved by the necessity for the organs (to which blood flows in great quantities) to discharge blood into the veins, unless they are to burst through plethora.

At the beginning of Chapter IX, Harvey, in order to lay a solid foundation for his statements, submits three propositions which he proves by experiment in the following three chapters. The first proposition is that, under the action of the heart's contraction, blood flows unceasingly from the *vena cava* into the arteries, and in such quantities that no new blood formed by the aliments would suffice did not a part of the blood return to its source.

This proposition is proved by an estimate of the amount of blood passing through the heart, for such a calculation leads to the conclusion that, if we take the amount expelled at each systole to be but a drachm (though it must be at least three drachms) and if we estimate a minimum of a thousand heart-beats every half-hour (though the figure should be in fact between sixteen and eighteen hundred) there would already have passed through the heart in a half an hour a volume of blood considerably greater than all that contained in the body.

'But do not let us confine our observations to but half an hour, let us consider an hour and then a whole day. It will then be but the more evident that by its contractions the heart expels altogether much more blood than could be supplied by aliments or that the veins could contain. The incessant and rapid flow of the blood through the heart can also be proved by what we may observe when animals are slaughtered by the butcher. When the jugular vein is severed (as in swine, sheep and lambs) the mass of blood expelled by the heart, while it has not yet been completely stilled, drains out in less than a quarter of an hour. We may also note the rapid death of men by abundant haemorrhages. The arteries in all these cases, play as great a part as and indeed a greater part than, the veins which get their blood direct from the arteries, while the arteries receive blood from the veins, only through the heart. And this is what explains why, in a dead body, after the heart has ceased to beat, the veins remain full of blood while the arteries empty into the veins with the last pulsations of the heart and the last movements of the lungs. All this affords additional proof of the circulation of the blood from the veins to the arteries. Here we have also an explanation of why, when the heart-beats are very faint or almost imperceptible in lipothymic conditions or in syncopes, it is no longer possible to observe any haemorrhage from severed vessels. Since it is the heart-beats that command the movements of the arterial blood, it is easy to understand, again, why the butcher who has just felled an ox (unless he allows the blood to drain out by at once severing the carotid before the heart has quite ceased to beat) leaves in the body of an animal not thus opportunely bled a very great quantity of blood.'

By such remarks, presented by Harvey and adduced by him as proof of that general circulation of the blood he was the first to teach, we may learn how great were the powers of observation and the genius of reflection in the mind of this great man of science.

In Chapter X Harvey offers confirmation of his premiss, not only from observation but from effective experiment, thus, 'in serpents and several fish, by tying the veins some way below the heart you will perceive a space between the ligature and the heart speedily to become empty, so that unless you would deny the evidence of your senses, you must needs admit the return of the blood to the heart. ... If, on the contrary, the artery instead of the vein be compressed or tied, you will observe that the part between the obstacle and the heart and the heart itself becomes inordinately distended, to assume a deep purple or even livid colour, and at length to be so much oppressed with blood that you will believe it about to be choked; but the obstacle removed, all things immediately return to their natural state in colour, size, and impulse.'

Furthermore, it can be seen in a snake that if a ligature be applied to the section of vein entering the heart, as soon as that vein is emptied the heart, not receiving any more blood, becomes dis-coloured, pale and slows down; it then stops and is soon to all appearance dead. But if then the ligature is loosened the heart immediately resumes both its movements and its coloration. On the other hand, if a similar ligature be applied to the arteries shortly after the point where they leave the heart, we see that all that is above the ligature (and especially the heart) becomes turgescent, turns purple and is soon so full of blood that it threatens to burst and the heart soon stops. These two sorts of death, and death by the retention of arterial blood in the heart, fully confirm that there is a continuous circulation through the heart, from the veins to the arteries.

After furnishing these proofs that the blood flows from the *vena cava* through the lungs and the heart, Harvey sets himself in Chapter XI to confirm his second proposition: *i.e.* that in the members and in all parts of the body the blood passes from the arteries into the veins.

Here we have the celebrated experiments of ligatures applied to the limbs, and then we have the conclusions which are drawn from such experiments. Harvey remarks on the different effects observed when a ligature is drawn very tightly and when it is less constricted. He then notes that in the case of extreme constriction, such as is applied before the amputation of a limb, the hand (for instance) keeps its colour. Nothing flows from the strangulated veins, but the hand does not become swollen since no blood can reach it from the arteries, which are also tightly constricted. In fact, there is in the hand the *status quo ante* that the ligature was applied (*see* Plate XVI).

On the other hand, a loose ligature—such as that applied when a simple blood-letting is to be performed—does not constrict the arteries (which are embedded deeply) and so blood reaches the hand. However, the superficial veins are constricted so that the blood is hindered from leaving the hand and the portion of the limb below the ligature soon shows a considerable degree of venous turgescence; there is also a collapse of the veins in the portion of the limb above the ligature. If the ligature is then completely loosened we see the veins at the extremity of the limb subside and those in the upper part of the limb to appear filled once more, until a perfect equilibrium is established between the two areas. From this it follows clearly that the blood returns through the veins to the heart and that these, at their roots, are fed by the arteries, for when a ligature is drawn so tight as to compress the arteries the veins do not swell. For this reason we practise a blood-letting in the region between a moderately tight ligature and the extremity of the limb, and not in the region between the ligature and the heart. An attempted blood-letting in the latter region will give no results, and this proves that the venous blood does not flow from the heart to the extremities.

There is an amusing remark in this chapter, and one that shows that Harvey's faculty of observation was always remarkable when it came to his favourite studies. He once fell out of his carriage and the fall rapidly induced a large sero-sanguineous lump in his temporal region—*i.e.* at the side of his head. 'Immediately after the shock,' he writes, 'after about twenty heart-beats'—evidently he kept all his wits about him—'there arose a tumefaction about the size of a hen's egg that was not inflamed and gave me no great pain. By reason of the proximity of the artery the blood had flowed rapidly and in greater quantities than usual to the region of the contusion.'

D'Arcy Power makes some interesting comments on Chapter XI, especially with regard to Harvey's notions of the connection between the veins and arteries. Harvey deduced logically that such a communication must exist, but he did not actually observe the communicating vessels for his magnifying glass was not powerful enough. D'Arcy Power notes this, and then goes on to make some statements which I find difficult to accept. He says:

'Later commentators have given to Cesalpino the credit due to Harvey by translating "capillamenta" into our term "capillaries". But this process of "reading into" the writings of man what he never knew is one of the commonest pitfalls of defective scholarship.'

I think that here are two incompatible statements. First, we have referred earlier to the relevant texts of Caesalpinus and I cannot see anything to prevent us from holding that his word *capillamenta* is an equivalent term to our word 'capillaries', meaning the minute vessels whose existence Harvey suspected. Since Caesalpinus wrote that the blood which leaves the left ventricle through the aorta returns to the right auricle through the *vena cava* and that then the *vena arteriosa* carries the blood through the lungs to the *arteria venosa*, the same logical conclusion to which Harvey came (that is to say, that there must exist capillary passages connecting the arteries to the veins) must also have come to Caesalpinus. It does not seem to me that the latter's *capillamenta* can be confounded with Aristotle's *neura*, since the passages referred to by Caesalpinus are to be found in the lungs and in other parts of the body where there are no *neura* at all.

Second, it seems to me most unlikely that we can suppose Harvey could have remained in ignorance of Caesalpinus and his work during the three years or so that he spent at Padua. Caesalpinus was then still living and teaching in Rome. He enjoyed a very great reputation as an anatomist and 'naturalist'. His *Quaestiones Peripatericarum Libri V* and his *Quaestiones Medicarum Libri II* had only just (1593) been reprinted at Venice in an edition that soon became widely read, and Venice is but a few miles from Padua. Some British authors were among the first to recognize that Caesalpinus must have had some influence upon Harvey, since in the film made in 1928 (*see* p. 180) to commemorate the tercentenary of the publication of Harvey's Treatise, mention is specifically made of Caesalpinus as having contributed towards moulding Harvey's thought. That Harvey himself nowhere cites Caesalpinus (though he mentions

Colombo and Fabricius, both of whom were professors at Padua University) is most probably due to the fact that Harvey considered, not without justification, that his own personal contribution to the subject was so much more important than the almost casual allusions of Caesalpinus (who adduced hardly any proof of his contentions) that he had no reason to mention Caesalpinus at all. Indeed, there is in Harvey's work an entirely novel method of approach, and such a cohesion and co-ordination of argument and proof that nothing written on the subject before is of much value—save to show the incomparable superiority of the English physician.

D'Arcy Power makes also another remark—this time picturesque and historically true—concerning the imprecise and inconvenient means available in the 17th century for measuring the smaller subdivisions of time:

'The ordinary watch had only a single hand marking the hours, so that neither minutes nor seconds could be registered by them.' And he adds that according to Dr. Norman Moore, the pulse itself served for long to regulate the water-clocks and the number of pulse-beats was not measured by means of a watch until after the publication in 1707 of Sir John Floyer's book, *The Physician's Pulse-watch, or an Essay to explain the old art of feeling the Pulse*. But in Harvey's time, and long afterwards, physicians contented themselves with estimating the character of the pulse, rather than its precise rate.

Norman Moore, in referring to Mirfield's *Breviarium Bartholomei*, says: 'The mixture of prayers with pharmacy seems odd to us; but let it be remembered that Mirfield wrote in a religious house, that clocks were scarce, and that in that age and place time might not inappropriately be measured by the minutes required for the repetition of so many verses of Scripture or so many prayers. Thus Mirfield recommends that chronic rheumatism should be treated by rubbing the part with olive oil. This was to be prepared with ceremony. It was to be put into a clean vessel while the preparer made the sign of the cross and said the Lord's Prayer and an *Ave Maria*. When the vessel was put to the fire the Psalm "Why do the heathen rage" was to be said as far as the verse, "Desire of Me, and I shall give thee the heathen for thine inheritance." The *Gloria*, *Pater Noster*, and *Ave Maria* are to be said, and the whole gone through seven times. Which done, let that oil be kept. The time occupied I have tried, and found to be a quarter of an hour.'

But to return to Harvey's great work. In Chapter XII he summarizes and links up all that has gone before and shows the heart, the arteries and veins co-operating together to effect the complete circulation of the blood, as a necessary result of the preceding proofs. For instance, in practising phlebotomy the arm may be tied up properly and the puncture duly made, yet if from alarm or any other cause a state of faintness supervenes in which the heart pulsates more languidly, the blood does not flow freely but distils by drops only. But 'now a contrary state of things occurs when the patient gets rid of his fears and recovers his courage, the pulse strength is increased, the arteries begin again to beat with greater force, and to drive the blood even into the part that is bound, so that the blood now springs from the puncture in the vein, and flows in a continuous stream'.

Chapter XIII contains the confirmation of the truth of the third proposition advanced by Harvey at the commencement of Chapter IX. This stated that the veins must of necessity carry from each and all of the members, and uninterruptedly, the blood to the heart, and also conduct it round again in a continuous circulation. 'Now this remaining proposition will be made sufficiently clear from the valves which are found in the cavities of the veins themselves, from the uses of these, and from experiments cognizable by the senses.'

Then follows a very closely reasoned account of the venous valves which close by extending their free edges towards the centre of the vein, though towards the end of the vein they become progressively more open. 'This arrangement of the valves, although their discoverer (some say Fabricius of Aquapendente, or Sylvius according to Jean Riolan) did not rightly understand their role, is by no means explained as a method of preventing the blood from flowing into the lower parts of the body on account of its weight, for the edges of the valves in the jugular veins hang downwards, and are so contrived that they prevent the blood from rising upwards.' These valves also provide another proof that there is a current of venous blood flowing towards the heart, for if a probe be introduced into the opening of a vein it will be found that the instrument is obstructed by the valves, while if the probe be inserted from the opposite direction it passes by the valves more easily by pushing them aside. 'In fact, the valves interrupt any flow of blood that might attempt to pass from the heart towards the *venae cavae* . . . the valves also present a barrier to any passage of blood from the greater into the lesser veins, while the valves aid in the flow of blood from the lesser veins into the greater.'

Harvey then proceeds to show how all this may be confirmed by means of experiments with a ligature on an arm, and by the observations he made on the 'valvular nodules' thus caused.

The author begins his Chapter XIV by this statement: 'And now I may be allowed to give in brief, my view of the circulation of the blood, and to propose it for general adoption. Since all things, both argument and ocular demonstration, show that the blood passes through the lungs and heart by the force of the ventricles, and is sent for distribution to all parts of the body, where it makes its way into the veins and pores of the flesh, and then flows by the veins from the circumference on every side to the centre from the lesser to the greater veins, and is by them finally discharged into the *vena cava* and the right auricle of the heart.'

Thus, in this chapter, he recapitulates all the new doctrine. In the three last chapters, Nos. XV, XVI and XVII, Harvey seeks only to make still more plain his demonstration of the circulation of the blood. Chapter XV sets forth a number of reasons of a 'probable' nature and Chapter XVI the consequences to be drawn from facts that are to be daily observed in medical practice, and these are clearly explained. Chapter XVII contains much comparative anatomy relating to the heart, from which Harvey deduces that none other than a circulatory movement is possible.

If, after this rather detailed account of the ideas that Harvey developed in the *Exercitatio* of 1628, we move forward twenty years, we shall see what the great scientist, in his desire to explain to Riolan what he and others did not appear to have grasped, has to say in his *Exercitationes duae Anatomicae ad Johannem Riolanum, filium, Parisiensem*. Harvey used the phrase *quoniam multos video haerere*—'because I see many hesitate'—and we may observe that in this final recapitulation of his doctrine only one essential is changed, so firmly established was the original thesis.

In the Letters we have the same affirmations, the same demonstrations of the way the heart works, of the functions of the arteries, of the return of the blood by means of the veins—in a word, the same description of the circuit but with overwhelming answers to all possible objections. Despite his seventy-one years Harvey still shows himself to be an admirable dialectician, though one who always relied upon observation and upon carefully executed experiments.

In the First Letter Harvey once more denies the supposed lateral anastomoses, that is, the arterio-venous anastomoses which, according to Riolan, would permit of local and partial displacements of blood in certain regions of the body without there being any need for a general circulation. Furthermore, in the Second Letter he makes a witty attack upon those obliging 'spirits' which had been recklessly multiplied by some anatomists according to the needs of their theories, where they played the effective role of *Deus*—or rather *Dei*—*ex machina*. For Harvey, indeed, there was but one spirit, one sole 'vital force' which comes from the blood and, thanks to the circulation, is everywhere distributed by the blood.

In these two Letters additional proofs of the circulation of the blood are adduced. The explanations, indeed, are such that it is sufficient to read these Letters to obtain a thorough grasp of Harvey's conception and his way of proving his doctrine. Therefore I do not at all share the opinion of D'Arcy Power and others that the interest of the Letters is 'secondary'. Although I would agree with D'Arcy Power that the Letters refer, primarily, to certain points in the attacks which had been made on Harvey's discovery, still, I cannot think that these Letters 'are less clear', and still less that the Second Letter 'amidst a mass of unprofitable speculation . . . contains one or two gems of pathological observation'. I think, on the contrary, that it is to these Letters (and especially to the end of the Second Letter) that we must turn in order to see the final and definite expression of Harvey's thought concerning what he considered to be the reasons for the circulation.

These reasons are not quite the same as those imagined in 1628. Harvey's conceptions had, indeed, ripened and become perfected during meditations spread over twenty years. We may remember, however, that an 'interpretation' is after all a matter of opinion, and has not the same certitude as an enumeration of observed facts. Harvey's later 'explanation' undoubtedly accords better with the movement and mechanism of the heart, and I am rather astonished that none of the commentators on Harvey's work appears to have noticed this fact. But the two *Exercitationes* of 1649 are little read in the text and so are generally dismissed as being uninteresting *parerga* or very secondary works.

Perhaps we may follow the course of Harvey's thought. In his *Exercitatio* of 1628 he demonstrated the following sequence in the activities of the heart. First, a passive distension of the auricles, then their 'active' contraction with, as a consequence of this contraction, the filling and 'passive' distension of the ventricles. Second, the ventricles, acting in a way similar to that of the auricles, contract and expel the blood-stream, one ventricle sending blood into the pulmonary artery and the other into the great artery or aorta. Obviously, it could be thought that the distension is caused by the 'ferment' and 'heat' of the heart, which would put into a state of 'ebullition' the venous blood arriving in the heart. In 1628 this was, as a matter of fact, Harvey's position. He thought that it was in the right auricle that this fermentative dilatation of the blood began and that the blood thus distended the right auricle itself, immediately afterwards producing, *ipso facto*, the contraction of the auricle, and the auricle could justly be regarded as the true source of the regenerated blood.

But by 1649 this interpretation no longer completely satisfied Harvey, who was now inclined to see the 'fermentation' and 'ebullition' of the blood as taking place in the *vena cava* before the auricle was reached. The latter, then, dilated only when under the influence of the blood that reached it in full 'ebullition' from the *vena cava*. All this is admirably expressed in the remarkable passage at the end of the Second Letter where Harvey summarizes all his doctrine, a passage that begins *Quoniam multos video haerere*. This little-known passage is so interesting and important for the understanding of Harvey's real conception of the circulation of the blood, and of the logical point of departure of the blood circuit, that I give below the Latin text together with my translation:

> *Quoniam multos video haerere et de circulatione dubitare, et aliquos oppugnare ea quae de me non penitus intellexerunt, in eorum gratiam breviter quid dictum velim, quae ex libello de cordis et sanguinis motu, recapitulabo. Sanguis in venis contentus (suo quasi fundo), ubi coposissimus (in vena scilicet cava) juxta cordis basim et auriculam dextram, sensim ab interno suo calore incalescens, et attenuatus turget et attolitur (fermentantium in modum) unde auricula dilatata, sua facultate pulsifica se contrahens, propellit eum confestim in dextrum cordis ventriculum qui, impletus. . . .*

> Since I see many people hesitate and doubt about the circulation and some even to oppose and attack that which they have not well understood in me, I wish to recapitulate briefly for them what I wanted to say and what this little book expresses regarding the motions of the heart and the blood. The blood that is contained in the veins (as in its proper place) and which is especially accumulated in the *vena cava* near the base of the heart and the right auricle, becoming warmed there by a faculty of heat inherent in it, becomes heated so as to give off vapour and rises into it (in the manner of substances in a state of fermentation). Thus the auricle becomes filled with it and then contracts owing to its own property of contractibility, thus forcing the blood into the right ventricle of the heart which, in its turn, fills. . . .

Thus it is quite clear that in 1649 it was in the *vena cava*—*in vena scilicet cava juxta cordis basim et auriculam dextram*—that Harvey conceived the blood to enter into 'fermentation' and to 'overflow' —*fermentantium in modum*—while it was not until afterwards that the auricles became filled and dilated—*unde auricula dilatata*. First of all the *vena cava*, and then the auricle; that is the order and sequence well expressed by the word *unde* 'from there', 'from that place'. The initiative, so to speak, in all these operations lay so little, in Harvey's opinion, in the motor or heart, that (several pages farther on and in a memorable declaration) he solemnly dethrones the heart from the position of 'initiator'. The remarks are addressed to those who would make him support this heresy which, moreover, we still blatantly persist in attributing to him, although the error is but our own. Says Harvey:

'If, in truth, we understand by this term "heart" the substance only of the heart itself with its ventricles and auricles, I do not believe that it is the regenerator of the blood, nor do I think that the blood receives, as coming from the heart, its force, its virtue, its essence, its animation or its heat. . . .'

Is not this categorical enough?

Harvey, then, in 1649, placed the 'fermentative' and re-generating processes of the blood in the *vena cava*, and he considered, therefore, that the *vena cava* was the starting-point of his circulation of the blood. I think I am right in stating that no one, up to now, has pointed out or noted this final expression of Harvey's views—the results of his meditations and reflections made since the publication of the *Exercitatio* in 1628. If we refer only to the book of 1628 we shall conclude that Harvey attributed to the heart the function of recharging of the blood with 'heat' and 'vital spirit'. But the motor action of the heart cannot be adduced as a valid reason for the start of the circulation, for a pump that propels a flow of water along a sluggish stretch of a river cannot be regarded as the source of the river. If, then, the fermentative process in the heart causes the blood to be recharged with heat and 'vital spirit' in that organ, Harvey's explanation in 1628 might justify the start of the circulation in the heart, how much better does the interpretation of 1649 (that of 'fermentation' in the *vena cava*) agree with the successive operations performed by the auricles and the ventricles!

For these reasons I have frequently declared, and still insist, that to read the *Exercitatio* of 1628 is not enough for a proper appreciation of Harvey's teaching. We must read also the two Letters of 1649. I venture to think that those who have not realized this cannot fully understand Harvey's mature conception, but I shall have more to say on these matters in the last chapter. For Harvey, as for all the men of his day, the essential function of the blood was to distribute to all the organs of the body both 'heat' and 'vital spirit'—*calorem et spiritum*. Consequently he held by an unhappy *a priori* assumption (the only one, I think, that Harvey advanced without the support of experiment and observation) that the blood must be deprived of 'heat' and 'spirit' on leaving the organs.

Harvey was, however, deprived of all means of exploring and of checking the condition of the blood, and therefore it was quite logical that he should expect it to return to the *vena cava* 'cool and devitalized' after delivering its 'heat' and 'vital spirit' to the organs. It then occurred to him that it must be in the *vena cava* that a regeneration of the blood must take place. The principles that had been lost in the organs were here renewed, thanks to a fermentation like that of new wine in a barrel, by which both heat and spirit are released. Harvey's own words are *sicut calorem et spiritum vini*.

In several passages, notably in the Second Letter, he discusses this comparison. He likens the 'vital spirit' to the 'subtile spirit' that is distilled by wine and by which this liquid manifests its virtue and energy. The ancient mystical ideas, as old as Man's history, died hard, for they had dominated all the ancient world and that of the Middle Ages. Men would always compare the two liquids, blood and wine, and Harvey's mind (in its efforts to explain the 'regeneration' of the blood) could not free itself of this venerable myth. The old image of heat and spirits of wine, of heat and the spirit of blood, loomed up before him and suggested to him the best interpretation that he could discover. It may be that here I have been able to point out another hitherto unrecognized fact, though it seems to me that if we read Harvey's texts with attention what I have advanced can hardly be denied.

I have ventured to base my story of Harvey's walk in the Padua countryside (*see* Chapter III) on his undoubted powers of generalization and his powerful ratiocinative mind and there cannot be much doubt that then, already in his Italian university days, the antique myth of Blood and Wine occupied his thoughts, though maybe in a more or less confused manner. So, the regeneration of the blood must take place in a central 'vat' or 'retort', and this he placed first of all in the heart, and then, later on, in the *vena cava*.

Now that we have delved as deep as possible into the main and fundamental works of Harvey, the *Exercitatio* of 1628 and the two Letters of 1649, we may turn to the *De Generatione Animalium*, which is a collection of notes brought together over a long term of years but not published until 1651, at the request (as we have seen) of

Dr. (later Sir George) Ent, Harvey's adept and disciple. But before we attempt an analysis of the *De Generatione* we must mention what Harvey says in Exercise No. 67 of the *De Generatione* regarding the deplorable loss, during the pillage of the Civil War, of his MS. on Insects. He writes:

'While I am discussing these things I must crave indulgence of my readers, if in recalling the irreparable losses I have suffered I allow myself the expression of regrets. The reason of my grief is this: while I was giving my professional services to His Majesty the King during the recent troubles, or rather civil wars, not only with the permission, but also on the orders of the Parliament, pillagers sacked my house of all its furniture, and, what is worse and causes my keenest sorrow, carried off my museum, and fruit of several years of assiduous research and observations. Thus a great number of my notes perished, especially those on the generation of insects, to the detriment, I think I may say, of the Republic of Letters.'

Now let us consider the text of the *De Generatione* itself. This was published simultaneously at Cambridge and Amsterdam in 1651 under the supervision of Dr. Ent, whose dedicatory epistle to the College of Physicians we give in full on pages 153 to 156. *De Generatione animalium* is a small but thick octavo volume of 568 pages, and Harvey introduces the work with a Preface on his method of studying natural science. Then come seventy-nine 'exercises' and the following '*Addimenta*': *de Partu, de Uteri membranis et humoribus*, and *de Conceptione*. We must say at once that, despite the aim and scope of this thesis, the *De Generatione* is far from having the importance of the two documents concerning the circulation of the blood. The *De Generatione*, moreover, is not so well ordered nor so coherent as the *Exercitatio* and the Letters, and it gives rather the impression of being a collection of stray notes brought together without any overriding general plan. Of course, one of the main reasons for this is that Harvey's material means for investigating the puzzling problems of generation were very inferior to those he had at his disposal for the observation of the movements of the heart and the blood. What, indeed, can be done in this matter without a microscope, except a little preliminary and rough research? To gain any exact knowledge of the processes of generation and reproduction we must at least have a knowledge of the spermatozoon, of which the first mention was made a few years after Harvey's death when the Dutch scientist, Leeuwenhoek, had invented and perfected his new optical instrument. Moreover, for a hundred years and more after Leeuwenhoek's time the nature and functions of the spermatozoon were subjects of controversy and the most violent discussion.

In order to give a just idea of the quality of Harvey's *De Generatione*, we cannot do better than to quote from the really masterly study of this work by the late Dr. H. P. Bayon, which was published (between Jaunary, 1938, and October, 1939) in the *Annals of Science* under the title 'William Harvey, Physician and Biologist: his Precursors, Opponents and Successors'.[1] The following excerpt will be found on pages 72 *et seq.*:

'*De generatione* can be considered to some extent a commentary on the posthumously published *De formatione ovi et pulli* (Patavii— *i.e.* Padua—1621) of Gerolamo Fabrizio da Aquapendente (1537–1619) with whose conclusions Harvey respectfully and yet frequently disagreed.

'No less than 62 out of the 72 "Exercises" of *De generatione* refer to matters connected with fowl embryology, together with anecdotal matter, which at times reminds the reader of Pliny, as, for example, with regard to Mrs. Harvey's parrot (*Exer. 5*). Still there are numerous observations of lasting interest; for Harvey recognized the *bursa Fabricii*, the vestigial organ first described by Gerolamo Fabrizio, which the Paduan anatomist thought was a receptacle in the hen for the semen of the cock, thus explaining the (erroneous) lasting insemination of hens. Harvey noted that the bursa was present in both pullets and cockerels, and that it did not contain semen (*Exer. 5*). As to its proper function, we are still in the dark, just as Harvey was. Fabrizio believed that one mating was sufficient to fertilize all the eggs during a season; Harvey controlled the statement by experiment and found that fertile eggs were still laid twenty days after separation from the cock (*Exer. 6*). Spallanzani (1784) confirmed this and in recent researches Curtis and Lambert observed that the mean duration of fertility was about 11 days with 21 days as the extreme limit (*Poultry Science*, 1929, 8, 142), though Crew secured a fertile egg 32 days after the removal of the cock (*Proc. Roy. Soc. Edin.*, 1926, 46, 230).

'Fabrizio considered that the chick originated from the chalazae, which Ulisse Aldrovandi (1522–1605) thought were the cock's

[1] Published by Taylor & Francis, Ltd., London. I should like to take this opportunity of paying a tribute to the memory of my distinguished British *confrère*, Dr. Bayon, from whose work I have borrowed freely. I owe my introduction to his researches to Sir Geoffrey Keynes, who was kind enough to send me a bound reprint of the *Annals of Science* papers.

sperm. Harvey showed that both views were wrong and that the chalazae performed a simple mechanical function. He then observed that the chick originated in what Fabrizio called the *cicatricula* (*Exer.* 2 and 44) since he believed it represented the scar where the yolk had detached itself from the ovary. Harvey remarked that it was not a *cicatrix* or scar (*Exer.* 61).'

Dr. Bayon discovered in a book by Sir Thomas Browne (1605–82), called *Pseudodoxia Epidemica or, Enquiries into Very many Received Tenents, And commonly presumed TRUTHS* (London, 1658, Book iii, Chap. xxviii, p. 151), this interesting remark:

> . . . and how in the Cicatricula or little pale circle formation first beginneth, how the Grando or tredle, are but the poles and establishing particles of the tender membrans, firmly conserving the floating parts in their proper places, with many other observables, that occular Philosopher and singular discloser of truth, Dr. *Harvey*, in that excellent discourse of Generation; So strongly erected upon the two great pillars of truth, experience and solid reason. That the sex is discernible from the figure of egg, or that Cocks and Hens proceed from long or round ones, as many contend experiments will easily frustrate.

Dr. Bayon further states that:

'Numerous other details are recorded by Harvey, but of more interest are his opinions in relation to general biological laws and principles. For example, Fabrizio taught that the process of embryonic development was essentially a metamorphosis; Harvey admitted this in relation to insects, but by apt observations in animals with red blood he confirmed the Aristotelian doctrine of epigenesis of successive formation of parts (*Exer.* 45).

'This is a positive achievement to Harvey's credit, because for a whole century after his time the hypothesis of preformation held the field; this was originally propounded by the physician Giuseppe degli Aromatari (1588–1660), who in his *Epistola de Generatione Plantarum ex Seminibus* (Venice, 1625) said:

> 'As to the chick hen's egg, we consider that the chick is sketched out in the egg before being formed by the hen.'

Harvey mentions having met Aromatari in Venice (*Exer.* 11). Cole remarks:

> 'Such was the simple beginning of an hypothesis which was to hang like a millstone round the neck of the embryologist for over a century.'

Bayon then names the main upholders of this preformation hypothesis: Nathanial Highmore (1613–84), Henry Power (1625–68), Jan Swammerdam (1637–80), Marcello Malpighi (1628–94)—Malpighi thought he could discern the form of an embryo in an unincubated egg—William Croone (1633–84), Charles Bonnet (1720–93)—who corresponded actively with Spallanzani (1729–99). The doctrine flourished for more than fifty years after the appearance of *Theoria Generationis* (Halle, 1759), a remarkable dissertation by Caspar Friedrich Wolff (1733–94), who, by means of accurate microscopical observations and sound reasoning, showed that if organs were preformed, then they would increase in size, not alter in shape, while the chick develops out of unformed elements as the result of what he calls *vis essentialis*.

Bayon continues:

'It can be granted that Wolff was too radical in some of his conclusions, for modern researches on egg-axes and the generic disposal of characters by chromosomes allow the admission of a slight degree of preformation or, more exactly, predetermination.

'Admittedly, many of the numerous authors, like Malpighi or Spallanzani, who supported preformation obtained their opinions from actual observations, which they wrongly interpreted, while Harvey asserted his belief in epigenesis, in all probability for the purpose of agreeing with Aristotle. But it can be said that Harvey was right while others were wrong, so that his work was not a complete failure in the end.'

Then Bayon, under the title of *A Slightly Inaccurate Quotation*, deals with the question of the famous phrase incorrectly attributed to Harvey, *omne vivum ex ovo*, and shows that if such was indeed the general sense of his belief he expressed it in other terms. For instance, *Exer.* 51 is headed *Ovum esse primordium commune omnibus animalibus*. The much-discussed picture opposite the title-page in *De Generatione* (1651) shows a figure of Jupiter holding in his hand an egg whence issue different sorts of animals and also a spider. On the egg is the legend *ex ovo omnia*. It was Wahlbom who wrote in 1746 that 'Harvey also long ago exclaimed *omne vivum ex ovo*', and this is the source of the modern misquotation.

Bayon points out that in identifying the mammalian embryo in its membranes with the primordial egg, Harvey had perceived but part of the truth:

'The recognition of the true mammalian ovum was a matter requiring considerable microscopical skill and was accomplished by Carl Ernst von Baer (1792–1876) in *De Ovi Mammalium et*

Hominis Genesi (Lipsiae, 1827): the exact date of the observation is in doubt, but it is worth recording that von Baer obtained his results by working backwards from embryo to ovum instead of trying to detect the "egg" in the ovary.'

This conception of *omne vivum ex ovo* leads us to the subject of spontaneous generation and Harvey's texts. Although the possible appearance of life from elements thought to be inert or deteriorated is once more being discussed, the modern discovery of crystalline viruses is very far removed from the ancient and absurd idea that highly evolved organisms could be generated from waste material. Nothing can be adduced from Harvey's texts to prove that he adhered to the thesis of generation without a 'generator', either male or female. Harvey's opinion was, indeed, directly opposed to such concepts, as we may see (making due allowance for the reticent language employed) from this passage in *Exer.* 40:

'But on these points we shall say more when we show that many animals, especially insects, arise and are propagated from elements and seeds so small as to be invisible (like atoms flying in the air), scattered and dispersed here and there by the winds; and yet these animals are supposed to have arisen spontaneously, or from decomposition, because their ova are nowhere to be found.'

Now let us consider the normal process of generation as it was conceived in Harvey's mind, and let us see how he regarded the fertilization of those eggs destined to give rise to living animals. Harvey does not appear to have dealt with the problem of parthenogenesis, at least not in the way in which we should approach it today, although it is almost permissible to say that he seems to have had an inkling of it in the hypothesis (which he did not reject out of hand) that the activity and development of the maternal ovum may be excited without direct contact with the male fluid but by the action of this at a distance.

Dr. Bayon says, 'by suitable observations and cogent reasoning he made clear the error of Aristotle's hypothesis that conception was due to the mixing of sperm with menstrual blood (*Exer.* 40)'.

After having examined the oviducts of fowls and the wombs of mammals, Harvey thought he was justified in denying that they contained free blood or that semen could reach the uterus. Indeed, he seems to have decided that sperm could exercise its influence at a distance 'like the essence of the stars' (*Exer.* 50), about which Bayon remarks, 'In presenting these views, Harvey becomes discursive and shows a definite astrological bias, which is reminiscent of Fludd's writings.'

Robert Fludd (1574–1657) was an exact contemporary of Harvey and was, moreover, a strange and prolix author. This English physician (who calls himself *armiger et in medicina doctor oxoniensis* on the title-page of his many books) wrote between 1600 and 1657 a number of works, several of which were published in Germany at either Oppenheim or Frankfort. One of them (*Medicina Catholica*, i.e. *Universal Medicine*) was printed in 1629 at Frankfurt by W. Fitzer (apparently an Englishman) who, the year before, had printed Harvey's *Exercitatio*. Bayon discovered in one of Fludd's compilations (*Integrum Morborum Mysterium*, Frankfurt, 1631), in the third part of the third section, which is devoted to the 'Science of the Pulse', the first known printed mention that is favourable to Harvey and his *De Motu Cordis et Sanguinis*. For a long time this remark was to remain the only one of its kind. It runs:

> My most dear countryman and colleague, W. Harvey, a distinguished anatomist and a profound philosopher, has confirmed and declared, with many ocular demonstrations, that blood moves in a circuit.

Fludd was a Rosicrucian of mystical tendencies and his vivid imagination saw the cosmos as full of symbolism. He made these matters the subject of his books and his solemn addresses on such things to his patients must have secured him no little renown and success in his profession. It must, however, be admitted that this astrologically and possibly alchemistically minded physician was a man of keen observation who conducted a number of remarkable experiments. He divined several of the laws of physics and dynamics and was, indeed, in some ways not only a subtle thinker but one in advance of his age. Pagel (in the *Bulletin J. H. Inst. Med. Hist.*, 1933) has pointed out that if Fludd so soon accepted Harvey's doctrine of the circulation of the blood, it was probably because he saw in it one of those 'circles' that agreed with his ideas on the relation of Man to the universe. Fludd has, moreover, approached the problems of generation on his own account and linked them with his theory of the three spheres or circles—those of the heart, the liver and the brain. It would not seem, however, that Fludd had any appreciable influence upon Harvey, a man who relied so entirely upon his own personal researches. But both Fludd and Harvey broke away from the beaten track, the one with his fanciful ideas about the cosmic influences of the universe, and the other with his admirably explicit and well-demonstrated theory of the circulation of the blood.

But to return to Harvey and the problems of generation and

fertilization. Bayon pertinently points out that such a skilful anatomist as Harvey would have been able to conduct such experiments as artificial insemination, after ligature of the oviduct, and that these would have shown him the truth or the falsity of his theories. We must, however, remember that in Harvey's time there was still much discussion as to whether the oviducts played any part at all in the processes of reproduction. It was only in 1656 that Thomas Wharton (in his *Adenographia*, Cap. XXXIII, London) suggested that fertilization was effected by the sperm reaching the 'female testicles' (*i.e.* the ovaries) through the uterus and the Fallopian tubes. And it was in 1672 that Reinier de Graaf (1641–73), in his *De Mulierum Organis Generationis Inservientibus* (printed at Leyden by Lugduni Batavorum), demonstrated that he had by observation and by methodical experiment upon female rabbits proved the generative function of the vesicles of the ovaries.

Harvey, of course, knew nothing of the male element, the spermatozoon, since it was only in 1677 that Leeuwenhoek revealed its existence by means of the microscope. Furthermore, despite Leeuwenhoek's discovery controversy was to rage for a century or more between the 'Ovists' and the 'Animalculists', since the great Spallanzani himself still affirmed as late as about 1780 that the male seed or sperm, when deprived of its animalcules, still retained its fecundating properties. Furthermore, at the beginning of the 19th century John Haighton (1755–1828) thought himself justified in concluding from a great number of experiments that 'the ovaries can be affected by the stimulus of impregnation without the contact either of palpable semen or of the *aura seminalis*'. Again, in 1822 and in 1828, in *Observations on the Changes the Egg undergoes during the Incubation in the Common Fowl*, Sir Everard Home (1758–1832) managed to conclude that the spermatozoa were the figment of imagination and error!

If we know today that reproduction by means of the conjunction of two distinct substances, male and female, is the general rule among evolved animals and plants, we must not forget that among more lowly living creatures there are modes of reproduction which are of a different sort, where new individuals, so to speak, bud out of organisms that are apparently sexually undifferentiated, as soon as these have reached a certain stage of maturity. Moreover, in quite highly organized living creatures there occur, from time to time (as though to remind us of the primitive tendency to reproduction without bisexual conjunction), cases of asexual reproduction, admittedly rare and abnormal but recalling the immemorial past.

Now that we have shown, from a consideration of *De Generatione Animalium*, the kind of problem that presented itself to Harvey's mind (a kind often insoluble for him and his contemporaries yet well within his powers of definition), we may conclude our account of the book. Its insufficiencies are redeemed by Harvey's treatment of his last subject—*De Partu, i.e.* parturition, the last act of the mystery of generation. Here, he had to deal with obstetrical problems, one of which seemed to him to be in direct contradiction with Fabricius's theories. Fabricius thought, quite justifiably, that the ejection of the foetus resulted from the combined contractions of the abdominal muscles (we should say today the abdomino-pelvic) and those of the uterus. Harvey, on the other hand, tended to minimize the role of the abdominal muscles and he justified his point of view by several rather impressive facts observed in cases of spontaneous parturition in animals whose bellies had been ripped open. Harvey was, in this matter, influenced by a discovery he had already made concerning the supposed appeal of the chick in the egg. The traditional belief was that the chick makes little noises which incite the mother-hen to crack the shell with her beak and thus allow the chick to emerge, but by a number of observations and experiments Harvey showed that it is the chick itself that makes the hole necessary for its emergence. No doubt he thought that the mammalian foetus might act in a somewhat similar manner, *motu proprio*, and itself make its way out of the enveloping womb once the time for birth had arrived. We know today that, normally, there is a simultaneous action of both sets of muscles; that is to say, the uterus contracts within the body and the abdomino-pelvic muscles also contract in the surface of the body.

Perhaps we have now said enough about *De Generatione Animalium* in its various aspects—at least, enough to give the reader some idea of the labours that occupied Harvey's time and to which he devoted so much of his prodigious intellectual activity. The *De Generatione* is valuable for the light it throws upon the history and philosophy of the whole subject of generation, though there is one important point in that history which Harvey mentions not in *De Generatione* but in the *De Motu Cordis*, at the end of his embryological observations quoted in support of his new doctrine of the circulation of the blood.

It was, perhaps, no more than an inspired guess of Harvey's genius, yet it foreshadowed the doctrine of 'recapitulation' which was, two hundred years later, to lay the foundation of the doctrine of the origin of species. It seems that Harvey was the first to have suggested that during the time of development that elapses between fecundation of the egg (of any given species) and the birth of the fully-formed individual, there occurs what may be regarded as a repetition, or an abbreviated version, of the slow and progressive stages traversed by living matter from the most primitive creatures to the stage in evolution of the species in question.

In a word, as the modern terminology has it, ontogenesis presents a kind of abridged 'cinematographic' review of the gradual modifications to be observed all along the phylogenetic chain of the species. It is, of course, true that today we no longer hold that there exists an absolutely faithful recapitulation of all the history of the phylum. There are many trials and errors, and forms appear which look as though they were headed for one direction but then develop quite differently. It is nonetheless true that we can recognize the general history of the line or phylum in the particular history of the foetal development of the individual that is the heir of that phylum.

In connection with this pregnant suggestion, which, as we have said, lies at the basis of the modern doctrine of evolution, it is interesting to listen to a son of Geoffroy Saint-Hilaire pay homage to the priority of Harvey's suggestions. My friend, the eminent biologist Jean Rostand—to whom, I may say in passing, I owe much for the encouragement he has given me during the writing of this book—was good enough to send me the following extract from a work entitled *Vie, travaux et doctrine scientifique d'Etienne Geoffroy Saint-Hilaire*, published in Paris in 1847 by his son Isidore. He is referring to an essay dealing with the bony head of vertebrates, published in 1806:

'What then is lacking if the method of anatomical philosophy is not to be found in its entirety on the first page of this memoir? One idea only—that of the analogy presented by the transitory and impermanent character of the more evolved animals with the permanent characters of less evolved creatures. Now, this all-embracing and most important idea, although in a measure grasped by Harvey as early as the 17th century . . .'

Isidore Geoffroy Saint-Hilaire quotes in support of his reference to Harvey the following words from the *Exercitationes de Generatione Animalium* (Chapter XII):

Sic natura perfecta et divina, nihil faciens frustra, nec cuipiam animali cor addidit, ubi non erat opus, neque, priusquam esset ejus usus, fecit, sed iisdem gradibus in formatione cujuscumque animalis, transiens per omnium animalium constitutiones (ut ita dicam: ovum, vermem, foetum,) perfectionem in singulis acquirit.

The following would seem to me to be the faithful and exact translation of this important passage:

Thus perfect and divine nature does nothing in vain, has not given a heart to every sort of animal, nor has, in those which possess a heart, introduced it before the need for it presented itself. But, for all animals, nature advances in successive stages (as I would say: egg, embryo, foetus) by the same stages until there is reached the perfection proper to each species.

Isidore Geoffroy Saint-Hilaire continues:
'We must say that it is from the starting-point of these views, that Harvey expressed as early as 1651 in his *Exercitationes de Generatione Animalium*, that we have come today to give the explanations of certain organic anomalies. The way from Harvey was followed in the 18th century by Haller, Wolf and especially by Autenrieth.'

The *De Generatione Animalium*, published in 1651 at the demand of and under the auspices of Dr. Ent, the *Exercitatio Anatomica de Motu Cordis et Sanguinis* of 1628, and the *Exercitationes Duae* of 1649, are usually regarded as the *Opera Omnia* of Harvey. No doubt we can find sidelights on his temperament in thoughts contained in his Notes (*Praelectiones* for the 'visceral' and 'muscular' lectures) and in those letters addressed by him or to him which have been preserved. We have referred to these, here and there, in the course of this book, when it was sought to portray Harvey as a man. We must now consider the sort of reception accorded to Harvey's many novel, original and even revolutionary theories, especially those relating to the motions of the heart and the blood.

Chapter IX

The Judgement of Contemporaries and of Posterity

Attacks against the doctrine of the circulation of the blood—Primerose, Plempius, Parisanus—Opposition from the Faculties of Medicine at the Paris and provincial universities—Riolan, Gui Patin, etc.—The 'hybrid' case of René Descartes—A victory for experiment over theory—Louis XIV and his surgeon Dionis—Harvey's theory taught by Royal Order in the *Jardin du Roy*—Valuable support given to Harvey's discovery by the Men of Letters of the *Grand Siècle*—Molière, Boileau, La Fontaine and others instructed by Dionis—Scathing criticism by Dionis of Descartes's anatomy and physiology—Increasing support of Harvey's teaching among scientists at the end of the 17th and beginning of the 18th centuries—Steno, Lower, Willis, Malpighi, Leeuwenhoek, Rusch, Vieussens, Sénac—Surprising silence of Sydenham, Van Helmont, Stahl and the 'phlogisticians'—Offray de la Mettrie: his pertinent judgements on Harvey and Descartes

HARVEY'S marvellous constructive work, in its two essential aspects—that of the movement of the heart and that of the circulation of the blood—became the object of violent, even passionate, attacks immediately after the publication of the *Exercitatio*. Although, little by little, there was formed a party favourable to the doctrines of Harvey, the 'anti-circulators' conducted a ferocious campaign of ridicule from Venice, Paris, Leyden, and in London itself.

In addition to the French opposition which, as we shall soon see, was led by Riolan and Gui Patin (supported by almost all the professors at the faculties of medicine), the most immediate and vindictive opposition was displayed by three individuals, namely Primerose in England, Parisanus in Venice and Plemp in the Low Countries. It will be sufficient if we deal with the 'anti-circulators' by examining the attitudes of these three men, since many of their objections were widely shared by others.

218

The British physician James Primerose (1592–1659) was, perhaps, the leader of the opposition to Harvey's doctrines in England. Of Scots origin and, moreover, the son and the brother of physicians, Primerose was born in the French province of Saintonge (now the Charente Maritime department) at Saint-Jean d'Angély, about the year 1592. After studying first at Bordeaux and then at Paris (thanks to the generosity of James I) Primerose was capped doctor at Montpellier in 1617. Later, he went to Oxford and then to the town of Hull, Yorkshire, where he died in 1659, two years after Harvey. We have already noted (in Chapter V) that at the end of 1629 Primerose came to London where, on 9th December, he passed his examination for the licentiate of the College of Physicians, Harvey being at that time one of the eight Elects from among whose number the three examiners were always chosen. It may be, indeed, that Harvey was among these latter when Primerose passed his examination.

However that may be, the Scots physician published in the following year (1630) his first dissertation *Against the Thesis of Harvey*, and, as Bayon points out, this was the first attack on Harvey that was actually printed. The full title of the book is *Exercitationes et Animadversiones in Librum de Motu Cordis et Sanguinis adversum Guillelmum Harveum* (London, 1630). A physician of repute and a man of undoubted honesty, Primerose was unlucky enough to cherish throughout his life quite erroneous views concerning the circulation of the blood. In 1639, and again in 1640, he renewed his attacks, though this time they were directed against two of Harvey's followers. These two works of Primerose are entitled, respectively, *Animadversiones in Johannis Walleii Disputationem quam pro Circulatione Sanguinis proposuit* (Amsterdam, 1639), and *Animadversiones in Theses quas pro Circulatione Sanguinis in Academia Ultra Jectinei Henricus Le Roy proposuit* (Leyden, 1640).

Parisanus (Emilio Parisano) was an Italian born at Rome in 1567. He studied at Padua under Fabricius da Aquapendente (before Harvey's time) and then practised at Venice, where he died in 1643. Parisanus was rather a poor anatomist, but, still, he carried on a series of controversies, without rhyme or reason, with Jean Riolan, who was also a fanatical opponent of Harvey's doctrine. In 1635 Parisanus published (at Venice) his *De Cordis et Sanguinis Motu ad Guillelmum Harveium*.

In 1639, the printer Jean Maire issued from his press at Leyden a volume of 270 pages. In this book the combined 'refutations' (in Latin) of both Parisanus and Primerose were compared, passage by passage, with Harvey's original text. This same Jean Maire had also published (in French) the *Discours de la Méthode* of Descartes (1637). The frontispieces of the two books bear the same symbol of the printer and are interesting to compare.

Plemp, or Plempius (Volpisque-Fortune), was a physician of Dutch origin born at Amsterdam in 1601. After having studied at Ghent, Leyden and Bologna, he settled in the Belgian city of Louvain where he occupied a chair in the University. At Louvain he published a number of works on various medical subjects and, in particular (in 1638), his *De Fondamentis Medicinae, Libri Sex*. An interesting feature of Plemp's case is that, after having been a declared and outspoken adversary of Harvey, he was finally converted to a belief in the circulation of the blood. It was Descartes who won over Plemp to the Harveian doctrine, and thereafter the Dutch physician became 'more royalist than the King', so to speak —*i.e.* more pro-Harvey than Harvey himself. Indeed, though Descartes, as we shall see, did not accept Harvey's thesis in its entirety, Plemp adopted all Harvey's ideas and defended them against Descartes, who accepted the fact of the circulation of the blood but rejected the explanations Harvey gave concerning the contraction and dilatation of the heart. Descartes, indeed, put forward a rival theory of his own. Plempius died at Louvain in 1675.

The essential points in the objections preferred against Harvey by his detractors may be conveniently summarized along the lines given in Professor Richet's translation of Harvey.[1] With regard to the air that was still considered to be contained in the arteries, together with 'spirit' and a little blood, Richet wrote:

'Harvey confutes this error by means of a quite simple experiment. When an artery is severed nothing but blood is seen to gush forth from it, while when the trachea is cut, air is seen both to leave by and enter through the wound. Consequently we can say that the lungs contain air while the arteries contain blood.

'This rigorous logical reasoning, this close examination aroused the indignation of Primerose and Parisanus: *Deus plus quam optime! An haec similitudo quatuor pedibus currit!* exclaims the latter. The lungs are constantly open while the arteries are shut. When the lungs are punctured they continue to emit and to take in air, for they are not hindered by any violent flow of blood. It is quite different with the arteries which cannot, at one and the same time, pour out blood and take in air. And if we seek for a reason

---

[1] *Harvey, La Circulation du Sang*, translated with an historical Introduction and Notes by Charles Richet (Masson et Cie., Paris, 1879).

why the air in the arteries does not escape, is it not true that Democritus lived solely upon inhaling scents and odours? Odours —'spirits'—reach the heart. It is a fact known to all. So, when an artery is cut open, the air contained in it rushes to the heart, while air from outside the body cannot enter the artery because of the spurt of blood that issues forth from the wound.

'As for Primerose, he found a still more simple objection. It is this. When an artery is cut, there is, in all probability, some penetration into the artery of air from the outside while there is some ejection of air from the artery itself, but we cannot perceive these things because of the rapidity of the artery's movement.'

Regarding the pulmonary vein that was supposed to contain air, Richet remarks:

'Harvey multiplied his proofs that the vessel can contain nothing else but blood.

'First of all, it has the characteristics of a vein and not of the trachea. Why, he said, if the pulmonary vein contained air, should it be constructed like a vein? Parisanus found an excellent answer to this objection. He declared that things were so because nature wished them to be!

'By blowing air into the trachea, the air cannot be made to pass into the heart or into the pulmonary vein . . . to this demonstration Harvey's opponents made childish objections. . . . "Do not let us seek," wrote Parisanus, "to make nature contradict herself . . . if we inject air into the lungs of a corpse, it is not astonishing that the air does not reach the heart, for it is the heart, alone, by its proper movements that attracts the air from the lungs, and in a dead body the heart is no longer in movement. Moreover, the heart of a corpse is cold and the passage of air is prevented by the constriction, through the absence of heat, of the pores."

'By some extraordinary coincidence, Primerose confronted Harvey with an actual experiment, but it was one that was wretchedly interpreted. "There is," he says, "an experiment made by the learned Vesalius which shows that the heart attracts air from the lungs. If we removed from a living animal the bony thoracic wall, the lungs collapse and the heart ceases to beat. But if, then, we immediately blow air into the lungs, we see them swell up and the heart begin to beat again while the arteries resume their pulsations." It is interesting to note that Vesalius already knew about artificial respiration and that he interpreted the fact of it so ill.'

Richet wrote as follows concerning the veins, which were thought to begin at the liver and carry blood to the organs:

'Harvey devoted several chapters to the refutation of this error, and it was, moreover, a refutation which Caesalpinus had already quite effectively sustained. Nothing is more curious than the objections raised in this connection.

' "All the veins," said Primerose, "are not provided with valves, and since from one particular fact we cannot deduce a general theory, the fact that some veins have valves does not justify us in concluding that the blood of all the veins returns to the heart. The arteries have no valves, while the veins are provided with them. Consequently, the flow of blood is more rapid in the arteries than in the veins, so more blood would enter the veins than leaves them, which is absurd. If the blood really does circulate and if the arterial blood is constantly being forced into the veins, the valves are useless. The valves, moreover, can never entirely obstruct the passage of the veins, so what is their use except to strengthen the venous walls?"

'And Parisanus goes even farther:

' "Let us see: place a ligature upon the arm of some poor wretch, torture him to please Harvey, and see what happens. The innocent man, thus subjected to torment, will feel sharp pains in his arm and will soon be half dead without being able to describe what he experiences. The terrible pain attracts blood into his veins. Is it any wonder that they appear swollen? As for the valves, their existence is of no value in determining the direction of the blood stream. It is obvious that two valves in each vein should suffice, but as there is a much greater number they are useless." '

Perhaps it is hardly worth while to continue any further exposition of such wretched reasoning which, moreover, is frequently interspersed with invective and abuse. However, to give an idea of the tone adopted by some of Harvey's opponents, here is a passage from Primerose in which he complains of the importance accorded to the study of inferior animals in physiology:

'Thou hast observed a sort of pulsatile heart in slugs, flies, bees and even in squill-fish. We congratulate thee upon thy zeal. May God preserve thee in such perspicacious ways. But why dost thou say that Aristotle would not admit of small animals possessing a heart? Dost thou declare, then, that thou knowest what Aristotle did not? Those who mark in thy writings the names of so many and diverse animals will take thee for the sovereign investigator of nature and will believe thee to be an oracle seated upon the tripod and dictating thy decisions. I speak of those who are not physicians and have but a smattering of the science. But if we read the works of real anatomists, such as Galen, Vesalius, the illustrious Fabricius and Cassertius, we see that they have provided us with engraved plates representing the animals they dissected. As for Aristotle, he made observations on all things and no one should dare contest his conclusions.'

Primerose had been the pupil of Riolan in Paris and was, more-over (as we have noted), a licentiate of the College of Physicians. The College at that time contained another antagonist who, with-out displaying any violence of language, was content to teach, in the Barber-Surgeons' amphitheatre in Monkwell Street, the exact con-trary of the doctrine Harvey was demonstrating in his Lumleian Lectures at the College of Physicians. This man was Alexander Reid,[1] whom we have already mentioned several times. If we wish to learn of how tenaciously Galen's classical doctrine was held and how long it survived we have only to refer to the lectures delivered by Reid, for he collected them for publication in a *Manual of Anatomy* that was first issued in 1634. Reprints followed in 1637 and 1638, and (after Reid's death) in 1642, 1650, 1653 and 1658, with no change at all in the text. This affords an example of the disdainful attitude towards Harvey's discovery which persisted for so long in some quarters—the attitude of ignoring Harvey completely but continuing to pour forth the pure milk of Galenical orthodoxy. Of course, it is a classical method to pursue. Those who have not the courage to discuss the ideas which disconcert and displease, just ignore them. Such an attitude is not seldom proof of the cogency and irrefutability of the new theories.

Let us now consider the reactions of the professors of medicine in France. Their attitude gives us a good idea of the development of the dispute, though generally speaking the war of words was not carried on with as much animosity in France as elsewhere. Still, most of the teachers were lined up solidly behind Riolan, admittedly a great anatomist. The chief of Riolan's supporters was Gui Patin, who succeeded Riolan as Dean of the Faculty of Medicine of Paris and whose renown (such as it was) was acquired more by his deliberate and aggressive opposition to any sort of novelty than by serious and considered observation. We shall see how, later on, certain other distinguished Frenchmen acquiesced in the English physician's doctrine. These were men such as Dionis, surgeon to Louis XIV, who persuaded his royal master to order the hostile Faculty to hearken to the new teaching established by royal com-

[1] The name is spelt indifferently 'Read' or 'Reid'. I have used the latter form since the physician was a Scotsman. (*Translator's note.*)

mand in the *Jardin du Roy* (the future *Muséum d'Histoire Naturelle*), a teaching conducted by Dionis himself. But before we get to that interesting incident, let us glance, for a moment, at some of the French opponents of Harvey.

Jean Riolan fils (1577–1657) was almost an exact contemporary of Harvey himself. He was celebrated throughout France both for his passion for anatomical dissection (conducted, of course, so as to conform in all points with the doctrines of Galen) and for the highly classical nature of his teaching, which had earned him his appointment of Dean of the Faculty (*see* Plate XI). When we think of Riolan, perhaps we should bear in mind Flourens's rather severe remark, 'Riolan passed all his life searching for, rediscovering and finding out what the Ancients had already accomplished, and in rejecting everything achieved by the Moderns.'[1]

However, Riolan was a foeman of importance and his expressed opposition to the new doctrines (formulated, it must be admitted, in an indirect fashion and in academic style) undoubtedly contributed much more to the diffusion and spreading of Harvey's views than the snappish and old-maidish criticisms of the earlier opponents. We have seen that in the two *Exercitationes* of 1649 Harvey thought Riolan alone worthy of reply, although in a celebrated passage of the Second Letter there is a reference to Descartes.[2]

It was on the morrow of the publication in 1648 at Paris of Riolan's manual of anatomy which he called *Enchiridion*[3] and of which he sent a copy to Harvey[4] that the latter began the composition of his two *Exercitationes*. We have already sketched out the

---

[1] P. Flourens: *Histoire de la découverte de la circulation du sang*, 2nd edition, Paris, 1857, published by Garnier.

[2] *Ingenio pollens, acustissimus vir Renatus Cartesius.* See my translation, *Nouvelle traduction française de deux Lettres de William Harvey à Jean Riolan*, pages 164 and L, par. 77.

[3] *Enchiridium anatomicum et pathologicum. Enchiridium* is the Latin form of *Enchiridion*, that is, 'Manual'.

[4] As Harvey mentions at the beginning of his reply:

There appeared, a few months ago, a work on anatomy and pathology by the illustrious Riolan, a work that was sent to me by his own hand. . . . Harvey heads his epistle with the words: *Exercitatio de Circulatione sanguinis ad Johannem Riolanum filium, Parisiensem. . . . Professorem Regium egregium atque Decanum.* This contains an error, for Harvey salutes the French physician as '*Decanus*', but Jean Riolan (the son) was at no time *Decanus Facultatis.* Harvey may have confused him with Jean Riolan the father (1539–1606), who was *Decanus* from 1586 to 1587, or he may have used the term as a courtesy title. It is, perhaps, of interest to note that Harvey and Jean Riolan, the son, were of almost the same age (being born in 1578 and 1580, respectively), and died in the same year (1657). (*See* my translation, pages 107 and IX, par. 1.)

nature of the objections Riolan raised to Harvey's theory of the circulation of the blood, and the French physician's rather pitiful attempts to conciliate pathological facts with anatomical data. The reader will find this in Chapter VII, and there is no need to expatiate again upon a point which has, after all, but a slight retrospective interest.

Nevertheless, it must be recorded in favour of Riolan that he displayed good judgement in accepting the 'white vessels' that Aselli[1] had discovered in 1622 and had described as 'lacteal vessels' on account of their colour. While Riolan accepted these and interpreted them correctly as the passages whereby the digestive juices pass from the stomach and intestines into the blood, instead of travelling *via* the portal vein, Harvey wrote, in his First Letter to Riolan:

'I do not see how, when once this (*i.e.*, the general circulation of the blood) is admitted, there do not vanish all the difficulties which formerly existed concerning the distribution of the chyle and the blood by the same passages, and how, consequently, it would not appear quite superfluous to seek for or to find separate and distinct passages for the chyle. By the liquids in the egg, the umbilical veins absorb the alimentary juices and cause them to nourish and develop the chick while it is still an embryo. What, then, is there to prevent us from inferring that, in a similar way, the mesaric veins carry the chyle from the intestines and the liver, and that, indeed, they perform the same service in the adult? So would disappear all the difficulties raised, since we should have not two contrary currents but a continuous flow through the mesaric veins from the intestines towards the liver. What we should think of the "lacteal vessels" I will say elsewhere when I deal with the milk found in the diverse organs of newly born animals, particularly of human infants. We find milk in the mesentery and in all its glands and also in the thymus, the arm-pits and the breasts of infants. This is the milk that midwives press out and remove for reasons of health, as they think.'

Admittedly, this was a great mistake on Harvey's part, but as

[1] Gaspardo Aselli was born at Cremona in 1581 and died at Milan in 1626, after having held a chair at Pavia where, in 1622, he discovered the 'lacteal vessels' in a dog killed soon after a meal. It was only after his death that his writings were collected and published by his disciples under the title of *De lactibus sive lacteis venis quarto vasorum genere mesaricorum* (Milan, 1627). As is well known the study of the 'lacteal vessels' was pursued and developed by the Frenchman Jean Pecquet, the Swede Olaus Rudbech, and the Dane Thomas Bartholinus, who held a chair at Copenhagen and who is responsible for giving the vessels their accepted name of the lymphatics (1651–52).

we have pointed out, we cannot expect even a genius like Harvey to know everything. What he accomplished in other directions is imposing enough for us to be able to pardon this error. We have now to consider Gui Patin, a celebrated professor in the Faculty of Medicine at Paris for thirty years and Dean of the Faculty from 1650 to 1652.

A doughty polemist and partisan, Patin (who was by temperament busy with all sorts of matters, in all sorts of places) did not fail to let fling his missiles at the 'circulators' in his celebrated Letters, which are of great value for the picturesque light they throw upon his times. His attacks on Harvey's teaching and its supporters were as spirited as those he directed with much better excuse against the cult of 'antimony', as it may be called, and its fanatical propagator the physician Guénault,[1] or against that novelty introduced by the Jesuits—cinchona bark or quinine. Here is Patin discussing the circulation of the blood:[2]

'If Monsieur Duryer knows only how to lie and how the blood circulates, he would know but two things. I hate the first and I am indifferent to the second. . . . If he returns to the fray I will lead him, by other paths—more important paths—into the way of sound medicine, a way more significant than that of the supposed circulation of the blood.'

So much for Harvey. Now for Pecquet:

'All Pecquet's assertions constitute a novelty that I shall perhaps be ready to believe when they have been satisfactorily proved, and when they introduce something useful and convenient *in morborum curatione, quo excepto,* I will have nothing to do with them.'[3]

All this is a rather diverting sort of frivolity. Together with Riolan and Gui Patin we might name among the opponents of the doctrine of the circulation almost all the professors of the Faculty of Medicine at Paris, and many of those in the provinces, all of whom were horrified by the daring of the English innovator.

Having noted something of the weakness of the objections raised against Harvey's teaching by his enemies, we may now consider the curious case of a half-way position between obstinate opposition to and the whole-hearted support of the new system. It

[1] This was the Guénault whom Boileau classes among the nuisances of Paris. 'Guénault upon his horse that bespatters me as he passes by.'—Satire VI.

[2] Gui Patin, as Flourens remarks, was passionate in all things, in politics and in medicine; what he detested most in the first were the Jesuits and Mazarin, and in the second, antimony and Guénault. *See* Chapters VI and VII of Flourens's *Histoire de la découverte de la circulation du sang* (Paris, 1854 and 1857).

[3] Jean Pecquet, mentioned in the note on Aselli (p. 225).

is a singular case, since in one and the same man—no less a person than Descartes—we find at one and the same time a fervent apologist for Harvey and a no less obstinate opponent of the most original part of Harvey's work; that is to say, the mechanism of the heart's action which causes the circulation.

Nevertheless, we should not forget that Descartes (*see* Plate XVII) was the first man of science to welcome and to accept Harvey's admirable demonstration of the fact of the circulation of the blood, although Descartes did maintain that he himself had had a sort of inkling of the discovery before he ever read the *Exercitatio* and that he had expressed this sort of intuition in the MS. of his *Traité du Monde*. It is known that this treatise was to have been published in 1633 but that, since Galileo had been condemned by the Holy Office at the June solstice of 1632, Descartes did not dare to have the whole treatise printed, but printed from it in 1637 some of the less compromising portions under the title of *Discours de la Méthode*. The *Traité du Monde*, in fact, was not published in full until 1664, fourteen years after Descartes's death.

Anyway, it was in 1632, before Galileo's condemnation on 22nd June, that Descartes wrote from Holland to Father Mersenne, the celebrated Minim friar (with whom he maintained a correspondence), in the following words:

'I shall speak of Man in my (*Traité du*) *Monde* a little more than I had intended, for I undertake to explain all his principal functions. I have already described those which relate to life, such as the digestion of food, the beating of the pulse, the distribution of nourishment and the five senses. I am now engaged in dissecting the heads of various animals in order to discover what imagination, memory, etc., are made up of. . . . I have seen the book *De Motu Cordis* which you mentioned to me some time ago and I find myself not far from his opinion[1] although I read it only after having written on this question.'

This letter, moreover, should be compared with another from the Abbé Gassendi—who was, later on, so often to disagree with Descartes—in which this eminent scientist and mathematician, in addressing Pieresc as early as 28th August, 1629 (and thus three years before the exchange of letters between Mersenne and Descartes), expresses himself thus regarding Harvey's work:

'The book about which M. Valois has spoken to you M. du Puy has and will send it to you. I had already seen it before leaving

---

[1] *Peu différent*, that is to say, 'not far from'; not *un peu différent*, or 'a little different from', as is sometimes printed.

for Germany, and gave my opinion about it to Father Mersenne . . . his views about the constant circulation of the blood by means of the arteries and veins seems very probable and well founded, but what I object to in his work is that he imagines the blood cannot pass from the right ventricle of the heart to the left ventricle by the septum, for I remember that the Sieur Payen (a cunning surgeon of Aix) showed us, some years ago, that there existed not only pores but open channels.'

This proves that as early as 1629 Gassendi had spoken of Harvey to Mersenne and we may be sure that the latter lost no time in informing Descartes about Harvey's discovery, since in 1632 Descartes wrote, 'The book De Motu Cordis which you mentioned to me some time ago . . .', while in the MS. of Le Monde[1] (1632) he notes:

'The greater portion (of the blood) returns into the veins by the extremities of the arteries which are to be found, in several places, joined to those of the veins. And from the veins there passes also some part of the blood to nourish the members, but most of the blood returns to the heart and from there goes straightway into the arteries, so that the movement of the blood in the body is one of a perpetual circulation.'

We cannot help thinking on reading this passage that Descartes, when he wrote it, must have been under the influence of that old conversation he had had with Mersenne, and that the philosopher owed to Harvey the notion of the circulation which, moreover, had been 'in the air' since the end of the 16th century. Furthermore, Descartes, with perfect candour, recognized the priority and the precedence of Harvey and gave the English physician the entire credit for his discovery when, a few years later, the Frenchman wrote in the Discours de la Méthode:

'If one should enquire why the blood in the veins does not run dry by thus continually emptying itself into the heart, and how the arteries do not become over-filled, since all that passes through the heart returns back again to it, I have no need to add anything to what has been written by an English physician to whom we must all render a hommage of praise, since he was the first to break the

---

[1] Le Monde, as we have said, appeared for the first time (and then in part only) in 1664, under the title of 'The World of Descartes or the Treatise on Light' (Le Monde de Descartes ou Traité de la Lumière). The second part, devoted to animals and Man (which in the original MS. formed Chapter XVIII) was published only by Clerselier (1677) in a separate volume, to which he gave the title of Traité de l'Homme. It is there that the above passage is to be found.

ice in this matter and the first to teach that there are several small passages at the extremities of the arteries by which the blood which these receive from the heart enters into the little branches of the veins, through which it moves at once towards the heart, so that its course is nothing else than a perpetual circulation.'

This last phrase is, we see, merely a repetition of what Descartes wrote in the MS. of his *Monde*, and, as though to confirm the high opinion he had of Harvey, Descartes wrote in section 18, *Of the Formation of the Foetus*:

'This' (*i.e.*, the circulation of the blood) 'has already been so clearly proved by Harveius that it can now be doubted only by those who are so bound by their prejudices, and so used to dispute everything, that they cannot distinguish between real and certain opinions and those which are false and uncertain.'

However, this excellent beginning is followed by these words:

'But Harveius, to my way of thinking, has not been so successful in dealing with the movement of the heart, for he imagines, against the opinion of other physicians, and against the common judgement of the eye,[1] that when the heart becomes elongated its cavities become enlarged, and that, on the contrary, when the heart becomes shortened the cavities become more narrow, instead of—as I claim to be able to show—they then become wider.'

If Descartes, the pure mathematician and natural philosopher, found it quite superfluous to search for any other causation but that which showed itself so simply and evidently to 'reason', there would seem to be always a danger, in physiology, of reason's being substituted for prolonged and careful observation, a danger that specious evidence may lead to precipitate and ill-founded conclusions—in a word, a danger of the Cartesian methods being applied ill-advisedly.

The 'simple and evident' explanation to which Descartes clung so tenaciously (though it was opposed to the conclusions to be drawn from all Harvey's observations and experiments on a great variety and number of animals) was that the heat of the two ventricles of the heart (each one of them receiving simultaneously and rhythmically its large drop of cold blood which had dropped from the auricles) was enough to explain the distension of the two ventricles, which were thus forced into diastole, and to explain also the opening or gap which was produced in the two arterial exits by the separation of their sigmoid valves. A mechanism, we might say

---

[1] It is not a little amusing to find Descartes, the man who overthrew Scholasticism and the 'errors of sense', invoking the 'common opinion of physicians' and the 'judgement of the eye'.

nowadays, like that of the internal combustion engine with its piston-action caused by the huge expansion of the puff of enflamed petrol.

There is also this phrase: 'In supposing the heart to move in the way Harveius describes, we must imagine some faculty or inherent power that causes the movement.' But, of course, Harvey names this 'faculty'—it is just the contractile faculty of muscular tissue. 'Instead, in considering solely the dilatation of the blood which must necessarily follow from the heat that everyone recognizes to be greater in the heart than in any other part of the body,[1] it is obvious that this dilatation alone is sufficient to move the heart in the way I have described.'

We see that all this 'reasoning' of Descartes is, as far as the physiology of the heart is concerned, merely imaginative ratiocination. As a result, Descartes thought that it was in diastole that the heart emptied and in systole that it filled, while Harvey's admirable and irrefutable observations and experiments had established just the contrary. In the face of the great French philosopher's obstinacy in trusting to reason rather than to experiment, we feel like echoing d'Alembert's words on the science of his day:

'The mechanism of the human body, the speed of the blood's flow, the action of the blood on the vessels, are all matters which cannot be subjected to theory. We are ignorant of the actions, of the nerves, of the elasticity of the vessels, of their variable capacity, of the consistence of the blood, of the various degrees of heat. When nature's effects are too complicated for our calculations, the sole remaining guide for us must be experiment. The reactions of the human body are unknown, multiple, combined; the nicest calculations serve but to measure our ignorance.'

To this appeal of d'Alembert for experiment, always more experiment, the great physiologists of the 19th and 20th centuries reacted. Men such as Magendi, Claude Bernard, Vulpian and many others made experiment the base and foundation of all their researches. Once, when Claude Bernard was discussing a biological problem with his friend Joseph Bertrand, the mathematician, he said:

'There's only one creature that can beat you at integral calculus, and that is the dog I have just been experimenting on.'

---

[1] We have here a starting-point based on a 'general consensus of opinion' whose reliability should, first of all, have been solidly established concerning the evidence of the 'element fire' as the special property of the animal heart. We may remember that in Descartes's time the 'four elements' were still fire, earth, air and water.

By this, he meant to say that in such problems it is only the 'experimental response' of the animal that certainly comprises and takes into account all the factors.

But to return to Descartes. Although the philosopher had a preference for introspection and for the answers given by his 'interior reason' (that he liked to think of as divinely provided with clarity and truth) still, at the end of his *Discours de la Méthode*, and in words that seem to betray some inkling of the weakness of his position, he comes out with a paean of praise for experiment in order to further the progress of science. So marked, indeed, is this eulogy of experiment, that we may well ask ourselves whether the whole Discourse was not written in order to demand of his country the means to realize the experiments he desired to make.[1] We may judge of this attitude from a passage taken from the sixth and last section, *What Things are Needful to Advance Farther this Research into Nature*:

'The other reason that obliges me to write this is that I become more and more conscious, every day, of the delay occasioned to my programme of investigation by reason of the multitude of experiments that I must make yet cannot without another's help. Though I do not flatter myself that the public takes much interest in the things that interest me, all the same, I wish to do myself justice, and I should not like those who survive me to reproach me for not doing better than I have merely because I neglected to inform them how they might assist me.'

Instead of waiting for somebody to help him to make the necessary experiments, it is a pity that Descartes did not pay proper attention to the experiments of Harvey instead of judging them hastily and irrelevantly by his mathematician's pure 'reasoning reason'. Harvey, moreover, made a splendid reply to Descartes. At the end of the *Exercitatio Altera ad Iohannem Riolanum*—the Second Letter of 1649—Harvey expresses himself thus:

'A man remarkable for his brilliant genius, René Descartes. whom I thank for the eulogistic mention he has made of me, having removed the heart of a fish placed it upon a table and observed its pulsations. He thinks that the heart, in contracting, rises and becomes more rigid, opens, enlarges and swells its ventricles. I hold, however, that this opinion is not the right one, for it is certain that when the heart is contracted and more compact[2] it is in systole and not in

---

[1] I have dealt with this at length in my *Commentaires d'un Médecin d'aujourd'hui sur le Discours de la Méthode*.

[2] That is, the heart, being a muscle, appears 'thicker' when it is contracted though its cavities are then smaller.

diastole. But when the heart, as though exhausted, becomes less rigid and more slack, it is dilated and in diastole, and the cavities of the ventricles are larger. Thus, in a dead body we do not say that the heart is in diastole, although it is not in systole, but that it is slack, flabby, immobile, without movement. However, it is not distended; indeed, it is not distended and properly speaking in diastole except when it is filled by the flow of blood pumped in by the auricles. And this is more clearly visible during vivisections.'

Now that we have defined the rather equivocal position taken up by Descartes, partly favourable and partly unfavourable to Harvey's doctrines, we must repeat that it was the *Discours de la Méthode* that began to popularize Harvey's discovery in France, and indeed, in the world (since Descartes's reputation was very widespread). However, at the end of the 17th century it was perhaps the men of letters rather than the men of science who secured the triumph of Harvey's ideas. As Flourens wrote in another connection, 'It is always thus, it is always the writer who determines the fate of words.'

After Descartes, then, and in France first of all, it was other influential masters of words and ideas, men who were eagerly listened to by both Court and public, that entered the lists and took up a frankly 'pro-circulation' attitude. Moreover, they did not take sides between Harvey and Descartes on the further question of the heart's mechanism, for they were men of letters—not men of science —who attended Dionis's lectures in the spirit of enquiring laymen.

In the first rank of the 'circulatory' men of letters we have Molière, Boileau, La Fontaine and Racine, a group sometimes called the 'Auteuil Literary School' because the four often met together at what was then a village in the environs of Paris. Listen to Molière in *Le Malade Imaginaire* (1673), where he puts these words into the mouth of the blockhead Diafoirus when speaking of his booby of a son:

'What I like in him is that he is firmly attached to the opinions of the Ancients and never will consent to understand, or even listen, to the reasoning and the experiments connected with supposed discoveries about the circulation of the blood and other matters of the like sort.'

In another passage it is Thomas Diafoirus, the son, who thus addresses Angélique:

'I have defended, as against the circulators, a thesis that I make so bold as to present to you, Mademoiselle; please accept it as a hommage that I owe to you of the first-fruits of my brain.'

Boileau, in his turn, showed himself to be a mordant critic of the 'anti-circulators' when he published (in 1675) his *Arrêt Burlesque en la Grande Chambre en faveur des Maîtres-ès-Arts, Médecins, Professeurs de l'Université de Stagyre, au Pays des Chimères, pour le maintien de la doctrine d'Aristote*. That is, 'The burlesque Sentence of the High Court of Justice delivered in favour of the Masters of Arts, Physicians, Professors of the University of Stagira, in the Land of the Chimaeras, for the Maintenance of the Doctrine of Aristotle'. Boileau makes the Public Prosecutor say during his leading speech:

'Against the accused Reason for having recognized that the heart carries the blood all over the body and that the said blood has full authority to wander about, saunter and circulate with impunity by means of the veins and arteries.'

The sentence of the Court is delivered in a burlesque judgement by which the blood is forbidden 'any more to play the vagabond or to wander about and to circulate throughout the body, at risk of being delivered into the hands of the Faculty for punishment'.

Then we have La Fontaine in a poem that is but little known—and which, indeed, adds very little to his reputation as a poet. It was a piece he was commissioned to write on cinchona and quinine. La Fontaine composed the verses in 1682 at the request of a benefactress whose wishes he could not well ignore. She was the turbulent Madame de Bouillon, Marie-Anne Mancini, the youngest of Mazarin's five nieces, all or almost all of whom (beginning with Olympe or Olimpia, the eldest, who had hoped to marry Louis XIV) had enjoyed the royal favours. Their uncle, the Cardinal, had as hard a job to keep these ladies in order as Napoleon later had to restrain the conduct of his imperial sisters.

This Marie-Anne Mancini became very enthusiastic about the novel drug introduced into France by the Jesuits in 1649, which formed the principal ingredient in a 'health powder' the secret prescription which Louis XIV had purchased in 1679 from an Englishman, known in France as the 'Chevalier Talbot'.[1] So she asked

---

[1] The 'Chevalier Talbot' was in reality an English physician by the name of Tabor or Talbor (1642?-81), who was born near Cambridge and started life as an apprentice to an apothecary in the university city. Later, he turned his attention to the uses of the 'Jesuits' Bark' (*i.e.* quinine) in the treatment of fevers, for the employment of the drug was then attended by certain disagreeable results. Often the patients' reactions were violent and even alarming. The better to study the effects of quinine young Tabor moved to Essex, a county in those days much scourged with fevers. Here he devised a method of administering the drug mingled with wine and given in small doses. When he was thirty years old, in 1672, he published, if not his secret, at least an account of his observations in a book called

La Fontaine to write a eulogy on the drug. It was called *Le Quin-quina*. It seems, furthermore, that in the lady's mind there was some idea of getting again into the King's good graces. In fact the poem was to be a sort of eirenicon put forward by her and her sisters, almost all of whom—if not all—were suspected of having been in some way implicated in the lamentable affair of the woman La Voisin and her *poudre de succession* (or 'inheritance powder'), the principal ingredient of which was arsenic.[1] Marie-Anne may therefore have thought that it was good policy to pay tribute to the 'health powder' that Louis XIV had just bought from Chevalier Talbot for the sizable sum of 40,000 livres and a pension of 2,000 livres. In any case, the fabulist, always ready to oblige his friends (as we may see in the cases of Fouquet, Madame de La Sablière and others), 'went over', as he said, 'to science', and in a passage designed to explain the physiological effects of quinquina showed himself to be an out-and-out 'circulator'.

Here are some quotations from the poem. On reading it one has

Pyretologia or a Rational Account of the Cause and Cure of Agues with their Signs (London). Tabor was called in to treat King Charles II, despite the opposition of Richard Lower and owing to the recommendation of Thomas Short. Tabor administered his remedy, which was completely successful. As a result he was appointed Physician in Ordinary to the King and, in July, 1678, knighted at Whitehall. That same year, Tabor repaired to France there to treat the Dauphin. Again, the treatment was successful. In 1679 Louis XIV made Tabor a knight of one of his Orders and purchased from him the secret of the remedy. Tabor was then called to Spain to attend Queen Luisa Maria (as recounted in Madame de Sevigné's Letters). Tabor died in 1681 and was buried at Trinity Church in Cambridge where a monument was erected to his memory. In 1682 Louis XIV rendered Tabor's secret public by having issued at Paris a short work entitled *Le Remède anglais pour la guérison des fièvres.*

[1] In the second half of the 17th century two notorious poisoners, following the methods employed at the Italian Courts in the 16th century, introduced at the French Court the use of arsenic to secure the removal of fathers, husbands or troublesome lovers. The first of the two criminals was the notorious Marquise de Brinvilliers (Marie-Madeleine d'Aubray), the mistress of the impoverished officer Sainte-Croix, who seems to have been largely responsible for her life of crime. In 1676 she was beheaded, her body burned and her ashes scattered to the winds at the Place de Grève, in Paris. This was ten years after her first murder, that of her own father! The second poisoner was a professional midwife and abortionist called La Voisin, who was executed in 1679. Both women had as customers many ladies of high society. The scandal reached right to the steps of the Throne, so that Louis XIV, after celebrated inquests and interrogations conducted before the tribunal known as the *Chambre Ardente*, saw fit to hush the whole matter up because members of his own immediate suite were implicated in this unsavoury affair.

almost the impression that La Fontaine had just come from attending one of Dionis's lectures at the *Jardin du Roy*:

> *Deux portes sont au coeur; chacune a sa valvule,*
> *Le sang, source de vie, est par l'une introduit,*
> *L'autre huissière permet qu'il sorte et qu'il circule,*
> *Des Veines, sans cesser, aux artères conduit.*

> Two doors there are in the heart, each has its valve,
> Blood, the source of life, is by the one introduced,
> The other allows it to go forth and circulate
> Through the veins, without ceasing, to the arteries.

Here we have described, first, the introduction of venous blood by the sigmoid valve of the *vena arteriosa* (our pulmonary artery) and its arrival through the lungs to the left ventricle, and second, the propulsion through the exit valve (the sigmoid valves of the aorta) of blood that has been 'arterialized' by the left heart, towards the arteries that conduct the blood-stream all over the body. Now for the other quotation:

> *Quand le coeur l'a reçu, la chaleur naturelle*
> *En forme ses esprits qu'animaux on appelle.*
> *Ainsi qu'en un creuset il est rarefié;*
> *Le plus pur, le plus vif, le plus qualifié*
> *En atomes, extrait, quitte la masse entière,*
> *S'exhale et sort enfin par le reste attiré.*
> *Ce reste rentre encore, est encore épuré.*
> *Le chyle y joint toujours matière sur matière.*

> When the heart has received it, the natural heat
> Of it forms those spirits we call animal.
> Thus, as in a retort, it is rarefied;
> The purest extract, the most lively and most charged
> With atoms, leaves the whole mass,
> Comes out and issues forth, drawn by the remainder.
> This goes back again and is again purified.
> The chyle is elsewhere continually adding more matter to it.

Here, in twelve lines of verse, we have Harvey's circulation theory admirably set forth. There is even, it seems, special stress laid on certain points (such as the importance attributed to the chyle) and a hint of the two peripheric sources: the general *cava* and the *porto-cava* systems. ('The chyle is elsewhere continually adding more matter to it.') There are a number of reasons, as we shall see in the last chapter of this book, why I think we should adopt this view today, but it is remarkable that La Fontaine should have had a similar conception.

It might be amusing to give further quotations from this curious poem, quotations that relate to the mechanism of the nervous functions of sensibility and movement which are interpreted in the Cartesian spirit. There is, moreover, further reference to these matters in La Fontaine's *Discours*, addressed to Madame de la Sablière, at the beginning of the first fable in Book X, *The Two Rats, the Fox and the Egg*. This work is, however, partly critical in intention, for La Fontaine was too fond of animals to accept the idea that they were just machines, without consciousness or sensibility. But we have not time to linger more over La Fontaine, for I have, I think, done what I set out to do which was to prove that La Fontaine, like Molière and Boileau, was an out-and-out 'circulator'.

If we reflect upon this rather strange and apparently sudden entry into the lists, almost simultaneously, of three of the greatest French writers of the *Grand Siècle*, and upon their all choosing to deal with a scientific question which, one would have thought, would have left them indifferent, we naturally wonder what it was that induced them thus to defend the new doctrine. It is even more curious that these writers actually did more to gain universal acceptance of the circulation of the blood than the scientists themselves. I proposed an answer to this problem in the French medical review *La Presse Médicale*, 11th September, 1954, and give here a summary of my argument.

At the beginning of the year 1672, Louis XIV, then thirty-five years of age, having been advised by one of his medical consultants, the young surgeon Dionis (aged thirty-one) that the Faculty of Medicine had ostracized the new doctrine of the circulation of the blood, decided that an independent chair of anatomy should be set up in the King's own preserve, that is to say in his royal *Jardin du Roy*, where the teaching of Harvey should be imparted. The sovereign therefore issued a decree establishing, or rather re-establishing, the teaching of anatomy in the 'King's Garden'. We say re-establishing since the former chair of anatomy there had been suppressed at the request of the Medical Faculty of the University of Paris. When the monarch's decision became known there was a great outcry, as may well be imagined, and the *Parlement*[1] took sides with the Professors. In fact, much the same situation arose as in 1635, when Louis XIII had ordained that chemistry should be taught in the *Jardin du Roy*.[2] Once again, as in 1635, the *Parlement* made use of its privilege to address 'Remonstrances' to the King. But Louis XIV was even less likely to be swayed by such tactics than his father, and the *Roi Soleil* went in person to the *Parlement* and there signified his commands.

The whole business was summarized by Dionis (*see* Plate XVIII), who was to occupy the new chair and there to lecture upon 'The Anatomy of Man according to the Circulation of the Blood and the newest Discoveries'. In the first edition (1690) of his lectures (which he had been delivering since 1673) he writes:

'If anatomy owes much to Harvey who discovered the circulation of the blood, to Virsungus who first described the pancreatic canal, to Asellius who pointed out the lacteal veins, to Pecquet who was the first to prove the existence of the thoracic canal, and to several others who in our days have studied anatomy with success, the science owes no less to the refounding, by His Majesty's gracious command, of public demonstrations in the Royal Garden where He has desired that human anatomy should be explained as we know it today. It was in 1672 that the teaching of anatomy was resumed in the *Jardin Royal* where it had been interrupted for several months.

'This resumption, although of the great usefulness to the public, met with opposition, naturally enough, from those who maintained that they alone had the right to teach and to explain anatomy. But the King, by a special declaration which he had confirmed and registered by the *Parlement*, His Majesty being present in person, in the month of March of the year 1673, ordered that demonstrations of anatomy and of the operations of surgery should be held in the Royal Garden and should be open to all comers, free of charge, and that the said demonstrations should take place in an amphitheatre which he had built especially for the purpose. Moreover, the King ordained that the specimens and subjects necessary for these demonstrations should be delivered to his professors in the Royal Garden in preference to all others.

[1] The ancient French parlements (of which that at Paris was but one of several) were not 'parliaments' in the English sense of the word but supreme courts of justice. (*Translator's note.*)

[2] '. . . Chemistry of which the said Faculty is suspicious for good reasons and considerations and which had already been condemned by the *Parlement*', as is written in the *Rémontrances sur la Création du Jardin du Roy* (reproduced in *Historical Notices on the Museum of Natural History*, by Laurent de Jussieu, in the *Annales du Muséum d'Histoire Naturelle*, I, 12).

'It was in execution of His Majesty's commands that I conducted public demonstrations during a period of eight years, that is to say, beginning in 1673 and lasting until 1680, in which latter year I had the honour of being chosen by the King to be first Surgeon in Ordinary to Her Royal Highness the Dauphine, so that I was obliged to cease my anatomical demonstrations since the appointment I had received did not allow of my continuing them.'

The inauguration of this anatomical chair and of the ideas which had led to its foundation created, therefore, during the entire year 1672, a great deal of commotion and discussion. There can be but little doubt that the conflict much impressed a man such as Molière, who was always on the look-out for topical subjects for his plays so that he could enrich them with a presentation of the follies and eccentricities that he saw before his eyes. Molière was, indeed, a forerunner of the modern newspaper reporters, topical journalists and columnists. It was quite natural that he should seize the opportunity of ridiculing a profession for which he had not much esteem, that of the official physicians. So he launched the first attacks against the 'anti-circulators' in his Le Malade Imaginaire early in 1673.[1]

Thus, when Dionis began his series of lectures and demonstrations Molière, who knew well what the whole commotion was really about and was a remarkably speedy writer, had already composed his piece informed with the spirit of the 'perfect circulator'.

Two years later, in 1675, it was Boileau, Molière's firm friend, who wrote the moving verses of the Épître à Racine:

> Avant qu'un peu de terre obtenue par prière
> Pour jamais sous la tombe eût enfermé Molière.

> Before Molière in the tomb was laid to rest
> Beneath a plot of earth, granted by request.

And it was Boileau, possibly instructed by attendance at Dionis's lectures, who published the famed 'prohibition of the blood to circulate in the body'. La Fontaine, anyway, undoubtedly went to

[1] Molière's Thomas Diafoirus is supposed to be a burlesque of Gui Patin (see page 226) who died in 1672 at the age of seventy. His medical skill is summed up in the rhyme:

> clysterium donare
> postea saignare
> ensuita purgare
> —Le Malade Imaginaire—Cérémonie Finale.

the *Jardin du Roy* to learn from Dionis exactly what Harvey's doctrine was—otherwise, we could hardly have had a description as detailed and as exact as that in *Le Quinquina*. I concluded my article in the *Presse Médicale* with these words:

'Before we discuss Harvey, Descartes and Riolan next time[1] let us remember Molière, Boileau and La Fontaine, pro-Harveists converted to the doctrine of the circulation of the blood . . . by Louis XIV and Dionis, which is itself curious enough.'

Before we leave Dionis and the *Jardin du Roy*, we may perhaps mention that his lectures, in addition to being solid contributions to knowledge in the most strictly 'Harveian' vein, are remarkable for the elegantly and courteously worded thrusts which he inserted from time to time into his criticisms of the Cartesian system. These criticisms are most marked in those passages where Dionis attacks Descartes for his opposition to the great Englishman's proof of the nature and character of the heart's movements. After having disposed of the entirely false thesis propounded by Descartes (of a 'mechanism' emptying the heart in diastole and filling it in systole), Dionis continues, in his *The Anatomy of Man according to the Circulation of the Blood* (1698):

'We have there one of the most imaginative ideas of which it is possible to conceive, and it is certain that by this theory we can explain all the phenomena encountered in this connection. We are deeply obliged to this great man for having broken the ice, for having been the first to attempt a mechanical explanation of the heart's movements. Nonetheless, we must say that this hypothesis is contrary both to reason and to experiment, but at this we should not be astonished. He did not know enough about the structure of the heart, and his meditations took up so much of his time that he was not able to obtain any great knowledge of that structure. All the same, we must say that he did all a man could do, who knew nothing of the heart beyond what he knew of it.'

In my second article in the *Presse Médicale* I remarked, 'This is surely one of the most elegant and courteous ways, one in real accord with the spirit of the *Grand Siècle*, to make a most unpleasant remark, and one that was at the same time absolutely true—"he did all a man could do, who knew nothing of the heart beyond what he knew of it".'

If, in France, Harvey's doctrine of the circulation of the blood received the publicity that was to ensure its general acceptance

[1] Another article on these three men appeared in the *Presse Médicale* on 29th January, 1955.

chiefly from literary men, it must be admitted that, here and there, certain scientists in other countries (*e.g.* Steno, Lower, etc.) were already consolidating Harvey's work and, indeed, in some respects going beyond what Harvey had been able to achieve. There is, however, one Frenchman worthy of note who made an advance on Harvey's work in a little book called *Le Coeur Déthroné*, published in the second half of the 17th century. The author, one Pierre Vattier (1623-70), was a physician whose memory, like that of his book, has sunk into oblivion, though he was certainly a man of very sound judgement. I give a brief account of Vattier and his work on page 258, and pause here merely to note his name in the present context. Vattier, together with Dionis and one or two other men of independent mind, were alone in opposing the Faculty of Medicine until Duvernois (in the 18th century) and then Sénac (in his celebrated *Traité du Coeur*), completely routed the upholders of the medieval misconceptions.

Since I have mentioned Sénac, who was first Physician in Ordinary to King Louis XV, it may be worth while mentioning that, despite all the tales told by those who have not consulted the texts, there is no suggestion in the Latin thesis of young Fagon[1] in 1664 of any acceptance of Harvey's ideas. I have had the curiosity to read and to translate Fagon's thesis, *An a sanguine cor salit?* (Paris, 1664), and I can guarantee that the young man there showed himself what he was to be throughout his life, a careful and prudent opportunist. He does not go any farther than Descartes, and in this way he made sure that should his timid suggestions meet the disapproval of the jury before which he defended his thesis, he would be covered by the prestige of Descartes's name.

We may now consider some scientists of other countries who, at the end of the 17th century, showed themselves partisans of Harvey's doctrine and amended it in some respects. First, in order to show how potent was the influence of Harvey's method—in spite of furious rearguard attacks from the old scholasticism, and in a time as unpropitious as that of civil war—to infuse a new spirit in the younger students of medicine and science, I cannot do

[1] Guy Crescent Fagon (1638–1718) became Physician in Ordinary to Louis XIV after the dismissal of Antoine Daquin in 1693. Fagon, however, appears to have possessed, in addition to undoubted talents for intrigue, the qualities of a real clinician. He was, moreover, a skilful practitioner and a man who had observed much. To the end of his reign Louis XIV had full confidence in Fagon who, though born in the same year as the sovereign, survived him by three years.

better than quote these lines from a recent article by Sir Zachary Cope on *How Medicine became a Science:*[1]

'The year 1628 marks one of the great dates in the history of medicine for it indicates the birth of rational physiology. Harvey's discovery compelled an entirely new orientation in medicine and set a magnificent example of the correct method to be adopted in attempting further advances. More than anyone else, Harvey introduced the scientific spirit into medicine, and his influence was widely felt. It can hardly be an accident that, immediately after the time of Harvey there should have been so many medical men interested in science that they formed 22 out of the original 115 fellows of the Royal Society, which was formally started in 1660.'

In 1664, the great Danish anatomist (and geologist) Nicholas Steno (1639–87), who may be called the earliest of the brain anatomists since he clearly distinguished the fibres of the brain, wrote concerning the heart in his *De Musculis Specimen:*

'It is certain, and of a certainty as well demonstrated for the mind as for the eye, that the heart is a muscle, that it has all that other muscles possess and nothing but what they possess, so that it is not an organ of innate heat, nor the seat of the soul, neither does it produce vital spirit, nor blood nor any other humour whatsoever.'

At about the same time (1669) the English physician Lower (1631–91), the close friend and the heir of Willis, proved in the first (and following editions) of his *Tractatus de Corde* that it is in the lungs, and under the influence of air, that the 'black' blood is transformed into 'red' blood. Flourens describes Lower's experiments in the following words:

'If we examine the blood of the *vena cava*, that is to say the blood which has not yet traversed the right ventricle, and then the blood of the pulmonary artery, that is the blood that issues from the right ventricle, we shall find that these two sorts of blood are precisely identical. Both are of the same kind—venous or "black" blood.

'If we ligature the trachea in a living animal so that the lungs receive no more air, the blood of the carotid artery will be black like that of the jugular vein. That is to say, the blood which issues from the left ventricle is similar to that which has not yet entered it.

'If, in a dog that has just died, we force the still fluid blood from the *vena cava* into the lungs and if, at the same time we introduce air into the lungs, we see that at once the blood in the pulmonary vein will become red.

'Finally . . . if we open the thorax of a living dog, the lungs will

[1] *Journal of the Franklin Institute*, Vol. 261, No. 1, January, 1956.

collapse and receive no more air. Then the blood of the pulmonary vein is black. But if we introduce air, the blood becomes red, but only to become black again when we cease to pump in air, whereas if we begin again to introduce air, then the blood again assumes a red coloration.'

And one hundred and thirty years later, Bichat describes in his *Recherches physiologiques sur la Vie et la Mort* what he called 'the death of the organs through that of the lungs':

'One of the best methods of judging of the colour of the blood is, I think, that which I utilize. First of all, the trachea having been exposed and cut transversally, I adapt to it a faucet or tap which can be opened or closed at will. . . . Secondly, we open any artery, the carotid, the crural *etc.* . . . in order to observe the different variations and alterations in the colour of the blood.'

In this same work of Bichat's, under the heading 'On the death of the Heart by the Lungs', we read:

'(1) Adjust a tube with a tap to the trachea, which has been exposed and cut transversally high up. (2) Open the abdomen so as to be able to observe the intestines, the epiploon *etc.* (3) Shut the tap. After about two or three minutes, the reddish colour that pervades the white substance of the peritoneum (and which this membrane receives from the vessels which run beneath it) will change to a dark brown, which colour we can cause to disappear and to reappear by opening or shutting the tap.'

Bichat's experiments are, indeed, but the continuation of the admirable ones made by Lower. Contemporary with Lower, or following him, was a number of scientists whose names are most worthy of note, including Willis (1622–75) and Malpighi (1628–94). To their discoveries must be added that of the capillary vessels by Leeuwenhoek (1632–1723), the skilled microscopist. Then came the researches of Rusch (1638–1731), of Vieussen (1641–1716), of Duverney (1648–1730), of Lancini (1654–1720), of Boerhaave (1668–1758), of Winslow (1669–1760), of Morgagni (1682–1771) and of Haller (1708–77), all of which led up to the *Treatise of the Structure of the Heart, of its Action and its Diseases* (*Traité de Structure du coeur, de son action et de ses maladies*), published in 1749 by Jean de Sénac (1693–1770), senior Physician in Ordinary to Louis XV and one of the most acute-minded men of his time.

For twenty years (assisted during the latter part of that time by Portal, Professor of Medicine at the Royal College and member of the Academy of Science) Sénac laboured to perfect his work, which he enriched (thanks to Portal's collaboration) with admirable anatomical plates depicting the pericardium, the nerves of the heart, the ventricles, and the interauricular septum with the oval aperture. The final and most splendid edition of Sénac's work was published in 1777, after his death.

If we would give a complete list of the names of those responsible for the evolution of ideas about Harvey's great work during the 17th and 18th centuries, we should not only have to cite many others but we should also have to leave out the names of many illustrious men such as Sydenham (1624–89), sometimes termed the 'English Hippocrates'. He was more a clinician and a therapeutist than an anatomist or a physiologist, yet it is strange that he never mentions his compatriot Harvey. Maybe Sydenham's ardent republicanism during the Civil War led him to suspect not only Charles I's physician but also his teaching. There was also Van Helmont (who died, it is true, in 1644), who was more concerned with his *archeai* and with a desire to develop the ideas of Paracelsus than with devotion to exact anatomical science. The German physician Stahl (1660–1754), the father of 'phlogiston', was, in a measure, the continuer of Van Helmont's theories.

With Van Helmont and Stahl, whom we may think of as more or less opposed to those physicians who were experimenters well versed in anatomical learning, we have represented the other tendency, then so widely noticeable among medical men, to accept cheerfully the concepts of a rash imagination rather than the slowly delivered, but much more reliable, conclusions drawn from the patient dissection and vivisection of animals. Thus, we have two separate paths which were to diverge during the second half of the 18th century. On the one hand, there were the experimentalists such as Portal, Bichat, Vicq d'Azyr, not to mention Lavoisier, Nollet, Galvani and Volta. On the other, there were the mystics and doctrinaires such as Mesmer, whom we see a little later on (at the beginning of the 19th century) supporting Laënnec against Broussais.

I should like to point out, in passing, that this double tendency can be found well expressed, and perhaps combined, in the original character of a physician whose life extended over the transition period of two generations, namely Julien Offray de la Mettrie of Saint-Malo. He died at the age of forty-two in 1751, having taken the part of both the 'analysts' and the 'animists', and developing a balanced outlook not always apparent in his singularly sharp-tongued criticisms of both schools.

During his short life, La Mettrie displayed extraordinary activity and emitted a host of original ideas and judgements, often full of good sense, and I mention him here on account of two passages in his works relating to Harvey and Descartes. La Mettrie died at Berlin, the friend, confidant and Physician in Ordinary to Frederic the Great, at whose Court he was in a measure a rival of Voltaire. It was the King of Prussia who pronounced La Mettrie's funeral oration at the Berlin Academy of Sciences.

Now, here is La Mettrie talking of Harvey and his methods of work. The passage occurs in *Ouvrage de Pénélope*, that was published at Berlin in 1748:[1]

'You know Harvey, that immortal figure who, with great sagacity, related the causes of disease to his splendid discovery of the circulation of the blood, and who by his weighty works rendered the greatest services to medicine, since he dragged it out of the shadowy chaos of empiricism whereinto the blind children of Hippocrates had plunged it. Well, my son, how do you think that Harvey was regarded by his contemporaries?—As a dissector of fleas, snakes, butterflies and insects!'

Now let us hear La Mettrie judge Descartes, or rather explain him. This passage occurs in *L'Homme Machine*, published at Leyden in 1748:

'I think that Descartes would be a man worthy of all respect and admiration had he been born in an age that had no need of his enlightenment, had he known the value of experiment and of observation, and had he realized the danger of ignoring them or of neglecting them. Still, it is only just that I should here say something to rehabilitate his memory, something addressed to all the little facetious philosophers and poor imitators of Locke, who, instead of (in their impudence) making fun of that great man, would do better to realize that without him the whole field of philosophy would be lying fallow, like that of science if there had been no Newton.

'It is true that the great philosopher often erred. No one can deny this. Nevertheless, he did understand the nature of animals and was the first to demonstrate that animals are simply machines. And, after a discovery of that importance and one that presupposes so much sagacity, how can we not forgive him all his mistakes?'

We have dealt at some length with the hundred years or so that elapsed before the final triumph of Harvey's discovery and before

[1] I owe this part of my documentation to my friend M. Pierre Lemée, a learned authority on all pertaining to Saint-Malo and its neighbourhood. M. Lemée has published several pamphlets dealing with Offray de la Mettrie.

the discomfiture and defeat of the last opponents of the doctrine of the circulation of the blood,[1] but we cannot, without going beyond the limits assigned to this book, pursue the subject through the second half of the 18th century, the whole of the 19th and the first fifty years of the 20th. The manifold results that stemmed from the scientific revolution initiated by Harvey are plain to see. Modern physiological, pathological, therapeutic and hygienic knowledge is not merely based on his great discovery but was developed by the extension of his methods. I am dealing with this at length in my *Histoire de la Circulation du Sang avant et depuis Harvey* (not yet published).

Now that we have seen the doctrines of the great English physician securely maintained against the fierce early opposition we may, in our final chapter, point out certain erroneous interpretations of Harvey's teaching which have unfortunately become associated with it. The chief of these is that of the heart considered as the apparatus wherein the circuit of the blood begins. This is a concept that Harvey himself, who never entertained this idea, was careful not to express. It will be our privilege to suggest, in the light of modern knowledge, a new locus for the 'source' of the bloodstream, for we must bear in mind that Harvey, fully conscious of the imperfections of the science of his day, advanced only provisional and tentative suggestions on this question.

---

[1] It is curious to note that as late as the beginning of the second half of the 18th century (about 1760) an Italian physician, Homolo Piso (cited by the celebrated Dr. Tissot of Geneva in his little book *De la Santé des Gens de Lettres*, Paris, 1769), wrote a treatise, *De regimine magnor. Auxilior.*, against the circulation of the blood.

It is possible that, one day, De Motu Cordis will be carried farther along the path that I have opened up and that it will receive new interpretations

Chapter X

Harvey's Explanation of the Circulation of the Blood in the Light of Modern Knowledge

The 'topographical' accuracy of the circulation as established by Harvey—Its provisional character recognized by Harvey—The mistake that Harvey made owing to the imperfect science of his day—The source of the circulation assumed in the *vena cava*—The collapse of this explanation after the discoveries of Lavoisier and Claude Bernard—The new aspect of the circulation of the blood—Physiological and physiopathological facts in support of the new view—Therapeutical treatment suggested by these facts and the grave consequences of ignoring them

Aᴛ the head of this chapter I have quoted Harvey's prudent declaration at the beginning of his *Exercitatio* of 1628. It may be found in the last three lines of Chapter I, thus:

Illud forsan in cordis motu eveniat nunc, aut alii hinc saltem, hac data via, fœlicioribus freti ingeniis, rei rectius gerendæ, et melius inquirendi occasionem capient.

It is possible that the same thing will happen with my *De Motu Cordis*, and perhaps others more favoured will take advantage of the path that I have just opened for them to present the matter more exactly and carry on better researches.

I do not think that it is possible to offer a more striking proof of the breadth of Harvey's mind. Harvey was not one of those pompous investigators who (in his day as in our own) refuse to admit that their opinions may have to be modified in the light of later discoveries. He was as simple and modest as he was great. He judged that some part of his doctrine might need to be revised and he proclaimed the fact openly. Just as he was sure and unwavering in his affirmation of the reality of the circulation (for his experiments and observations enabled him to declare justly, 'this at least is certain, for I have seen and carefully studied it with my own eyes'), so also he showed himself prudent and reserved when confronted with the question, 'but *why* are these things so?'

In assigning a 'reason' we inevitably assume a hypothesis, and this is necessarily based on other hypotheses which are themselves formed from knowledge previously acquired—or thought to have been acquired. It is here that the weak point in our deductions resides, even if we arm ourselves with all the resources of logic. There need be only a little error at the starting-point—that first hypothesis may be a little rash or rickety—and sooner or later the whole edifice will come tumbling to the ground. Harvey realized all this so well that he offered the explanation of what he had seen and observed as an hypothesis only, and as one which might some day have to be modified, though within the framework of what he had certainly demonstrated—the circulation of the blood. Just before the noble declaration we have just quoted, Harvey reproduced these lines of Terence, in order to remind his readers of the prudence with which all scientific explanations should be advanced:

> *Numquam quisquam ita bene subducta ratione ad vitam fuit,*
> *Quin res, aetas, usus, aliquid apportet novi*
> *Aliquid admoneat ut illa quae te scire credas, nescias,*
> *Et quae tibi putaris prima in experiundo repudies.*

No one can produce a theory so sound but that facts, time or use may not bring forth something new to show one's fancied knowledge to be ignorance, and that one's first judgement is repudiated by experience.

It is just because Harvey realized that the over-confident assumption of a belief as true may ruin a theory elaborated by impeccable logic but built upon shifting foundations, that he offered his explanation as provisional only. His own theory did, in point of fact, contain an initial error that falsely coloured his conclusions.

Influenced by the ideas current in his day, Harvey supposed that the main function and object of the blood was to carry to the organs 'heat' and 'vital spirit'. Thus, he was led to conclude by an *a priori* argument that the blood must come back from the organs cooled and deprived of 'vital spirit'. We must admit that, given the premiss as to the function of the blood-stream, this conclusion does seem inescapable, yet had Harvey been able to measure the heat of the blood and of the tissues he would have observed that the blood is *not* cooler on leaving the organs than on entering them. Indeed, it is warmer on leaving them, and that by reason of the 'combustion' or oxidation that occurs in the tissues. But the two men who were to do most to explain thermogenesis in animals, Lavoisier and Claude Bernard, came long after Harvey's time—Lavoisier more than a hundred and fifty years after and Claude Bernard nearly two hundred and fifty.

The same considerations apply to the 'vital spirit'. And we should do well not to ridicule this idea of a 'vital spirit', this conviction of the presence of subtle essences imperceptible to the senses, for we now know that there are certain vital substances present in minute quantities which rule and regulate the equilibrium of the blood, and we call them hormones. The tradition that the blood, with its 'vital spirit', was a more mysterious fluid than it appeared may be interpreted as a vague sort of intuition of these *imponderabilia*. However, the blood does not leave the organs deprived even of this sort of 'spirit' but rather enriched by it.

So the two main reasons which induced Harvey to think that the blood came back, cold and deprived of 'vital spirit', to fill the *vena cava* were quite erroneous, but it was upon these ideas that he founded his explanation of the circulation of the blood. This explanation is skilfully set forth to Riolan (who, however, does not seem to have understood Harvey's thoughts in the matter) towards the end of the second of the two Letters of 1649. On page 205 I have already given this text and its translation and if we refer to it, we shall see at once why Harvey thought it necessary to suppose that in the *vena cava* there occurs a fermentation analogous to that of new wine in a barrel, bubbling and fermenting and thus generating considerable heat and 'subtle essence'. Harvey repeats this simile several times. The heat and spirit of wine in fermentation, the *calor et spiritus vini*, might indeed be analogous to the heat and 'vital spirit' that the blood acquired in the *vena cava*.

The comparison was a tempting one, all the more so because (as we saw in Chapter VIII) men had not ceased to compare blood with wine from the most remote antiquity down through the Middle Ages. There was indeed implicit in this comparison a sort of explicative mysticism that interpreted the one substance by the other.

For were there not the Dionysiac festivals of ancient Greece, and was not the mystery of the vine and the juice of the grape implicit in Christianity? We may be sure that Harvey's mind, like that of all men of his day, was conditioned to this comparison between wine and blood, and that he never rid himself of this prepossession. So, quite naturally, he thought of fermentation as being possible in blood as well as in wine.

Further, this interpretation of the blood's 'renovation' must have seemed all the more likely since everything else that he observed in the blood appeared to confirm the hypothesis. When the overheated blood overflowing from the *vena cava* had filled the auricle (*unde auricula dilatata*) and had thus provoked the auricle's natural contractibility to manifest itself so as to fill the ventricle, the ventricle, in its turn, was induced to contract and eject the blood towards the lungs, and this was surely evidence that the overheated blood needed cooling by the air drawn into the lungs. Harvey, of course, could not guess that the blood seeks oxygen in the lungs, for he knew nothing about oxygen. Thus, we can see how everything seemed to be satisfactorily explained by a hot fermentation of blood in the *vena cava*.

Harvey had noticed that the fermentation of wine in a barrel is always accompanied by (a) a considerable production of heat, and (b) the precipitation of the residues and waste-products of fermentation (*fulginositates*). Well then, he thought, if the blood has to be sent through the lungs in order that the fresh air they receive on inhalation may temper the excessive heat, the process of exhalation serves to free the blood of the waste matter produced by the fermentation—*a fulginositatibus*.

All most admirably reasoned out and indeed acceptable, had not the initial premiss—the arrival of blood cold and devoid of 'spirit' in the *vena cava*—been false. I have often felt it a great pity that so admirable an explanation should not be true. Harvey did all that he could in his time and age; he could not go farther. Like the great scientist he was, he was careful to set only a provisional value on his theory, and perhaps we may now be permitted to fulfil Harvey's hope and expectation that the future would 'present matters more exactly'.

Now, the system of the circulation as universally taught today locates the starting-point of the blood-stream in the 'motor' of the right auricle. This system—right auricle, lungs, left heart, organs, right auricle, etc.—is commonly but erroneously attributed to Harvey, in spite of the fact that the great physiologist was quite incapable of confusing a 'motor' with a 'spring'. Before we attempt to show that even this conception is absurd, let us here set out Harvey's real scheme, which puts the starting-point of the circulation in the *vena cava* (the supposed regenerator of the blood-stream). Harvey's sequence of the circulation was, then—*vena cava*, lungs, left heart, organs, *vena cava*, etc. (*see* Fig. 13).

In order to drive home an essential point and to defend Harvey's memory from the aspersion that he declared the starting-point to

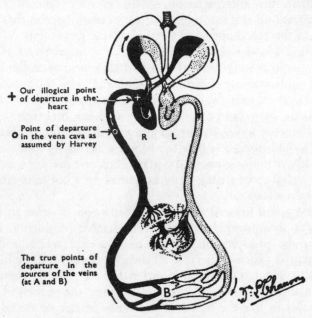

Our illogical point of departure in the heart

Point of departure in the vena cava as assumed by Harvey

The true points of departure in the sources of the veins (at A and B)

FIG. 13.   The true source of the blood-stream compared with that taught by Harvey (o) and an unfortunate modern assumption (+). R: right heart. L: left heart.

be in the 'motor' of the right auricle, I venture to quote here some passages from my *Place aux Veines*, in which I assemble what seem to me to be cogent reasons for seeking the starting-point of the blood-circuit in the venous exits of all the organs—that is to say, in the thousand little rivulets that carry away the matter produced by the processes of digestion or convey venous blood out of the organs themselves.

'Some declare, with astonishing thoughtlessness, that the blood circuit being a closed one it is of little importance, after all, what point we take to be the starting-point, since we continue round and round the circle. Others again, almost as thoughtless, maintain that the heart, and in particular the right auricle (*primum movens, ultimum moriens*), is very rightly regarded as the starting-point of the circuit, since it is the motor that excites all the movement of the blood-stream.[1]

'We can hardly accept this reasoning. We need not spend much time in examining the first contention, that of the closed (!) blood circuit, without any starting-point. Obviously the blood which continually exhausts itself by nourishing the organs must—if it is not to dry up—receive constant supplies from without in order to make up for what it loses in the tissues. The blood circuit is only apparently closed, for somewhere or other it must have supply lines which constitute the "source" of the blood-stream, as we shall see later on. Of course, everyone really knows this but hardly thinks about it enough to draw the logical conclusions from the facts.

'The second point of view, that the heart must be the starting-point of the cycle because the heart is the great motor of the blood, is very much the same thing as saying that the source and beginning of the River Seine was in the old Marly Machine[2] (if we assume, for a moment, that this apparatus was constructed in order to improve the flow of a slow-moving river). The heart, as regards the circulation of the blood, does nothing but secure a steady propulsion, and, unless I am seriously misinformed, it is not the heart that restores to the blood all those primary and essential substances which the organs demand—phosphorus, calcium, magnesium, proteins, lipoids, glucosides, etc.

'However, masters and pupils still agree "unanimously" that it is quite allowable thus to confuse the "source" with the "pump" on the stream. So we read in all the treatises and manuals that "the starting-point of the circulation of the blood must be sought in the right auricle, as Harvey taught".

[1] See my *Circulation du Sang, schema nouveau*, Paris, 1933.

[2] The Marly Machine, we may remember, was the pumping apparatus erected on the Seine a little upstream from Paris. The machine was designed in Louis XIV's time to carry water to Versailles, where immense quantitities were needed for the canals, basins and fountains of that royal residence. We may imagine, for our present purpose, that the Marly Machine was put up in order to increase the flow of the Seine towards its mouth, because at Marly the current had become sluggish, or slowed down as is the blood-stream when it reaches the heart. There would not, indeed, be anything so very extraordinary in installing what we might call 'an auxiliary motor' to aid in the flow of the river's waters downstream. But, had this been the avowed purpose of the Marly Machine, no one, I think, would have thought of calling Marly the source of the Seine. But we do something just as illogical when we situate the 'source' of the blood-stream in the right auricle.

'Harvey never made any such statement. Indeed, I think he would have been incapable of saying such a thing, for he was a physiologist of the highest intelligence and, therefore, incapable of putting the starting-point for his circulation anywhere else but where he saw the real source. He most emphatically did not see the source in the heart, which is just a motor in the middle of a stream that has its source far from the heart.'

There is no need to repeat what I have said above concerning the 'heat' and 'vital spirit' that Harvey (in accordance with the ideas of his time) thought were produced in the *vena cava* by a process of regeneration. But it was thus here that Harvey placed the source of the blood-stream, and his idea was undoubtedly logical although it could not survive the discoveries of Lavoisier and Claude Bernard. Harvey naturally put the starting-point of the blood-stream at its imagined source and not in a motor situated some distance along the circuit.

We can see how careful Harvey was *not* to place the starting-point of his circulation in the 'motor' of the heart, for in the Second Letter of 1649, a few pages after he had explained to Riolan his idea of the 'fermentation' in the *vena cava*, he wrote the important passage I have already quoted (page 206) and which I repeat here:

'If truly we mean by the term "heart" the substance only of the heart, with its ventricles and auricles, I do not believe that it is the enricher of the blood, or that the blood receives from the heart its force, its virtue, its essence, its movement or its heat. . . . I think that the prime cause of the heart's distension is innate heat, and that the first dilatation is wholly due to the blood itself becoming suddenly vaporous and turgescent like substances which ferment. . . .'

This explicit refusal by Harvey to place the beginning of the circuit in the heart is categorical enough, and incidentally we may ask on what grounds those critics base their opinions who declare that the Letters of 1649 are of no interest and not worth translating!

Now that we have made Harvey's own mature conception quite plain we must, of course, admit that his 'point of departure' in the *vena cava* is no longer admissible. But neither can we accept the doctrine that the blood starts from the 'motor' of the right auricle. We must therefore search for another starting-point, one that is acceptable in the light of modern knowledge. I have demonstrated elsewhere[1] what seems to me to be the right interpretation, and here

[1] As early as 1923, in the first instance, and then in 1926 in *La Machine Humaine enseignée par la Machine Automobile* (*The Human Machine Explained by the Automobile Engine*), published by Doin, Paris.

content myself with a brief quotation from a paper I read to the French Academy of Medicine in April, 1949:[1]

'We can easily follow the course of the Seine from Marly right up to the source. Well, let us in like manner follow up the course of the blood-stream from the right auricle of the heart. First of all we find the big terminal trunk of the *vena cava*, then the two great roots of this: the sub-hepatic and porto-hepatic root, and the general root. At the origin of the portal root we find thousands and thousands of little gastric and intestinal veins by which the blood-stream receives the primary substances for its reconstitution (phosphorus, calcium, sulphur, magnesium, amino-acids, sugars, fats, etc.), for there is no way that we can restore our blood except by eating. Therefore, it appears to me, it can hardly be erroneous to see in these venous and lymphatic gastro-intestinal channels at least one of the sources of the blood-stream. And in this matter the Ancients did not err, nor did the anatomists and physiologists of Galen's school, who have been so much ridiculed. Though they knew nothing of the circulation of the blood, nevertheless they justly recognized its prime source in the digestive passages. Here are to be found the counterparts of the "radicles" (as in botany the nourishing roots of plants are called) or first suppliers of that rising "sap" by which the Ancients typified the blood.

'The portal vein with its gastro-intestinal roots is just what an engineer would call a "feed-pipe"—that is to say, a passage which brings in from the exterior the necessary supply of fuel. If we now return to the cavo-hepatic confluence and take the alternative route through the great *vena cava*, we eventually reach the thousands of other little veins that issue from all the active organs (other than those of digestion)—the skin, muscles, brain, etc.—and carry away from them both blood that has been utilized and much that has not, and is therefore "recuperable".

'By means of the various apertures in the human body, the vents that allow of pulmonary exhalation, the excretion of sweat, urine, mucous matter and so forth, the blood that is recuperable purges itself of waste products (such as carbonic acid, excess water, urea, etc.) and moves onwards until it finds at the cavo-hepatic confluence the new blood entering from the intestines. Henceforth, these two sorts of blood commingle and go where all fuel must go if it is to produce energy—that is to say, somewhere where oxygen can be obtained.

---

[1] Published in the *Bulletin de l'Académie Nationale de Medicine*, Nos. 15 and 16, 1949. This paper was largely taken from my *La Circulation du Sang, schéma nouveau*, 1933.

'Thus, just as I have called the portal vein the "feed-pipe", the general *vena cava* might be termed the "recuperation pipe" (as in some of our machines), while the section of the circulatory passage which goes from the cavo-hepatic confluence to the lungs *via* the right heart and the pulmonary artery seems to me to play the part of the "jet" in regard to the "carburettor" of the lungs, where the blood must take in a supply of oxygen.'

The simplicity of the scheme is plainly shown in Fig. 14, where the main events of the circulation are indicated as follows. There is first the initial stage of alimentation and recuperation, in which the blood proceeds from all the venous issues of the organs to the cavo-hepatic confluence (I and II). Then comes the oxygenation stage, to which the blood proceeds from the cavo-hepatic confluence through the right side of the heart (the 'jet') to the lungs (III). Lastly, there is the distribution stage, in which the blood leaves the lungs and passes through the left side of the heart and the aorta, which together perform the functions of a 'supercharger'—that is to say, they dispatch the fuel to the place where it is to be consumed (IV).

This outline of the stages of the blood's progress by analogy with an engine is, I think, undeniably accurate. When I first elaborated my comparison between the human body and an automobile I was an out-and-out mechanist and soon found other astonishing parallels (irrelevant to the present theme) in the liver, nervous system, etc. I am still of the opinion that the mechanical model, properly interpreted and with due regard to its limitations, clarifies the point at issue better than any other. The late Professor Gley was much impressed by it and in his enthusiasm declared that it exhibits 'all the logical simplicity of something which lives and moves in the universality of the worlds'.

Be that as it may, my conviction that there is a physical explanation for every change led me to the conclusion that the evident source of the blood-stream in the venous issues of the organs could not be an inert one. It is, in fact, there powered and conditioned by considerable vaso-motor action, and the mass of blood sent to the heart is constantly varied. My paper to the Academy of Medicine thus continues:

'For example, there is the failure of the heart in states of syncope or collapse and, on the other hand, the over-charging of the heart and lungs by extreme peripheric venous vaso-constriction, which results in the blood's being propelled like an equinoctial tide to cause pulmonary oedema. Thus, new reasons (super-added to those —"nutritive" and "recuperative"—which I had at first noted) occurred

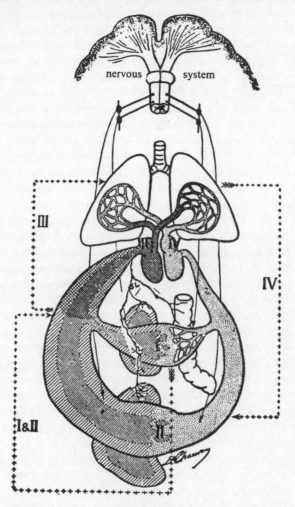

FIG. 14. The circulation of the blood—the logical development of Harvey's original conception in the light of modern knowledge. I: Source of new blood in the portal vein. II: Source of recuperable blood in the *vena cava*. III: Stage of oxygenation for the mixture of new and recuperated blood. IV: Circulation completed by distribution of arterial blood.

to me for establishing in the portal and *vena cava* roots the real source and point of departure of the circulation of the blood.

'From then on the central heart appeared to me in a new light, as one of those fluviatile "regulators" that we find in our countrysides where, on following the downstream course of a river, we get to a mill-race feeding a mill. We may find above the sluice-gates what is called a "ball-governor". If, after heavy storms at the far distant sources of the river, the current comes down in great force and threatens to flood the mill, the governor automatically lowers the sluice-gates and allows only a moderate amount of water to pass. On the other hand, if water becomes scarce upstream, the governor raises the sluice-gates and allows sufficient water through the mill-race to feed the mill in a normal and satisfactory manner.

'It seemed to me that the central heart must be considered as a second (though of course not a secondary) organ, situated in the course of the blood-stream but not at its source. Supplemented by all the other regulators which complete and strengthen the heart's action (such as the carotid sinus, etc.) it has to maintain the humoral and sanguineous optimum in the organism, whatever storms might be occurring at the source of the blood itself.

'You know what important deductions in the therapeutic field must be made from the foregoing physiological and physiopatho-logical considerations, both for the treatment of patients suffering from weakness of the heart's action (syncopes and states of collapse due to venous vaso-paresis at the sources of the blood) in which vaso-constrictor drugs of the adrenalin type are indicated, and also for the treatment of patients suffering from sudden vaso-constriction at the sources of the blood (cases of paroxysmal hypertension and crises of a cardio-pulmonary oedema nature) when vaso-dilating or vaso-paretic drugs, such as morphine, are indicated.

'It seems that from the point of view of legitimate reasoning, and also from the practical and utilitarian point of view, it is not logical to retain a conception which, today, affords no real explanation of the facts. Admittedly this conception was developed from Harvey's magnificent hypothesis, but it is surely contradicted by the dis-coveries of Lavoisier, of Claude Bernard and of all the great physio-logists of recent years. For the old scheme a new one must be substi-tuted, and it is one which guides us in our therapeutic action in such grave conditions as hypertension with collapse, or again, paroxysmal and pneumo-oedematous hypotension, not to mention such other conditions as those of paroxysmal diarrhoea. . . .

'To sum up, the vaso-motor action which is apparent in the small veins issuing from all the organs must be considered together with the alimentary supply by the portal vein and with the recuperation effected in the *vena cava*. This compels us to ascribe to the blood-stream a great venous peripheric origin. Harvey's central heart is a most powerful auxiliary motor that helps to regulate and distribute the great stream of blood that is delivered to it by the veins from all parts of the body.'

This is no mere logical quibble, or a dispute about terms, but a reorientation of our view of the circulation which is of vital importance in its therapeutic implications. I have gone into this aspect of the question in some detail in my *Place aux Veines*, but I will give here one example of the disastrous results of misapprehending the true pattern of the circulation.

Let us consider what is called a cardio-pulmonary oedema crisis, that dreadful and sudden suffocation caused by an oedematous condition of the lungs. The first stage of the drama is played in the peripheric venous circulation (Fig. 14, I and II), and consists of a violent and sudden contraction of the great mass of venous radicals spread almost all over the body. This contraction (which might be compared with the wringing out of a sponge) forces a stream of blood towards the heart and lungs with great violence. If, by ill chance, the patient is then treated by an injection of adrenalin (a powerfully vaso-constrictive substance) either in the veins or in the heart, on the pretext that that organ has begun to fail, the adrenalin at once provokes a still more powerful contraction of the peripheric field which, on the contrary, should be dilated and decongested (by morphine, for instance). The result of the adrenalin administration is instantaneous death by stoppage of the heart, which is overdriven and succumbs to the violence of the striction brought about by such ill-advised treatment.

Unfortunately such cases are by no means rare and, I think, are sufficient to show how important it is to know just where the source of the blood's circulation is situated, to recognize the role of the little streamlets that feed the blood-stream and to know just what happens in them. Moreover, this conception of the blood-stream *as* a stream, with a recognizable source, is the relevant and important point of it in the present work. Similarly, the recognition of the heart as the controller or accelerator of the blood-stream rather than as its generator is also essentially the *Harveian view*, and we may remember in this connection that the heart is actually absent in certain species of animals that nevertheless have circulatory systems.

In trying to set Harvey's great picture of the circulation in a modern frame I trust I have not exceeded the duties of a conscientious biographer. The effort has at least shown that certain schools of physiology, where Harvey's fundamental notion has long been misinterpreted to students, may still turn with profit to the three-hundred-years-old Latin texts of the great anatomist. I conclude with the admission that in my modification of Harvey's system I was unknowingly forestalled in certain particulars by an obscure 17th-century physician, one Pierre Vattier.

I came across Vattier's extremely rare little book of fifty-six pages quite by chance while rummaging among the second-hand stocks of the Paris booksellers—where I often amuse myself looking for curious and interesting volumes. I discovered Vattier, whose name has sunk into almost complete oblivion, only a few days before I was ready to write '*finis*' to this life of Harvey, and it is my opinion that he has not received the attention he deserves.[1]

Vattier was born in what is now the department of Calvados in Normandy, at Montreuil l'Eveillé or Montreuil-en-Auge, and he practised in Paris where he was physician to Gaston of Orleans. He must have been a singularly acute-minded man, full of learning and common sense. In his very small book, *Le Coeur dethrôné* ('The Heart Dethroned', Paris, 1660), he combats in really masterly fashion the error—already becoming widespread in his day—that Harvey's cycle of blood-circulation began in the heart. After adopting Harvey's thesis (and this in itself is greatly to his credit) Vattier concludes by recognizing that same source of the blood-stream that I have been proclaiming in my hospital lectures, and elsewhere, for the past thirty years!

Vattier naturally had his own simple arguments, based on the limited means of investigation at his disposal, whereas I had the discoveries of modern physiology at my command. I had the further advantage of my own previous study of the human body as a mechanism for the utilization of energy, which showed clearly (by an illuminating analogy) how the various sections of the circulatory system should be regarded. Nevertheless, Vattier had his feet on the right road, though he seems to have stood alone in his age.

---

[1] I have now dealt with Pierre Vattier in an article which appeared in *La Presse Médicale* of 31st December, 1955, entitled '*Le Docteur Pierre Vattier (1623–1670), Médecin de Gaston d'Orléans et Secrétaire du Roy en Langue Arabique*'.

Nothing can cover his high fame
but heaven;
No pyramids set off his memories,
But the eternal substance of his
greatness,—
To which I leave him

Chapter XI

Conclusion

The nature of this Life and Appreciation—William Harvey an even greater man
than is commonly thought

WHEN, having reached the end of my nine-chapter story of
the life and work of William Harvey, I ventured, contrary to
custom, to add a tenth chapter relating Harvey's discoveries to the
findings of modern science, I did so in full accord with the great
physician's expressed hope[1] that his work should be reconciled with
later discoveries. I have done this in an intimate and direct manner,
with due respect and affection for the Master, and not as a critic
declaiming from a vantage-point three centuries on in time. In
modifying Harvey's hypothesis I have been ever mindful of what
was immutable in the work of this great builder, that is, the
'circulatory course' but for which—*hac data via*, as he said—our
understanding of the human body might not have advanced
beyond medieval ignorance.

In striving to enter into the great Master's thoughts and to fall
into line with his wishes, and in thus writing this Life in the way that
I have, I feel I have shown a greater respect for his memory and a
greater admiration for him than I could have done by a common-
place and purely chronological account of his researches, for the

[1] See p. 189 and the Latin text on p. 246.

effects of Harvey's discoveries continue unceasingly to make themselves felt, and Harvey does not cease to live and to increase in stature as time goes on.

So, after nearly thirty years of almost daily study of Harvey's works, I may perhaps be permitted to repeat at the end of this book what I said at the beginning, namely that *the more we read Harvey and penetrate into his mind, the greater his figure seems to loom up through the ages. Greater than has as yet been acknowledged or numbered, he is, without shadow of doubt, among the three or four master intelligences of all time.*

Hempstead Church

Epilogue

At the end of my Harveian pilgrimage through England in October, 1955, I visited the tomb in the little parish church of Hempstead, in Essex. Harvey's body had been brought here all the way from Roehampton—a journey of several days—in fulfilment of his expressed wish to be laid in his family vault. During my two days' stay in the village I made notes of my impressions, and perhaps I may be permitted to quote from them in this brief epilogue.

For those who admire Harvey and his works a visit to Hempstead must evoke a crowd of memories. One reaches Hempstead, whose countryside Harvey so often covered during his solitary walks, from Saffron Walden by a road which was once but a pathway. The way is bounded by great slopes to the west and the east, and as one journeys along this sunken road one can see dotted about on either hand a few houses and farms that make up altogether a parish of less than three hundred inhabitants.

Two names are associated with Hempstead. First of all, that of Dick Turpin, the notorious highwayman:

Poor Dick Turpin
Of highway robbers king,
Hanged at York one fine morning.

It seems that Turpin's birthplace was the ancient *Rose and Crown* inn that still stands at the entrance to the village. The other name, still mentioned with respect in conversations you may have with the inhabitants, is, of course, that of William Harvey—'Doctor Harvey, the celebrated Doctor Harvey whose tomb you will see in the aisle of our little church up there.'

The humble parish church, that has suffered not a little from the ravages of time, lies, indeed, half-way up the slope of the rising ground to the east. The church is surrounded by a typical country village graveyard filled with crumbling and moss-grown grave-stones and monuments. However, in the chapel on the north side of the choir are the tombs of the Harveys, well looked after by Mr. Hooper, the vicar, who was kind enough to meet me and show me round although my visit fell upon those days in the week when he is most busy—a Saturday and a Sunday.

Immediately you enter the church the Harvey chapel with its white marble monuments attracts your eye. The outstanding memorial is that erected in 1883 to receive the remains of William Harvey when they were removed from the vault. I must record that before this tomb I felt an emotion similar to that which I experienced when, soon after the war, I stood alone for the first time in the mortuary chapel dedicated to the man whose creative life and character I had so much admired—my illustrious master, d'Arsonval. And there was aroused in me that rhythm of music, that desire to clothe thoughts in poetry which, I think, is the natural reaction of the human spirit when it is wrought to the pitch of sensibility. I was thus moved to write the following verses:

A Hempstead, sur le tombeau de Harvey
16 Octobre, 1955

Grand Will, je suis venu m'incliner sur tes restes,
Depuis dix lustres pleins que ta pensée m'étreint,
Que je me nourris d'elle et la cherche en tes textes,
M'attachant pas à pas à ton discours latin.
Quelque immense que fût le profil de ton Ombre,
Encore bien plus grand il s'en est dégagé
Pour ton lecteur fidèle—et dans le premier Nombre
Des vrais génies humains, il t'a trouvé placé.

Si tu fus moins connu de la foule amusée
Que le lyrique Will ton grand Frère en génie—
Etrange côte à côte en vos mûres années
Dans Londres turbulent où se croisent vos vies—
Les temps se sont chargés d'égaliser vos gloires
Et de vous venir prendre aux deux tombeaux cachés
De Stratford et d'Hempstead: en dépit des victoires
Les refuges chéris de vos Humilités.

Une petite Eglise en un petit village,
Voilà ton Westminster selon ta volonté:
'Le Hâvre de la paix au terme du Voyage'.
Que de grandeur encore en ta simplicité!
Grand Will, je puis partir, ma tâche est achevée,
De toi j'emporte aussi de la mort la leçon:
Terrestre enfouissement? Qu'importe, si l'Idée,
Survivante éternelle, immortalise un Nom!

BIBLIOGRAPHY

AUBREY, J.: *Lives of Eminent Persons.*

AVELING, J. H.: *Memorials of Harvey.* (London, 1875.)

BAYON, H. P.: 'William Harvey, Physician and Biologist. His Precursors, Opponents and Successors'. In *Annals of Science,* January, 1938, to October, 1939.

BINET, A., and RADOT, V.: *Histoire de la Faculté de Médecine de Paris.* (Paris, 1952.)

BOILEAU, N.: *Arrêt burlesque du Parlement de Stagyre.*

CAESALPINUS: *De Plantis.* (Florence, 1582.)
　　　　　Questionarum Peripaticarum. (1569.)
　　　　　Quaestionum Medicarum.

CHAULIAC, G. DE: *La Grande Chirurgie.*

COLOMBO, R.: *De Re Anatomica.* (1559.)

DESCARTES, R.: *Discours de la Méthode.* (1636.)

DIONIS, P.: *Anatomie de L'Homme suivant la Circulation du Sang.* (1690.)

DUHAMEL, G.: *Ouvrages et Chroniques.*

FABRICIUS DA AQUAPENDENTE: *De Venarum Ostiolis.*

FLOURENS, P.: *Histoire de la découverte de la circulation du sang.* (1854 and 1857.)

GALEN: *Works.*

GEOFFROY SAINT-HILAIRE, I.: *Works.*

GONTHIER D'ANDERNAC: *Works.*

HARVEY, W.: *Exercitatio Anatomica de Motu Cordis et Sanguinis in Animalibus.* (Frankfort, 1628.)
　　　　　Exercitationes duae Anatomicae de Circulatione Sanguinis ad Iohannem Riolanum. (Cambridge, 1649.)
　　　　　Exercitationes de Generatione Animalium. (Amsterdam and London, 1651.)

HERRINGHAM, W.: *William Harvey at St. Bartholemew's.* (A speech delivered at the hospital, June, 1928.)

HIPPOCRATES: *Works.*

IBN-AN-NAFIS and MUHYI-ED-DIN AT-TATAWI: *Works.* (Cairo, 1924, and Berlin, 1933.)

JUSSIEU, L. DE: *Works.*

KEYNES, G.: *A Bibliography of the Writings of Dr. William Harvey.* (Second Edition, 1954.)
　　　　　The Portraiture of William Harvey. (Thomas Vicary Lecture, 1948.)
　　　　　The Personality of William Harvey. (Linacre Lecture, 1949.)

LA FONTAINE, J. DE: *Le Quinquina.*

LOWER, R.: *Tractatus de Corde.* (1669.)

MALLOCH, A.: *William Harvey.* (New York, 1929.)

MALPIGHI: *Opera omnia.* (1686.)

MAUROIS, A.: *Histoire d'Angleterre.*

MERSENNE, M.: *Letters.*

METTRIE, O. DE LA: *Works.*

MOLIÈRE: *Le Malade Imaginaire.* (1673.)

MONDOR, H.: *Anatomistes et Chirurgiens.*

MOORE, N.: 'William Harvey', in the *Dictionary of National Biography.*

MUNK, W.: *Notae Harveianae.* (St. Bartholemew's Hospital Reports, Roll of the College of Physicians.)

PARÉ, A.: *Works.*

PARISANUS: *De Cordis et Sanguinis Motu ad Guilielmum Harveium.* (Venice, 1635.)

PATIN, G.: *Letters.*

PLEMPIUS: *De Fundamentis Medicinea Libri Sex.* (Louvain, 1638.)

POWER, D'A.: *William Harvey.* (London, 1897.)

PRIMEROSE, J. G. *Harveii de Motu Cordis cum Refutationibus.* (Leyden, 1630.)

RABELAIS, F.: *Pantagruel.*

RIOLAN, J.: *Anatomica seu Anthropographia—Enchiridion.* (1648.)

SERVETUS, M.: *Christianissimi Restitutio.* (1553.)

SINGER, C.: *The Evolution of Anatomy.*

VATTIER, P.: *Le Coeur déthrôné.* (Paris, 1660.)

VESALIUS: *De Corporis Humani Fabrica.* (1543, 1555.)

VINCI, LEONARDO DA: *Traités et Figures.*

WILLIS, R.: *William Harvey.* (Sydenham Society, 1897.)

INDEX